# Working Papers
## for use with

# Fundamental TWELFTH CANADIAN EDITION
# Accounting Principles

**VOLUME**

# Working Papers
for use with

# Fundamental
TWELFTH CANADIAN EDITION
# Accounting Principles

VOLUME

Kermit D. Larson
University of Texas–Austin

Tilly Jensen
Northern Alberta Institute of Technology

Prepared by
Tilly Jensen

 **McGraw-Hill**
**Ryerson**

Toronto Montréal Boston Burr Ridge, IL Dubuque, IA Madison, WI New York
San Francisco St. Louis Bangkok Bogotá Caracas Kuala Lumpur Lisbon London
Madrid Mexico City Milan New Delhi Santiago Seoul Singapore Sydney Taipei

**The McGraw·Hill Companies**

# McGraw-Hill Ryerson

Working Papers for use with
Fundamental Accounting Principles
Twelfth Canadian Edition
Volume 1

ISBN-13: 9780070953482
ISBN-10: 0-07-095348-1

3 4 5 6 7 8 9 10 MP 0 9

Printed and bound in Canada

Publisher: Nicole Lukach
Sponsoring Editor: Rhondda McNabb
Developmental Editor: Marcia Luke
Senior Marketing Manager: Joy Armitage Taylor
Senior Production Coordinator: Jennifer Wilkie
Page Layout: Jay Tee Graphics
Printer: Maracle Press, Ltd.

# Contents

_____
_____
_____
_____
_____
_____
_____
_____

## Quick Study 1-2

_____
_____
_____
_____
_____
_____
_____
_____
_____
_____
_____
_____
_____

## Quick Study 1-3

_____
_____
_____
_____
_____
_____
_____

## Quick Study 1-4

_____
_____
_____
_____
_____
_____
_____
_____

_____
_____
_____
_____
_____
_____
_____
_____
_____
_____
_____
_____
_____
_____
_____
_____
_____
_____
_____
_____

## Quick Study 1-6

_____
_____
_____
_____
_____
_____
_____

## Exercise 1-1

a. _____
b. _____
c. _____
d. _____
e. _____
f. _____
g. _____

## Exercise 1-2

| | *I or E* | | *I or E* |
|---|---|---|---|
| **Bank manager** | | **Parent** | |
| **Owner** | | **Canada Revenue Agency** | |
| **Toy supplier** | | **Cleaner contracted by TLC Daycare** | |

_____
_____
_____
_____
_____
_____
_____
_____
_____
_____
_____
_____
_____
_____
_____
_____
_____
_____

**Exercise 1-4**

a. _____
_____
_____

b. _____
_____
_____

c. _____
_____
_____

d. _____
_____
_____
_____

**Name** _____

**a.** _____

_____

_____

_____

_____

_____

_____

_____

**b.** _____

_____

_____

_____

_____

_____

_____

**c.** _____

_____

_____

_____

_____

_____

_____

_____

_____

## Exercise 1-6

1. _____
2. _____
3. _____
4. _____
5. _____

## Exercise 1-7

1. _____
2. _____
3. _____
4. _____
5. _____

1. _____
2. _____
3. _____
4. _____
5. _____
6. _____
7. _____
8. _____

## Problem 1-1A

| Characteristic | Type of Business Organization | | |
| --- | --- | --- | --- |
|  | Sole Proprietorship | Partnership | Corporation |
| Limited liability |  |  |  |
| Unlimited liability |  |  |  |
| Owners are shareholders |  |  |  |
| Owners are partners |  |  |  |
| Taxed as a separate legal entity |  |  |  |

## Problem 1-1B

a. _____

_____

_____

b. _____

_____

_____

1. _____        5. _____
2. _____        6. _____
3. _____        7. _____
4. _____

## Quick Study 2-2

a. _____
b. _____
c. _____

## Quick Study 2-3

1. _____        4. _____
2. _____        5. _____
3. _____

## Quick Study 2-4

| | | |
|---|---|---|
| | 1. | Delco performed work for a client located in China and collected 8,450,000 RMB (Chinese currency), the equivalent of about $1,320,000 Canadian. Delco recorded it as 8,450,000. |
| | 2. | Delco collected $180,000 from a customer on December 20, 2011 for work to be done in February, 2012.  The $180,000 was recorded as revenue during 2011.  Delco's year end is December 31. |
| | 3. | Delco's December 31, 2011 balance sheet showed total assets of $840,000 and liabilities of $1,120,000.  The income statement for the past 6 years has shown a trend of increasing losses. |
| | 4. | Included in Delco's assets was land and building purchased for $310,000 and reported on the balance sheet at $470,000. |
| | 5. | Delco's bank manager wants to verify the revenues and has asked for the sales receipts.  Delco says that they do not issue receipts but call customers and advise them of the amount owing. |
| | 6. | Delco's owner, Tom Del, consistently buys personal supplies and charges them to the company. |

## Quick Study 2-5

| | Assets | = | Liabilities | + | Equity |
|---|---|---|---|---|---|
| a. | | | | | |
| b. | | | | | |
| c. | | | | | |

*Fundamental Accounting Principles, 12th Edition*

| Assets | = | Liabilities | + | Equity |
|---|---|---|---|---|
| a. | | | | |
| b. | | | | |
| c. | | | | |

## Quick Study 2-7

**a.**

**Allin Servicing**
**Income Statement**
**Month ended April 30, 2011**

| Revenues | $300 |
|---|---|
| Expenses | ? |
| Net income (loss) | ? |

**Allin Servicing**
**Statement of Owner's Equity**
**Month ended April 30, 2011**

| Tim Allin, capital, April 1 | | $ 50 |
|---|---|---|
| Add: Investments by owner | $ 30 | |
| Net income | ? | ? |
| Total | | $255 |
| Less: Withdrawals by owner | | ? |
| Tim Allin, capital, April 30 | | ? |

**Allin Servicing**
**Balance Sheet**
**April 30, 2011**

| Assets | | Liabilities | |
|---|---|---|---|
| Cash | $ 60 | Accounts payable | $ 25 |
| Equipment | ? | **Owner's equity** | |
| | | Tim Allin, capital | ? |
| | | Total liabilities and | |
| Total assets | $265 | owner's equity | ? |

**b.**

**Allin Servicing**
**Income Statement**
**Month ended May 31, 2011**

| Revenues | ? |
|---|---|
| Expenses | $ 85 |
| Net income (loss) | ? |

**Allin Servicing**
**Statement of Owner's Equity**
**Month ended May 31, 2011**

| Tim Allin, capital, May 1 | | ? |
|---|---|---|
| Add: Investments by owner | $ 60 | |
| Net income | ? | $110 |
| Total | | ? |
| Less: Withdrawals by owner | | 75 |
| Tim Allin, capital, May 31 | | ? |

**Allin Servicing**
**Balance Sheet**
**May 31, 2011**

| Assets | | Liabilities | |
|---|---|---|---|
| Cash | $120 | Accounts payable | $ 45 |
| Equipment | ? | **Owner's equity** | |
| | | Tim Allin, capital | ? |
| | | Total liabilities and | |
| Total assets | ? | owner's equity | ? |

**1.** _____

**2.** _____

## Quick Study 2-9

| | | | |
|---|---|---|---|
| _____ | a. Income statement. | _____ | e. Owner's withdrawals account. |
| _____ | b. Cash flow statement. | _____ | f. Balance sheet |
| _____ | c. Telephone bill. | _____ | g. Bank statement. |
| _____ | d. Invoice from supplier. | _____ | h. Sales invoice. |

## Quick Study 2-10

| Assets | = | Liabilities | + | Equity |
|---|---|---|---|---|
| a. | | | | |
| b. | | | | |
| c. | | | | |
| d. | | | | |
| e. | | | | |

## Quick Study 2-11

| | | | |
|---|---|---|---|
| _____ | 1. Supplies | _____ | 8. Utilities expense |
| _____ | 2. Supplies expense | _____ | 9. Furniture |
| _____ | 3. Accounts receivable | _____ | 10. Fees earned |
| _____ | 4. Accounts payable | _____ | 11. Rent revenue |
| _____ | 5. Equipment | _____ | 12. Salaries expense |
| _____ | 6. Tim Roadster's withdrawals | _____ | 13. Tim Roadster's investments |
| _____ | 7. Notes payable | _____ | 14. Net income |

## Quick Study 2-12

| | |
|---|---|
| _____ | 1. Total revenues |
| _____ | 2. Total operating expenses |
| _____ | 3. Net income |
| _____ | 4. Total assets |
| _____ | 5. Total liabilities |
| _____ | 6. Tim Roadster, capital (April 30, 2011) |
| _____ | 7. Total liabilities and owner's equity |

| | | | | |
|---|---|---|---|---|
| _____ | 1. | Net loss ............................................. | $ | _____ |
| _____ | 2. | Rent expense ..................................... | 22 | _____ |
| _____ | 3. | Rent payable ...................................... | 6 | _____ |
| _____ | 4. | Accounts receivable........................... | 14 | _____ |
| _____ | 5. | Joan Bennish's investments in May .... | 30 | _____ |
| _____ | 6. | Interest revenue................................. | 2 | _____ |
| _____ | 7. | Joan Bennish, capital, May 1, 2011 ...... | 0 | _____ |
| _____ | 8. | Repair supplies.................................. | 5 | _____ |
| _____ | 9. | Notes payable .................................... | 25 | _____ |
| _____ | 10. | Joan Bennish's withdrawals in May..... | 5 | _____ |
| _____ | 11. | Truck .................................................. | 15 | _____ |
| _____ | 12. | Consulting fees earned ...................... | 18 | _____ |
| _____ | 13. | Joan Bennish, capital, May 31, 2011 .... | | _____ |
| _____ | 14. | Cash ................................................... | 20 | _____ |

## Quick Study 2-14

### Income Statement

| | | |
|---|---|---|
| | | |
| | | |
| | | |
| | | |
| | | |
| | | |
| | | |
| | | |
| | | |
| | | |

### Statement of Owner's Equity

| | | |
|---|---|---|
| | | |
| | | |
| | | |
| | | |
| | | |
| | | |

## Balance Sheet

| | | | |
|---|---|---|---|
| | | | |
| | | | |
| | | | |
| | | | |
| | | | |
| | | | |
| | | | |
| | | | |
| | | | |
| | | | |
| | | | |
| | | | |
| | | | |
| | | | |
| | | | |
| | | | |
| | | | |
| | | | |
| | | | |
| | | | |
| | | | |
| | | | |

## Exercise 2-1

**(a)** _____
_____
_____
_____

**(b)** _____
_____
_____
_____

**(c)** _____
_____
_____
_____

**(d)** _____
_____
_____
_____

| | (a) | (b) | (c) | (d) | (e) |
|---|---|---|---|---|---|
| Owner's equity, January 1 ................. | $     -0- | $     -0- | $     -0- | $     -0- | |
| Owner's investments during the year ................................................. | 60,000 | | 31,500 | 37,500 | 150,000 |
| Net income (loss) for the year .......... | 15,750 | 40,500 | (4,500) | | (8,000) |
| Owner's withdrawals during the year ................................................. | | (27,000) | (15,000) | (15,750) | (63,000) |
| Owner's equity, December 31 .......... | 51,000 | 49,500 | | 42,750 | 171,000 |

## Exercise 2-3

### Income Statement

| | | |
|---|---|---|
| | | |
| | | |
| | | |
| | | |
| | | |
| | | |
| | | |
| | | |
| | | |
| | | |
| | | |
| | | |
| | | |

## Exercise 2-4

### Statement of Owner's Equity

| | | |
|---|---|---|
| | | |
| | | |
| | | |
| | | |
| | | |
| | | |

*Analysis component:* _____

_____
_____
_____
_____

## Balance Sheet

| | | | |
|---|---|---|---|
| | | | |
| | | | |
| | | | |
| | | | |
| | | | |
| | | | |
| | | | |
| | | | |
| | | | |
| | | | |
| | | | |
| | | | |
| | | | |
| | | | |
| | | | |
| | | | |
| | | | |
| | | | |
| | | | |

*Analysis component:* _____

_____
_____
_____

**Exercise 2-6**

## Income Statement

| | | |
|---|---|---|
| | | |
| | | |
| | | |
| | | |
| | | |
| | | |
| | | |
| | | |
| | | |
| | | |

## Statement of Owner's Equity

| | | |
|---|---|---|
| | | |
| | | |
| | | |
| | | |
| | | |
| | | |
| | | |
| | | |
| | | |
| | | |
| | | |
| | | |

*Analysis component:*
_____
_____
_____
_____

**Exercise 2-8**

## Balance Sheet

| | | | |
|---|---|---|---|
| | | | |
| | | | |
| | | | |
| | | | |
| | | | |
| | | | |
| | | | |
| | | | |
| | | | |
| | | | |
| | | | |
| | | | |
| | | | |
| | | | |

*Analysis component:*
_____
_____
_____
_____
_____

1. _____
2. _____
3. _____
4. _____
5. _____

**Exercise 2-10**

**(a) Net Income (Loss) =** [          ]
    **Supporting Calculations:** _____
_____
_____
_____
_____
_____
_____

**(b) Net Income (Loss) =** [          ]
    **Supporting Calculations:** _____
_____
_____
_____
_____
_____
_____

**(c) Net Income (Loss) =** [          ]
    **Supporting Calculations:** _____
_____
_____
_____
_____
_____
_____

**(d) Net Income (Loss) =** [          ]
    **Supporting Calculations:** _____
_____
_____
_____
_____
_____
_____

**(a) Assets =**
**Owner's Equity  =** [                    ]
**Supporting Calculations:** _____

_____
_____
_____
_____
_____
_____

**(b) Liabilities =**
**Owner's Equity =** [                    ]
**Supporting Calculations:** _____

_____
_____
_____
_____
_____
_____

## Exercise 2-12

| | | ASSETS | | | = | LIABILITIES | + | OWNER'S EQUITY |
|---|---|---|---|---|---|---|---|---|
| CASH | + | ACCOUNTS RECEIVABLE | + | OFFICE SUPPLIES | = | ACCOUNTS PAYABLE | + | NOEL BRIDGES, CAPITAL |
| (a) | | | | | | | | |
| (b) | | | | | | | | |
| (c) | | | | | | | | |
| (d) | | | | | | | | |
| (e) | | | | | | | | |
| (f) | | | | | | | | |

| | ASSETS | | | = | LIABILITIES | + | OWNER'S EQUITY |
| CASH | + ACCOUNTS RECEIVABLE | + PARTS SUPPLIES | + EQUIPMENT | = ACCOUNTS PAYABLE | + | JANINE COMMRY, CAPITAL |
|---|---|---|---|---|---|---|
| (a) _____ | _____ | _____ | _____ | _____ | _____ |
| (b) _____ | _____ | _____ | _____ | _____ | _____ |
| (c) _____ | _____ | _____ | _____ | _____ | _____ |
| (d) _____ | _____ | _____ | _____ | _____ | _____ |
| (e) _____ | _____ | _____ | _____ | _____ | _____ |
| (f) _____ | _____ | _____ | _____ | _____ | _____ |
| (g) _____ | _____ | _____ | _____ | _____ | _____ |
| (h) _____ | _____ | _____ | _____ | _____ | _____ |
| (i) _____ | _____ | _____ | _____ | _____ | _____ |

## Exercise 2-14

a. _____
b. _____
c. _____
d. _____
e. _____
f. _____
g. _____

## Exercise 2-15

a. _____
b. _____
c. _____
d. _____
e. _____
f. _____
g. _____
h. _____

**Name** _____

| | ASSETS | | | = | LIABILITIES | + | OWNER'S EQUITY | |
|---|---|---|---|---|---|---|---|---|
| CASH | + | ACCOUNTS RECEIVABLE | + | EQUIPMENT | = | ACCOUNTS PAYABLE | + | ELLEN MANSON, CAPITAL | EXPLANATION OF CHANGE IN OWNER'S EQUITY |
| a. | | | | | | | | |
| b. | | | | | | | | |
| c. | | | | | | | | |
| d. | | | | | | | | |
| e. | | | | | | | | |
| f. | | | | | | | | |
| g. | | | | | | | | |
| h. | | | | | | | | |
| i. | | | | | | | | |
| j. | | | | | | | | |

## Exercise 2-17

a. _____

b. _____

c. _____

d. _____

e. _____

f. _____

| | | ASSETS | | | = | LIABILITIES | + | OWNER'S EQUITY | |
|---|---|---|---|---|---|---|---|---|---|
| CASH | + | ACCOUNTS RECEIVABLE | + SUPPLIES | + | EQUIP-MENT = | ACCOUNTS PAYABLE | + | ANNIE DEWEERD, CAPITAL | EXPLANATION OF CHANGE IN OWNER'S EQUITY |
| a. | | | | | | | | | |
| | | | | | | | | | |
| b. | | | | | | | | | |
| | | | | | | | | | |
| c. | | | | | | | | | |
| | | | | | | | | | |
| d. | | | | | | | | | |
| | | | | | | | | | |
| e. | | | | | | | | | |
| | | | | | | | | | |
| f. | | | | | | | | | |
| | | | | | | | | | |
| g. | | | | | | | | | |
| | | | | | | | | | |

## Annie Deweerd – Freelance Writing
## Income Statement
## For Month Ended March 31, 2011

Revenues:
    Freelance service revenue ....................................
Operating expenses:
    Salaries expense .................................................
    Rent expense ......................................................    _____
       Total operating expenses...................................    _____
Net income .............................................................    _____

## Annie Deweerd – Freelance Writing
## Statement of Owner's Equity
## For Month Ended March 31, 2011

Annie Deweerd, capital, March 1 ...............................
Add:  Investment by owner...........................................
       Net income ...............................................    _____
Annie Deweerd, capital, March 31 .............................

## Annie Deweerd – Freelance Writing
## Balance Sheet
## March 31, 2011

| Assets | | Liabilities | |
|---|---|---|---|
| Cash .......................... | | Accounts payable............................ | |
| Accounts receivable.. | | | |
| Supplies ..................... | | | |
| Equipment.................. | | **Owner's Equity** | |
| | _____ | Annie Deweerd, capital ...................... | _____ |
| Total assets................. | _____ | Total liabilities and owner's equity ... | _____ |

*Analysis component:* _____
_____
_____
_____
_____
_____
_____

| | | ASSETS | | | = | LIABILITIES | + | OWNER'S EQUITY | |
|---|---|---|---|---|---|---|---|---|---|
| CASH | + | ACCOUNTS RECEIVABLE | + SUPPLIES | + EQUIP- MENT | = | ACCOUNTS PAYABLE | + | PETE JONG, CAPITAL | EXPLANATION OF CHANGE IN OWNER'S EQUITY |
| a. | | | | | | | | | |
| | | | | | | | | | |
| b. | | | | | | | | | |
| | | | | | | | | | |
| c. | | | | | | | | | |
| | | | | | | | | | |
| d. | | | | | | | | | |
| | | | | | | | | | |
| e. | | | | | | | | | |
| | | | | | | | | | |
| f. | | | | | | | | | |
| | | | | | | | | | |
| g. | | | | | | | | | |
| | | | | | | | | | |
| h. | | | | | | | | | |
| | | | | | | | | | |

## Exercise 2-21

### Income Statement

| | | |
|---|---|---|
| | | |
| | | |
| | | |
| | | |
| | | |
| | | |
| | | |
| | | |
| | | |
| | | |
| | | |
| | | |
| | | |
| | | |
| | | |
| | | |
| | | |

## Statement of Owner's Equity

| | | |
|---|---|---|
| | | |
| | | |
| | | |
| | | |
| | | |
| | | |
| | | |
| | | |
| | | |
| | | |
| | | |

## Balance Sheet

| | | | |
|---|---|---|---|
| | | | |
| | | | |
| | | | |
| | | | |
| | | | |
| | | | |
| | | | |
| | | | |
| | | | |
| | | | |
| | | | |
| | | | |
| | | | |
| | | | |
| | | | |
| | | | |
| | | | |
| | | | |

*Analysis component:* _____

_____

_____

_____

_____

_____

_____

_____

_____

| | | ASSETS | | | = | LIABILITIES | + | OWNER'S EQUITY | |
|---|---|---|---|---|---|---|---|---|---|
| CASH | + | ACCOUNTS RECEIVABLE | + SUPPLIES + | EQUIP-MENT | = | ACCOUNTS PAYABLE | + | OTTO INGLES, CAPITAL | EXPLANATION OF CHANGE IN OWNER'S EQUITY |
| a. | | | | | | | | | |
| b. | | | | | | | | | |
| c. | | | | | | | | | |
| d. | | | | | | | | | |
| e. | | | | | | | | | |
| f. | | | | | | | | | |
| g. | | | | | | | | | |
| h. | | | | | | | | | |

## Exercise 2-23

### Income Statement

| | | |
|---|---|---|
| | | |
| | | |
| | | |
| | | |
| | | |
| | | |
| | | |
| | | |
| | | |
| | | |
| | | |
| | | |
| | | |
| | | |
| | | |
| | | |

## Statement of Owner's Equity

| | | |
|---|---|---|
| | | |
| | | |
| | | |
| | | |
| | | |
| | | |
| | | |
| | | |

## Balance Sheet

| | | | |
|---|---|---|---|
| | | | |
| | | | |
| | | | |
| | | | |
| | | | |
| | | | |
| | | | |
| | | | |
| | | | |
| | | | |
| | | | |
| | | | |
| | | | |
| | | | |
| | | | |
| | | | |
| | | | |
| | | | |

### Analysis component:

_____
_____
_____
_____
_____
_____
_____
_____
_____

**2009 Net Income (Loss) =** [                    ]
    **Supporting Calculations:** _____

_____
_____
_____
_____
_____
_____
_____
_____
_____
_____

**Problem 2-2A**

| Income Statement | | |
|---|---|---|
| | | |
| | | |
| | | |
| | | |
| | | |
| | | |
| | | |
| | | |
| | | |
| | | |
| | | |
| | | |
| | | |
| | | |
| | | |
| | | |
| | | |
| | | |

| Statement of Owner's Equity | | |
|---|---|---|
| | | |
| | | |
| | | |
| | | |
| | | |
| | | |
| | | |
| | | |

## Balance Sheet

| | | | |
|---|---|---|---|
| | | | |
| | | | |
| | | | |
| | | | |
| | | | |
| | | | |
| | | | |
| | | | |
| | | | |
| | | | |
| | | | |

**Problem 2-3A**
  **Part 1**

## Balance Sheet

| | | | |
|---|---|---|---|
| | | | |
| | | | |
| | | | |
| | | | |
| | | | |
| | | | |
| | | | |
| | | | |
| | | | |
| | | | |
| | | | |

## Balance Sheet

| | | | |
|---|---|---|---|
| | | | |
| | | | |
| | | | |
| | | | |
| | | | |
| | | | |
| | | | |
| | | | |
| | | | |
| | | | |
| | | | |

**Net Income (Loss) Calculation:**

_____
_____
_____
_____
_____
_____
_____
_____
_____
_____
_____
_____

*Analysis component:*

_____
_____
_____
_____
_____
_____
_____

**Problem 2-4A**

**Part 1: Company A**
**(a)** _____
_____
_____
_____

**(b)** _____
_____
_____
_____

**(c)** _____
_____
_____
_____
_____

**Part 2: Company B**

(a) _____
_____
_____
_____
_____

(b) _____
_____
_____
_____
_____

(c) _____
_____
_____
_____
_____

**Part 3: Company C**

_____
_____
_____
_____
_____
_____
_____
_____
_____
_____
_____
_____
_____
_____
_____
_____
_____

**Part 4: Company D**

_____
_____
_____
_____
_____
_____
_____
_____
_____
_____
_____
_____
_____
_____
_____
_____
_____
_____

**Part 5: Company E**

_____
_____
_____
_____
_____
_____
_____
_____
_____
_____
_____
_____
_____
_____
_____
_____
_____

|  | ASSETS | | | | | = | LIABILITIES | | + | OWNER'S EQUITY | |
|---|---|---|---|---|---|---|---|---|---|---|---|
| CASH | + ACCOUNTS RECEIVABLE | + OFFICE SUPPLIES | + OFFICE EQUIPMENT | + BUILDING | | = | ACCOUNTS PAYABLE | + NOTES PAYABLE | + | DAN MURRAY, CAPITAL | EXPLANATION OF CHANGE |
| (a) | | | | | | | | | | | |
| (b) | | | | | | | | | | | |
| Bal. | | | | | | | | | | | |
| _ | | | | | | | | | | | |
| Bal. | | | | | | | | | | | |
| (d) | | | | | | | | | | | |
| Bal. | | | | | | | | | | | |
| (e) | | | | | | | | | | | |
| Bal. | | | | | | | | | | | |
| (f) | | | | | | | | | | | |
| Bal. | | | | | | | | | | | |
| (g) | | | | | | | | | | | |
| Bal. | | | | | | | | | | | |
| (h) | | | | | | | | | | | |
| Bal. | | | | | | | | | | | |
| (i) | | | | | | | | | | | |
| Bal. | | | | | | | | | | | |
| (j) | | | | | | | | | | | |
| Bal. | | | | | | | | | | | |
| (k) | | | | | | | | | | | |
| Bal. | | | | | | | | | | | |
| (l) | | | | | | | | | | | |
| Bal. | | | | | | | | | | | |

**Murray Enterprises**
**Income Statement**
**For Month Ended March 31, 2011**

Revenues :
    Service revenue ......................................................
Operating expenses:
    Wages expense.....................................................
    Advertising expense............................................     _____
        Total operating expenses..................................
Net loss ..................................................................     _____

**Murray Enterprises**
**Statement of Owner's Equity**
**For Month Ended March 31, 2011**

Dan Murray, capital, March 1
Add:  Investment by owner
    Total                                                                         _____
Less:  Withdrawal by owner
        Net loss                                                                 _____
Dan Murray, capital, March 31

**Murray Enterprises**
**Balance Sheet**
**March 31, 2011**

| Assets | | Liabilities | |
|---|---|---|---|
| Cash | | Accounts payable | |
| Accounts receivable | | Notes payable | _____ |
| Office supplies | | Total liabilities | |
| Office equipment | | | |
| Building | | **Owner's Equity** | |
| | | Dan Murray, capital | |
| Total assets | _____ | Total liabilities and owner's equity | _____ |

*Analysis component:* _____
_____
_____
_____
_____
_____
_____
_____
_____

Name _____

| DATE | ASSETS | | | = | LIABILITIES | + | OWNER'S EQUITY | |
| --- | --- | --- | --- | --- | --- | --- | --- | --- |
| | CASH | + ACCOUNTS RECEIVABLE | + OFFICE SUPPLIES | = | ACCOUNTS PAYABLE | + | BEV NG, CAPITAL | EXPLANATION OF CHANGE |

**Analysis component:** _____
_____
_____
_____
_____
_____
_____

## Income Statement

| | | |
|---|---|---|
| | | |
| | | |
| | | |
| | | |
| | | |
| | | |
| | | |
| | | |
| | | |
| | | |
| | | |
| | | |

## Statement of Owner's Equity

| | | |
|---|---|---|
| | | |
| | | |
| | | |
| | | |
| | | |
| | | |
| | | |
| | | |

## Balance Sheet

| | | | |
|---|---|---|---|
| | | | |
| | | | |
| | | | |
| | | | |
| | | | |
| | | | |
| | | | |
| | | | |
| | | | |
| | | | |
| | | | |
| | | | |
| | | | |

*Analysis component:* _____

_____

_____

_____

_____

_____

_____

_____

_____

_____

_____

_____

_____

_____

| DATE | CASH | + | ACCOUNTS RECEIVABLE | + | OFFICE SUPPLIES | + | OFFICE EQUIPMENT | + | ELECTRICAL EQUIPMENT | = | ACCOUNTS PAYABLE | + | LARRY POWER CAPITAL | EXPLANATION OF CHANGE |
|------|------|---|---------------------|---|-----------------|---|------------------|---|----------------------|---|------------------|---|---------------------|------------------------|
| | | | | | | | | | | | | | | |

**ASSETS** = **LIABILITIES** + **OWNER'S EQUITY**

*Analysis component:*

_____
_____
_____
_____
_____
_____

## Problem 2-8A

### Income Statement

| | | |
|---|---|---|
| | | |
| | | |
| | | |
| | | |
| | | |
| | | |
| | | |
| | | |
| | | |
| | | |
| | | |
| | | |
| | | |
| | | |

### Statement of Owner's Equity

| | | |
|---|---|---|
| | | |
| | | |
| | | |
| | | |
| | | |
| | | |
| | | |
| | | |
| | | |

## Balance Sheet

| | | | |
|---|---|---|---|
| | | | |
| | | | |
| | | | |
| | | | |
| | | | |
| | | | |
| | | | |
| | | | |
| | | | |
| | | | |
| | | | |
| | | | |
| | | | |
| | | | |
| | | | |
| | | | |
| | | | |
| | | | |

*Analysis component:*

_____

_____

_____

_____

_____

_____

## Problem 2-9A

| | TRANSACTION | BALANCE SHEET | | | INCOME STATEMENT |
|---|---|---|---|---|---|
| | | TOTAL ASSETS | TOTAL LIABILITIES | EQUITY | NET INCOME |
| 1. | Owner invests cash | | | | |
| 2. | Sell services for cash | | | | |
| 3. | Acquire services on credit | | | | |
| 4. | Pay wages with cash | | | | |
| 5. | Owner withdraws cash | | | | |
| 6. | Borrow cash with note payable | | | | |
| 7. | Sell services on credit | | | | |
| 8. | Buy office equipment for cash | | | | |
| 9. | Collect receivable from (7) | | | | |
| 10. | Buy asset with note payable | | | | |

**Chapter 2    Problem 2-1B**    *Name* _____

**2010 Net Income (Loss) =**    [              ]
    **Supporting Calculations:** _____

_____
_____
_____
_____
_____
_____
_____
_____
_____
_____


**Problem 2-2B**

### Income Statement

| | | |
|---|---|---|
| | | |
| | | |
| | | |
| | | |
| | | |
| | | |
| | | |
| | | |
| | | |
| | | |
| | | |
| | | |
| | | |
| | | |
| | | |
| | | |


### Statement of Owner's Equity

| | | |
|---|---|---|
| | | |
| | | |
| | | |
| | | |
| | | |
| | | |
| | | |
| | | |

## Balance Sheet

| | | | |
|---|---|---|---|
| | | | |
| | | | |
| | | | |
| | | | |
| | | | |
| | | | |
| | | | |
| | | | |
| | | | |
| | | | |
| | | | |

**Problem 2-3B     Part 1**

## Balance Sheet

| | | | |
|---|---|---|---|
| | | | |
| | | | |
| | | | |
| | | | |
| | | | |
| | | | |
| | | | |
| | | | |
| | | | |

## Balance Sheet

| | | | |
|---|---|---|---|
| | | | |
| | | | |
| | | | |
| | | | |
| | | | |
| | | | |
| | | | |
| | | | |
| | | | |
| | | | |

**Net Income (Loss) Calculation:** _____

_____
_____
_____
_____
_____
_____
_____
_____
_____
_____
_____

*Analysis component:* _____

_____
_____
_____
_____
_____

**Problem 2-4B**
**Part 1:  Company V**

(a) _____

_____
_____
_____

(b) _____

_____
_____
_____

(c) _____

_____
_____
_____
_____

**Part 2: Company W**

**(a)** _____

_____

_____

_____

**(b)** _____

_____

_____

_____

**(c)** _____

_____

_____

_____

**Part 3: Company X**

_____

_____

_____

_____

_____

_____

_____

_____

_____

_____

_____

_____

_____

_____

_____

**Part 4: Company Y**

_____
_____
_____
_____
_____
_____
_____
_____
_____
_____
_____
_____
_____
_____
_____
_____
_____

**Part 5: Company Z**

_____
_____
_____
_____
_____
_____
_____
_____
_____
_____
_____
_____
_____
_____
_____

| | | ASSETS | | | | | = | LIABILITIES | | + | OWNER'S EQUITY | |
|---|---|---|---|---|---|---|---|---|---|---|---|---|
| | CASH | + ACCOUNTS RECEIVABLE | + OFFICE SUPPLIES | + OFFICE EQUIPMENT | + BUILDING | | = | ACCOUNTS PAYABLE | + NOTES PAYABLE | + | Judith Grimm, CAPITAL | EXPLANATION OF CHANGE |
| (a) | | | | | | | | | | | | |
| (b) | | | | | | | | | | | | |
| Bal. | | | | | | | | | | | | |
| (c) | | | | | | | | | | | | |
| Bal. | | | | | | | | | | | | |
| (d) | | | | | | | | | | | | |
| Bal. | | | | | | | | | | | | |
| (e) | | | | | | | | | | | | |
| Bal. | | | | | | | | | | | | |
| (f) | | | | | | | | | | | | |
| Bal. | | | | | | | | | | | | |
| (g) | | | | | | | | | | | | |
| Bal. | | | | | | | | | | | | |
| (h) | | | | | | | | | | | | |
| Bal. | | | | | | | | | | | | |
| (i) | | | | | | | | | | | | |
| Bal. | | | | | | | | | | | | |
| (j) | | | | | | | | | | | | |
| Bal. | | | | | | | | | | | | |
| (k) | | | | | | | | | | | | |
| Bal. | | | | | | | | | | | | |
| (l) | | | | | | | | | | | | |
| Bal. | | | | | | | | | | | | |

**Southwest Consulting**
**Income Statement**
**For Year Ended December 31, 2011**

Revenues:
   Consulting services revenue ................................
Operating expenses:
   Wages expense.......................................................
   Advertising expense.............................................    _____
      Total operating expenses....................................
Net income ................................................................    _____

**Southwest Consulting**
**Statement of Owner's Equity**
**For Year Ended December 31, 2011**

Judith Grimm, capital, January 1
Add:  Investment by owner
         Net income                                                   _____
   Total
Less:  Withdrawals by owner                                          _____
Judith Grimm, capital, December 31                                   _____

**Southwest Consulting**
**Balance Sheet**
**December 31, 2011**

| Assets | | Liabilities | |
|---|---|---|---|
| Cash | | Accounts payable | |
| Accounts receivable | | Notes payable | _____ |
| Office supplies | | Total liabilities | |
| Office equipment | | | |
| Building | | **Owner's Equity** | |
| | | Judith Grimm, capital | |
| Total assets | _____ | Total liabilities and owner's equity | _____ |

*Analysis component:* _____
_____
_____
_____
_____
_____
_____
_____
_____

| DATE | CASH | + | ACCOUNTS RECEIVABLE | + | CLEANING SUPPLIES | = | ACCOUNTS PAYABLE | + | Andrew Martin, CAPITAL | EXPLANATION OF CHANGE |
|------|------|---|---------------------|---|-------------------|---|------------------|---|------------------------|------------------------|
| | | | | | | | | | | |

ASSETS = LIABILITIES + OWNER'S EQUITY

**Part 3**

## Income Statement

| | | |
|---|---|---|
| | | |
| | | |
| | | |
| | | |
| | | |
| | | |
| | | |
| | | |
| | | |
| | | |

## Statement of Owner's Equity

| | | |
|---|---|---|
| | | |
| | | |
| | | |
| | | |
| | | |
| | | |
| | | |

## Balance Sheet

| | | | |
|---|---|---|---|
| | | | |
| | | | |
| | | | |
| | | | |
| | | | |
| | | | |
| | | | |
| | | | |

*Analysis component:*

_____
_____
_____
_____
_____
_____

| DATE | ASSETS | | | | | = LIABILITIES + | OWNER'S EQUITY | |
|---|---|---|---|---|---|---|---|---|
| | CASH | + ACCOUNTS RECEIVABLE | + OFFICE SUPPLIES | + OFFICE EQUIPMENT | + EXCAVATING EQUIPMENT | = ACCOUNTS PAYABLE | + Robert Cantu, CAPITAL | EXPLANATION OF CHANGE |

## *Analysis component:*

_____
_____
_____
_____
_____
_____
_____
_____

## Problem 2-8B

### Income Statement

| | | |
|---|---|---|
| | | |
| | | |
| | | |
| | | |
| | | |
| | | |
| | | |
| | | |
| | | |
| | | |
| | | |
| | | |
| | | |
| | | |
| | | |

### Statement of Owner's Equity

| | | |
|---|---|---|
| | | |
| | | |
| | | |
| | | |
| | | |
| | | |
| | | |
| | | |
| | | |
| | | |

## Balance Sheet

| | | | |
|---|---|---|---|
| | | | |
| | | | |
| | | | |
| | | | |
| | | | |
| | | | |
| | | | |
| | | | |
| | | | |
| | | | |
| | | | |
| | | | |
| | | | |
| | | | |

*Analysis component:* _____

_____

_____

_____

_____

_____

_____

_____

## Problem 2-9B

| | | BALANCE SHEET | | | INCOME STATEMENT |
|---|---|---|---|---|---|
| | TRANSACTION | TOTAL ASSETS | TOTAL LIABILITIES | EQUITY | NET INCOME |
| 1. | Owner invests cash | | | | |
| 2. | Pay wages with cash | | | | |
| 3. | Acquire services on credit | | | | |
| 4. | Buy store equipment for cash | | | | |
| 5. | Borrow cash with note payable | | | | |
| 6. | Sell services for cash | | | | |
| 7. | Sell services on credit | | | | |
| 8. | Pay rent with cash | | | | |
| 9. | Owner withdraws cash | | | | |
| 10. | Collect receivable from (7) | | | | |

1. _____ Buildings
2. _____ Building Repair Expense
3. _____ Wages Expense
4. _____ Wages Payable
5. _____ Notes Receivable
6. _____ Notes Payable
7. _____ Prepaid Advertising
8. _____ Advertising Expense
9. _____ Advertising Payable
10. _____ Unearned Advertising
11. _____ Advertising Fees Earned
12. _____ Interest Earned
13. _____ Interest Expense
14. _____ Interest Payable
15. _____ Earned Subscription Fees
16. _____ Unearned Subscription Fees
17. _____ Prepaid Subscription Fees
18. _____ Supplies
19. _____ Supplies Expense
20. _____ Rent Revenue
21. _____ Unearned Rent Revenue
22. _____ Prepaid Rent
23. _____ Rent Payable
24. _____ Service Fees Earned
25. _____ Jan Sted, Withdrawals
26. _____ Jan Sted, Capital
27. _____ Salaries Expense
28. _____ Salaries Payable
29. _____ Furniture
30. _____ Equipment

## Quick Study 3-2

| Accounts Receivable | |
|---|---|
| 1,000 | 650 |
| 400 | 920 |
| 920 | 1,500 |
| 3,000 | |

| Accounts Payable | |
|---|---|
| 250 | 250 |
| 900 | 1,800 |
| 650 | 1,400 |
| | 650 |

| Service Revenue | |
|---|---|
| | 13,000 |
| | 2,500 |
| | 810 |
| | 3,500 |

| Utilities Expense | |
|---|---|
| 610 | |
| 520 | |
| 390 | |
| 275 | |

| Cash | |
|---|---|
| 3,900 | 2,400 |
| 17,800 | 3,900 |
| 14,500 | 21,800 |
| 340 | |

| Notes Payable | |
|---|---|
| 4,000 | 50,000 |
| 8,000 | |

a. _____ Equipment

b. _____ Land

c. _____ Al Tait, Withdrawals

d. _____ Rent Expense

e. _____ Interest Revenue

f. _____ Prepaid Rent

g. _____ Accounts Receivable

h. _____ Office Supplies

i. _____ Notes Receivable

j. _____ Notes Payable

k. _____ Al Tait, Capital

l. _____ Rent Earned

m. _____ Rent Payable

n. _____ Interest Expense

o. _____ Interest Payable

## Quick Study 3-4

a. _____ To increase Notes Payable

b. _____ To decrease Accounts Receivable

c. _____ To increase Owner, Capital

d. _____ To decrease Unearned Fees

e. _____ To decrease Prepaid Insurance

f. _____ To decrease Cash

g. _____ To increase Utilities Expense

h. _____ To increase Fees Earned

i. _____ To increase Store Equipment

j. _____ To increase Owner, Withdrawals

k. _____ To decrease Rent Payable

l. _____ To decrease Prepaid Rent

m. _____ To increase Supplies

n. _____ To increase Supplies Expense

o. _____ To decrease Accounts Payable

## Quick Study 3-5

a. _____ Buildings

b. _____ Interest Revenue

c. _____ Bob Norton, Withdrawals

d. _____ Bob Norton, Capital

e. _____ Prepaid Insurance

f. _____ Interest Payable

g. _____ Accounts Receivable

h. _____ Salaries Expense

i. _____ Office Supplies

j. _____ Repair Services Revenue

k. _____ Interest Expense

l. _____ Unearned Revenue

m. _____ Salaries Payable

n. _____ Furniture

o. _____ Interest Receivable

## Quick Study 3-6

a. _____ Buildings

b. _____ Interest Revenue

c. _____ Bob Norton, Withdrawals

d. _____ Bob Norton, Capital

e. _____ Prepaid Insurance

f. _____ Interest Payable

g. _____ Accounts Receivable

h. _____ Salaries Expense

i. _____ Office Supplies

j. _____ Repair Services Revenue

k. _____ Interest Expense

l. _____ Unearned Revenue

m. _____ Salaries Payable

n. _____ Furniture

o. _____ Interest Receivable

|  Cash          101  |  Accounts Receivable   106  |
|  Furniture      161  |  Accounts Payable     201  |
|  Del Martin, Capital 301  |  Revenue          403  |

**Part 2**

_____
_____
_____
_____

**Quick Study 3-8**

## GENERAL JOURNAL                                    Page ____

| Date | Account Titles and Explanation | PR | Debit | Credit |
|------|-------------------------------|----|-------|--------|
|      |                               |    |       |        |
|      |                               |    |       |        |
|      |                               |    |       |        |
|      |                               |    |       |        |
|      |                               |    |       |        |
|      |                               |    |       |        |
|      |                               |    |       |        |
|      |                               |    |       |        |
|      |                               |    |       |        |
|      |                               |    |       |        |
|      |                               |    |       |        |
|      |                               |    |       |        |
|      |                               |    |       |        |
|      |                               |    |       |        |
|      |                               |    |       |        |
|      |                               |    |       |        |

## GENERAL JOURNAL    Page ____

| Date | Account Titles and Explanation | PR | Debit | Credit |
|------|-------------------------------|----|-------|--------|
|      |                               |    |       |        |
|      |                               |    |       |        |
|      |                               |    |       |        |
|      |                               |    |       |        |
|      |                               |    |       |        |
|      |                               |    |       |        |
|      |                               |    |       |        |
|      |                               |    |       |        |
|      |                               |    |       |        |
|      |                               |    |       |        |
|      |                               |    |       |        |
|      |                               |    |       |        |
|      |                               |    |       |        |
|      |                               |    |       |        |
|      |                               |    |       |        |
|      |                               |    |       |        |
|      |                               |    |       |        |
|      |                               |    |       |        |
|      |                               |    |       |        |
|      |                               |    |       |        |

## Quick Study 3-9

## GENERAL JOURNAL    Page ____

| Date | Account Titles and Explanation | PR | Debit | Credit |
|------|-------------------------------|----|-------|--------|
|      |                               |    |       |        |
|      |                               |    |       |        |
|      |                               |    |       |        |
|      |                               |    |       |        |
|      |                               |    |       |        |
|      |                               |    |       |        |
|      |                               |    |       |        |
|      |                               |    |       |        |
|      |                               |    |       |        |
|      |                               |    |       |        |
|      |                               |    |       |        |
|      |                               |    |       |        |
|      |                               |    |       |        |
|      |                               |    |       |        |
|      |                               |    |       |        |
|      |                               |    |       |        |
|      |                               |    |       |        |
|      |                               |    |       |        |
|      |                               |    |       |        |

## GENERAL JOURNAL                                    Page ____

| Date | Account Titles and Explanation | PR | Debit | Credit |
|------|-------------------------------|-----|-------|--------|
|      |                               |     |       |        |
|      |                               |     |       |        |
|      |                               |     |       |        |
|      |                               |     |       |        |
|      |                               |     |       |        |
|      |                               |     |       |        |
|      |                               |     |       |        |
|      |                               |     |       |        |
|      |                               |     |       |        |

## Quick Study 3-10

### Cash                                              ACCOUNT NO. ____

| DATE | EXPLANATION | PR | DEBIT | CREDIT | BALANCE |
|------|-------------|-----|-------|--------|---------|
|      |             |     |       |        |         |
|      |             |     |       |        |         |
|      |             |     |       |        |         |
|      |             |     |       |        |         |
|      |             |     |       |        |         |

### Office Supplies                                   ACCOUNT NO. ____

| DATE | EXPLANATION | PR | DEBIT | CREDIT | BALANCE |
|------|-------------|-----|-------|--------|---------|
|      |             |     |       |        |         |
|      |             |     |       |        |         |

### Equipment                                         ACCOUNT NO. ____

| DATE | EXPLANATION | PR | DEBIT | CREDIT | BALANCE |
|------|-------------|-----|-------|--------|---------|
|      |             |     |       |        |         |
|      |             |     |       |        |         |

### Accounts Payable                                  ACCOUNT NO. ____

| DATE | EXPLANATION | PR | DEBIT | CREDIT | BALANCE |
|------|-------------|-----|-------|--------|---------|
|      |             |     |       |        |         |
|      |             |     |       |        |         |
|      |             |     |       |        |         |
|      |             |     |       |        |         |
|      |             |     |       |        |         |

### Stan Adams, Capital                    ACCOUNT NO. ____

| DATE | EXPLANATION | PR | DEBIT | CREDIT | BALANCE |
|------|-------------|----|-------|--------|---------|
|      |             |    |       |        |         |
|      |             |    |       |        |         |

### Landscaping Services Revenue          ACCOUNT NO. ____

| DATE | EXPLANATION | PR | DEBIT | CREDIT | BALANCE |
|------|-------------|----|-------|--------|---------|
|      |             |    |       |        |         |
|      |             |    |       |        |         |

## Quick Study 3-11

### Trial Balance

|  | Debit | Credit |
|--|-------|--------|
|  |       |        |
|  |       |        |
|  |       |        |
|  |       |        |
|  |       |        |
|  |       |        |
|  |       |        |
|  |       |        |
|  |       |        |
|  |       |        |
|  |       |        |

## Quick Study 3-12

_____
_____
_____
_____
_____

## Quick Study 3-13

_____
_____
_____
_____
_____
_____
_____
_____

_____
_____
_____
_____
_____
_____
_____
_____
_____

## Exercise 3-1

| Cash | Accounts Receivable |
|------|---------------------|
|      |                     |

|  | Office Supplies |
|--|-----------------|
|  |                 |

| Office Equipment | Accounts Payable |
|------------------|------------------|
|                  |                  |

| Ella Tims, Capital | Ella Tims, Withdrawals |
|--------------------|------------------------|
|                    |                        |

| Fees Earned | Rent Expense |
|-------------|--------------|
|             |              |

| Cash | | | Accounts Receivable | | |
|---|---|---|---|---|---|
| Bal. | 700 | | Bal. | 1,200 | |

| | | | Prepaid Insurance | | |
|---|---|---|---|---|---|
| | | | Bal. | -0- | |

| Computer Equipment | | | Accounts Payable | | |
|---|---|---|---|---|---|
| Bal. | 480 | | | 60 | Bal. |

| Notes Payable | | | Neil Simon, Capital | | |
|---|---|---|---|---|---|
| | -0- | Bal. | | 800 | Bal. |

| Neil Simon, Withdrawals | | | Service Revenue | | |
|---|---|---|---|---|---|
| Bal. | -0- | | | 2,600 | Bal. |

| | | | Wages Expense | | |
|---|---|---|---|---|---|
| | | | Bal. | 1,080 | |

*Analysis component:* _____

_____
_____
_____
_____
_____
_____
_____
_____
_____

| Cash | | | | Accounts Receivable | |
|---|---|---|---|---|---|
| Bal. | 1,800 | | | Bal. | 4,800 |

| | | | | Repair Supplies | |
|---|---|---|---|---|---|
| | | | | Bal. | 1,400 |

| Equipment | | | | Accounts Payable | |
|---|---|---|---|---|---|
| Bal. | 7,400 | | | 500 | Bal. |

| Nels Sigurdsen, Capital | | | | Nels Sigurdsen, Withdrawals | |
|---|---|---|---|---|---|
| | 2,350 | Bal. | Bal. | 500 | |

| Repair Revenue | | | | Rent Expense | |
|---|---|---|---|---|---|
| | 14,000 | Bal. | Bal. | 950 | |

## Exercise 3-4

Parts 1 and 3

*Note: T-accounts may be used or the balance column format; both are provided for in Parts 1 and 3 of this exercise.*

| Cash | 101 | | Accounts Receivable | 106 |
|---|---|---|---|---|

| | | | Equipment | 150 |
|---|---|---|---|---|

| Accounts Payable | 201 | | Sue Ware, Capital | 301 |
|---|---|---|---|---|

| Sue Ware, Withdrawals      302 | Revenue      401 |
|---|---|

| Expenses      501 |
|---|

## Parts 1 and 3

*Note:  T-accounts may be used or the balance column format; both are provided for in Parts 1 and 3 of this exercise.*

### GENERAL LEDGER

**Cash**      ACCOUNT NO. 101

| DATE | EXPLANATION | PR | DEBIT | CREDIT | BALANCE |
|---|---|---|---|---|---|
|  |  |  |  |  |  |
|  |  |  |  |  |  |
|  |  |  |  |  |  |
|  |  |  |  |  |  |
|  |  |  |  |  |  |

**Accounts Receivable**      ACCOUNT NO. 106

| DATE | EXPLANATION | PR | DEBIT | CREDIT | BALANCE |
|---|---|---|---|---|---|
|  |  |  |  |  |  |
|  |  |  |  |  |  |
|  |  |  |  |  |  |

**Equipment**      ACCOUNT NO. 150

| DATE | EXPLANATION | PR | DEBIT | CREDIT | BALANCE |
|---|---|---|---|---|---|
|  |  |  |  |  |  |
|  |  |  |  |  |  |
|  |  |  |  |  |  |

**Accounts Payable**      ACCOUNT NO. 201

| DATE | EXPLANATION | PR | DEBIT | CREDIT | BALANCE |
|---|---|---|---|---|---|
|  |  |  |  |  |  |
|  |  |  |  |  |  |
|  |  |  |  |  |  |

### Sue Ware, Capital                                    ACCOUNT NO. 301

| DATE | EXPLANATION | PR | DEBIT | CREDIT | BALANCE |
|------|-------------|----|-------|--------|---------|
|      |             |    |       |        |         |
|      |             |    |       |        |         |

### Sue Ware, Withdrawals                                ACCOUNT NO. 302_

| DATE | EXPLANATION | PR | DEBIT | CREDIT | BALANCE |
|------|-------------|----|-------|--------|---------|
|      |             |    |       |        |         |
|      |             |    |       |        |         |

### Revenue                                              ACCOUNT NO. 401

| DATE | EXPLANATION | PR | DEBIT | CREDIT | BALANCE |
|------|-------------|----|-------|--------|---------|
|      |             |    |       |        |         |
|      |             |    |       |        |         |
|      |             |    |       |        |         |

### Expenses                                             ACCOUNT NO. 501

| DATE | EXPLANATION | PR | DEBIT | CREDIT | BALANCE |
|------|-------------|----|-------|--------|---------|
|      |             |    |       |        |         |
|      |             |    |       |        |         |

**Part 2**

### GENERAL JOURNAL                                      Page ____

| Date | Account Titles and Explanation | PR | Debit | Credit |
|------|-------------------------------|----|-------|--------|
|      |                               |    |       |        |
|      |                               |    |       |        |
|      |                               |    |       |        |
|      |                               |    |       |        |
|      |                               |    |       |        |
|      |                               |    |       |        |
|      |                               |    |       |        |
|      |                               |    |       |        |
|      |                               |    |       |        |
|      |                               |    |       |        |
|      |                               |    |       |        |
|      |                               |    |       |        |
|      |                               |    |       |        |
|      |                               |    |       |        |
|      |                               |    |       |        |
|      |                               |    |       |        |
|      |                               |    |       |        |
|      |                               |    |       |        |
|      |                               |    |       |        |
|      |                               |    |       |        |

## GENERAL JOURNAL                              Page ____

| Date | Account Titles and Explanation | PR | Debit | Credit |
|------|-------------------------------|----|-------|--------|
|      |                               |    |       |        |
|      |                               |    |       |        |
|      |                               |    |       |        |
|      |                               |    |       |        |
|      |                               |    |       |        |
|      |                               |    |       |        |
|      |                               |    |       |        |
|      |                               |    |       |        |
|      |                               |    |       |        |

**Part 4**

## Trial Balance

| | | |
|---|---|---|
| | | |
| | | |
| | | |
| | | |
| | | |
| | | |
| | | |
| | | |
| | | |
| | | |
| | | |

**Part 5**

## Income Statement

| | | |
|---|---|---|
| | | |
| | | |
| | | |
| | | |
| | | |
| | | |
| | | |
| | | |
| | | |
| | | |

## Statement of Owner's Equity

|  |  |  |
|---|---|---|
|  |  |  |
|  |  |  |
|  |  |  |
|  |  |  |
|  |  |  |
|  |  |  |
|  |  |  |
|  |  |  |
|  |  |  |

## Balance Sheet

|  |  |  |  |
|---|---|---|---|
|  |  |  |  |
|  |  |  |  |
|  |  |  |  |
|  |  |  |  |
|  |  |  |  |
|  |  |  |  |
|  |  |  |  |
|  |  |  |  |
|  |  |  |  |
|  |  |  |  |
|  |  |  |  |
|  |  |  |  |
|  |  |  |  |
|  |  |  |  |
|  |  |  |  |
|  |  |  |  |
|  |  |  |  |

### *Analysis component:*

| Account Number | Account Name | Account Number | Account Name |
|---|---|---|---|
| _____ | Cash | _____ | Wes Bosse, Withdrawals |
| _____ | Accounts Receivable | _____ | Consulting Revenues |
| _____ | Office Equipment | _____ | Salaries Expense |
| _____ | Accounts Payable | _____ | Rent Expense |
| _____ | Unearned Revenue | _____ | Utilities Expense |
| _____ | Wes Bosse, Capital | | |

## GENERAL JOURNAL

Page ____

| Date | Account Titles and Explanation | PR | Debit | Credit |
|------|-------------------------------|----|----|----|
| | | | | |
| | | | | |
| | | | | |
| | | | | |
| | | | | |
| | | | | |
| | | | | |
| | | | | |
| | | | | |
| | | | | |
| | | | | |
| | | | | |
| | | | | |
| | | | | |
| | | | | |
| | | | | |
| | | | | |
| | | | | |
| | | | | |
| | | | | |
| | | | | |
| | | | | |
| | | | | |
| | | | | |
| | | | | |
| | | | | |
| | | | | |
| | | | | |
| | | | | |
| | | | | |
| | | | | |

## Part 2

**Cash**

| Bal. | 11,500 | |
|------|--------|---|

**Accounts Receivable**

| Bal. | 6,000 | |
|------|-------|---|

**Office Equipment**

| Bal. | 12,500 | |
|------|--------|---|

| Accounts Payable | | | Unearned Revenue | | |
|---|---|---|---|---|---|
| | 3,000 | Bal. | | 500 | Bal. |

| Wes Bosse, Capital | | | Wes Bosse, Withdrawals | | |
|---|---|---|---|---|---|
| | 9,500 | Bal. | Bal. | 2,000 | |

| Consulting Revenues | | | Salaries Expense | | |
|---|---|---|---|---|---|
| | 37,500 | Bal. | Bal. | 10,000 | |

| 520 | Rent Expense | | 530 | Utilities Expense | |
|---|---|---|---|---|---|
| Bal. | 7,500 | | Bal. | 1,000 | |

**Part 3**

### Trial Balance

| | | |
|---|---|---|
| | | |
| | | |
| | | |
| | | |
| | | |
| | | |
| | | |
| | | |
| | | |
| | | |
| | | |
| | | |
| | | |
| | | |
| | | |

**Part 4**

## Balance Sheet

| | | | |
|---|---|---|---|
| | | | |
| | | | |
| | | | |
| | | | |
| | | | |
| | | | |
| | | | |
| | | | |
| | | | |
| | | | |
| | | | |
| | | | |
| | | | |

*Analysis component:* _____

_____

_____

_____

_____

_____

_____

_____

**Exercise 3-7**

### GENERAL JOURNAL      Page ____

| Date | | Account Titles and Explanation | PR | Debit | Credit |
|---|---|---|---|---|---|
| a. | | | | | |
| | | | | | |
| | | | | | |
| | | | | | |
| | | | | | |
| b. | | | | | |
| | | | | | |
| | | | | | |
| | | | | | |
| c. | | | | | |
| | | | | | |
| | | | | | |
| | | | | | |
| | | | | | |

### GENERAL JOURNAL
Page ____

| Date | Account Titles and Explanation | PR | Debit | Credit |
|------|-------------------------------|----|-------|--------|
| d. | | | | |
| | | | | |
| | | | | |
| | | | | |
| e. | | | | |
| | | | | |
| | | | | |
| f. | | | | |
| | | | | |
| | | | | |
| g. | | | | |
| | | | | |
| | | | | |
| | | | | |

### Exercise 3-8

### GENERAL JOURNAL
Page ____

| Date | Account Titles and Explanation | PR | Debit | Credit |
|------|-------------------------------|----|-------|--------|
| | | | | |
| | | | | |
| | | | | |
| | | | | |
| | | | | |
| | | | | |
| | | | | |
| | | | | |
| | | | | |
| | | | | |
| | | | | |
| | | | | |
| | | | | |
| | | | | |
| | | | | |
| | | | | |
| | | | | |
| | | | | |
| | | | | |

## GENERAL JOURNAL                                    Page ____

| Date | | Account Titles and Explanation | PR | Debit | Credit |
|------|--|-------------------------------|----|-------|--------|
| | | | | | |
| | | | | | |
| | | | | | |
| | | | | | |
| | | | | | |
| | | | | | |
| | | | | | |
| | | | | | |
| | | | | | |
| | | | | | |
| | | | | | |

## Exercise 3-9

## GENERAL JOURNAL                                    Page ____

| Date | | Account Titles and Explanation | PR | Debit | Credit |
|------|--|-------------------------------|----|-------|--------|
| | | | | | |
| | | | | | |
| | | | | | |
| | | | | | |
| | | | | | |
| | | | | | |
| | | | | | |
| | | | | | |
| | | | | | |
| | | | | | |
| | | | | | |
| | | | | | |

## Transactions not creating revenue and the reasons: _____

_____
_____
_____
_____
_____
_____
_____
_____
_____
_____
_____
_____
_____

## GENERAL JOURNAL                                    Page ____

| Date | Account Titles and Explanation | PR | Debit | Credit |
|------|-------------------------------|-----|-------|--------|
|      |                               |     |       |        |
|      |                               |     |       |        |
|      |                               |     |       |        |
|      |                               |     |       |        |
|      |                               |     |       |        |
|      |                               |     |       |        |
|      |                               |     |       |        |
|      |                               |     |       |        |
|      |                               |     |       |        |
|      |                               |     |       |        |
|      |                               |     |       |        |
|      |                               |     |       |        |
|      |                               |     |       |        |

**Transactions not creating revenue and the reasons:** _____

_____

_____

_____

_____

_____

_____

_____

_____

_____

_____

_____

_____

_____

_____

_____

## GENERAL LEDGER

### Cash                                                                ACCOUNT NO. 101

| DATE | EXPLANATION | PR | DEBIT | CREDIT | BALANCE |
|------|-------------|----|-------|--------|---------|
| 2010 | | | | | |
| Dec. 31 | Beginning balance | | | | 850 |
| | | | | | |
| | | | | | |
| | | | | | |
| | | | | | |
| | | | | | |
| | | | | | |

### Accounts Receivable                                   ACCOUNT NO. 106

| DATE | EXPLANATION | PR | DEBIT | CREDIT | BALANCE |
|------|-------------|----|-------|--------|---------|
| 2010 | | | | | |
| Dec. 31 | Beginning balance | | | | 300 |
| | | | | | |
| | | | | | |
| | | | | | |

### Equipment                                                    ACCOUNT NO. 167

| DATE | EXPLANATION | PR | DEBIT | CREDIT | BALANCE |
|------|-------------|----|-------|--------|---------|
| 2010 | | | | | |
| Dec. 31 | Beginning balance | | | | 1,500 |
| | | | | | |
| | | | | | |

### Accounts Payable                                      ACCOUNT NO. 201

| DATE | EXPLANATION | PR | DEBIT | CREDIT | BALANCE |
|------|-------------|----|-------|--------|---------|
| 2010 | | | | | |
| Dec. 31 | Beginning balance | | | | 325 |
| | | | | | |
| | | | | | |

### Jay Walker, Capital                                    ACCOUNT NO. 301

| DATE | EXPLANATION | PR | DEBIT | CREDIT | BALANCE |
|------|-------------|----|-------|--------|---------|
| 2010 | | | | | |
| Dec. 31 | Beginning balance | | | | 2,325 |
| | | | | | |
| | | | | | |

### Jay Walker, Withdrawals                    ACCOUNT NO. 302

| DATE | EXPLANATION | PR | DEBIT | CREDIT | BALANCE |
|------|-------------|----|-------|--------|---------|
| 2010 | | | | | |
| Dec. 31 | Beginning balance | | | | 300 |
| | | | | | |
| | | | | | |

### Fees Earned                    ACCOUNT NO. 401

| DATE | EXPLANATION | PR | DEBIT | CREDIT | BALANCE |
|------|-------------|----|-------|--------|---------|
| 2010 | | | | | |
| Dec. 31 | Beginning balance | | | | 1,800 |
| | | | | | |
| | | | | | |

### Salaries Expense                    ACCOUNT NO. 622

| DATE | EXPLANATION | PR | DEBIT | CREDIT | BALANCE |
|------|-------------|----|-------|--------|---------|
| 2010 | | | | | |
| Dec. 31 | Beginning balance | | | | 1,500 |
| | | | | | |
| | | | | | |

*Analysis component:*

_____
_____
_____
_____
_____
_____
_____
_____
_____
_____
_____

## GENERAL JOURNAL                    Page ____

| Date | Account Titles and Explanation | PR | Debit | Credit |
|------|-------------------------------|----|-------|--------|
|      |                               |    |       |        |
|      |                               |    |       |        |
|      |                               |    |       |        |
|      |                               |    |       |        |
|      |                               |    |       |        |
|      |                               |    |       |        |
|      |                               |    |       |        |
|      |                               |    |       |        |
|      |                               |    |       |        |
|      |                               |    |       |        |
|      |                               |    |       |        |
|      |                               |    |       |        |
|      |                               |    |       |        |
|      |                               |    |       |        |
|      |                               |    |       |        |
|      |                               |    |       |        |
|      |                               |    |       |        |
|      |                               |    |       |        |
|      |                               |    |       |        |
|      |                               |    |       |        |
|      |                               |    |       |        |
|      |                               |    |       |        |
|      |                               |    |       |        |
|      |                               |    |       |        |

## Exercise 3-13

### Cash                                ACCOUNT NO. 101

| DATE | EXPLANATION | PR | DEBIT | CREDIT | BALANCE |
|------|-------------|----|-------|--------|---------|
|      |             |    |       |        |         |
|      |             |    |       |        |         |
|      |             |    |       |        |         |
|      |             |    |       |        |         |
|      |             |    |       |        |         |
|      |             |    |       |        |         |

### Office Supplies                        ACCOUNT NO. 124

| DATE | EXPLANATION | PR | DEBIT | CREDIT | BALANCE |
|------|-------------|----|-------|--------|---------|
|      |             |    |       |        |         |
|      |             |    |       |        |         |

### Prepaid Rent                                    ACCOUNT NO. 131

| DATE | EXPLANATION | PR | DEBIT | CREDIT | BALANCE |
|------|-------------|----|-------|--------|---------|
|      |             |    |       |        |         |
|      |             |    |       |        |         |

### Photography Equipment                          ACCOUNT NO. 167

| DATE | EXPLANATION | PR | DEBIT | CREDIT | BALANCE |
|------|-------------|----|-------|--------|---------|
|      |             |    |       |        |         |
|      |             |    |       |        |         |

### Tara Harper, Capital                            ACCOUNT NO. 301

| DATE | EXPLANATION | PR | DEBIT | CREDIT | BALANCE |
|------|-------------|----|-------|--------|---------|
|      |             |    |       |        |         |
|      |             |    |       |        |         |

### Photography Fees Earned                         ACCOUNT NO. 401

| DATE | EXPLANATION | PR | DEBIT | CREDIT | BALANCE |
|------|-------------|----|-------|--------|---------|
|      |             |    |       |        |         |
|      |             |    |       |        |         |

### Utilities Expense                               ACCOUNT NO. 690

| DATE | EXPLANATION | PR | DEBIT | CREDIT | BALANCE |
|------|-------------|----|-------|--------|---------|
|      |             |    |       |        |         |
|      |             |    |       |        |         |

### Trial Balance

|  | Debit | Credit |
|--|-------|--------|
|  |       |        |
|  |       |        |
|  |       |        |
|  |       |        |
|  |       |        |
|  |       |        |
|  |       |        |
|  |       |        |
|  |       |        |

*Analysis component:*

_____

_____

_____

_____

| Cash | 101 | | Office Supplies | 124 |
|------|-----|-|----------------|-----|

| Prepaid Rent | 131 | | Photography Equipment | 167 |
|--------------|-----|-|-----------------------|-----|

| | | | Photography Fees Earned | 401 |
|-|-|-|-------------------------|-----|

| Tara Harper, Capital | 301 | | Utilities Expense | 690 |
|----------------------|-----|-|-------------------|-----|

## Trial Balance

| | Debit | Credit |
|---|-------|--------|
| | | |
| | | |
| | | |
| | | |
| | | |
| | | |
| | | |
| | | |
| | | |
| | | |
| | | |

*Analysis component:*

## Income Statement

|  |  |  |
|---|---|---|
|  |  |  |
|  |  |  |
|  |  |  |
|  |  |  |
|  |  |  |
|  |  |  |

## Statement of Owner's Equity

|  |  |  |
|---|---|---|
|  |  |  |
|  |  |  |
|  |  |  |
|  |  |  |
|  |  |  |
|  |  |  |
|  |  |  |

## Balance Sheet

|  |  |  |  |
|---|---|---|---|
|  |  |  |  |
|  |  |  |  |
|  |  |  |  |
|  |  |  |  |
|  |  |  |  |
|  |  |  |  |
|  |  |  |  |

*Analysis component:* _____

_____

_____

_____

_____

_____

_____

_____

## Income Statement

| | | |
|---|---|---|
| | | |
| | | |
| | | |
| | | |
| | | |
| | | |
| | | |
| | | |
| | | |
| | | |

## Statement of Owner's Equity

| | | |
|---|---|---|
| | | |
| | | |
| | | |
| | | |
| | | |
| | | |
| | | |
| | | |
| | | |
| | | |

## Balance Sheet

| | | | |
|---|---|---|---|
| | | | |
| | | | |
| | | | |
| | | | |
| | | | |
| | | | |
| | | | |
| | | | |
| | | | |
| | | | |
| | | | |
| | | | |
| | | | |

## Income Statement

| | | |
|---|---|---|
| | | |
| | | |
| | | |
| | | |
| | | |
| | | |
| | | |
| | | |

## Statement of Owner's Equity

| | | |
|---|---|---|
| | | |
| | | |
| | | |
| | | |
| | | |
| | | |
| | | |
| | | |
| | | |

## Balance Sheet

| | | | |
|---|---|---|---|
| | | | |
| | | | |
| | | | |
| | | | |
| | | | |
| | | | |
| | | | |
| | | | |
| | | | |
| | | | |
| | | | |
| | | | |

| | Description | (1) Difference between Debit and Credit Column | (2) Column with the Larger Total | (3) Identify account(s) incorrectly stated | (4) Amount that account(s) is overstated or understated |
|---|---|---|---|---|---|
| a. | A $2,400 debit to Rent Expense was posted as a $1,590 debit. | $810 | Credit | Rent Expense | Rent Expense is understated by $810 |
| b. | A $42,000 debit to Machinery was posted as a debit to Accounts Payable. | | | | |
| c. | A $4,950 credit to Services Revenue was posted as a $495 credit. | | | | |
| d. | A $1,440 debit to Store Supplies was not posted at all. | | | | |
| e. | A $2,250 debit to Prepaid Insurance was posted as a debit to Insurance Expense. | | | | |
| f. | A $4,050 credit to Cash was posted twice as two credits to the Cash account. | | | | |
| g. | A $9,900 debit to the owner's withdrawals account was debited to the owner's capital account. | | | | |

## Exercise 3-19

a. _____

b. _____

c. _____

d. _____

e. _____

## Exercise 3-20

Case A: _____

Case B: _____

Case C: _____

| Cash | | Land |
|---|---|---|

| Accounts Receivable | | Accounts Payable |
|---|---|---|

| Office Supplies | | Long-Term Notes Payable |
|---|---|---|

| Automobiles | | Jeff Bridges, Capital |
|---|---|---|

| Office Equipment | | Jeff Bridges, Withdrawals |
|---|---|---|

| Building | | Fees Earned |
|---|---|---|

| | | Wages Expense |
|---|---|---|

| | | Utilities Expense |
|---|---|---|

## GENERAL JOURNAL                          Page ____

| Date | Account Titles and Explanation | PR | Debit | Credit |
|------|-------------------------------|----|-------|--------|
|      |                               |    |       |        |
|      |                               |    |       |        |
|      |                               |    |       |        |
|      |                               |    |       |        |
|      |                               |    |       |        |
|      |                               |    |       |        |
|      |                               |    |       |        |
|      |                               |    |       |        |
|      |                               |    |       |        |
|      |                               |    |       |        |
|      |                               |    |       |        |
|      |                               |    |       |        |
|      |                               |    |       |        |
|      |                               |    |       |        |
|      |                               |    |       |        |
|      |                               |    |       |        |
|      |                               |    |       |        |
|      |                               |    |       |        |
|      |                               |    |       |        |
|      |                               |    |       |        |
|      |                               |    |       |        |
|      |                               |    |       |        |
|      |                               |    |       |        |
|      |                               |    |       |        |
|      |                               |    |       |        |
|      |                               |    |       |        |
|      |                               |    |       |        |
|      |                               |    |       |        |
|      |                               |    |       |        |
|      |                               |    |       |        |
|      |                               |    |       |        |
|      |                               |    |       |        |
|      |                               |    |       |        |
|      |                               |    |       |        |
|      |                               |    |       |        |
|      |                               |    |       |        |

GENERAL JOURNAL                                    Page ____

| Date | Account Titles and Explanation | PR | Debit | Credit |
|------|-------------------------------|----|-------|--------|
|      |                               |    |       |        |
|      |                               |    |       |        |
|      |                               |    |       |        |
|      |                               |    |       |        |
|      |                               |    |       |        |
|      |                               |    |       |        |
|      |                               |    |       |        |
|      |                               |    |       |        |

**Problem 3-3A**

GENERAL JOURNAL                                    Page ____

| Date | Account Titles and Explanation | PR | Debit | Credit |
|------|-------------------------------|----|-------|--------|
|      |                               |    |       |        |
|      |                               |    |       |        |
|      |                               |    |       |        |
|      |                               |    |       |        |
|      |                               |    |       |        |
|      |                               |    |       |        |
|      |                               |    |       |        |
|      |                               |    |       |        |
|      |                               |    |       |        |
|      |                               |    |       |        |
|      |                               |    |       |        |
|      |                               |    |       |        |
|      |                               |    |       |        |
|      |                               |    |       |        |
|      |                               |    |       |        |
|      |                               |    |       |        |
|      |                               |    |       |        |
|      |                               |    |       |        |
|      |                               |    |       |        |
|      |                               |    |       |        |
|      |                               |    |       |        |
|      |                               |    |       |        |
|      |                               |    |       |        |
|      |                               |    |       |        |
|      |                               |    |       |        |
|      |                               |    |       |        |
|      |                               |    |       |        |
|      |                               |    |       |        |

## GENERAL JOURNAL                                      Page ____

| Date | Account Titles and Explanation | PR | Debit | Credit |
|---|---|---|---|---|
|  |  |  |  |  |
|  |  |  |  |  |
|  |  |  |  |  |
|  |  |  |  |  |
|  |  |  |  |  |
|  |  |  |  |  |
|  |  |  |  |  |
|  |  |  |  |  |
|  |  |  |  |  |
|  |  |  |  |  |
|  |  |  |  |  |
|  |  |  |  |  |
|  |  |  |  |  |
|  |  |  |  |  |
|  |  |  |  |  |
|  |  |  |  |  |
|  |  |  |  |  |
|  |  |  |  |  |
|  |  |  |  |  |
|  |  |  |  |  |
|  |  |  |  |  |
|  |  |  |  |  |
|  |  |  |  |  |
|  |  |  |  |  |
|  |  |  |  |  |
|  |  |  |  |  |

## Problem 3-4A    Parts 1 and 2

### GENERAL LEDGER

Cash                                          ACCOUNT NO. 101

| DATE | EXPLANATION | PR | DEBIT | CREDIT | BALANCE |
|---|---|---|---|---|---|
|  |  |  |  |  |  |
|  |  |  |  |  |  |
|  |  |  |  |  |  |
|  |  |  |  |  |  |
|  |  |  |  |  |  |
|  |  |  |  |  |  |
|  |  |  |  |  |  |
|  |  |  |  |  |  |
|  |  |  |  |  |  |

## Accounts Receivable     ACCOUNT NO. 106

| DATE | EXPLANATION | PR | DEBIT | CREDIT | BALANCE |
|------|-------------|----|-------|--------|---------|
|      |             |    |       |        |         |
|      |             |    |       |        |         |
|      |             |    |       |        |         |

## Office Supplies     ACCOUNT NO. 124

| DATE | EXPLANATION | PR | DEBIT | CREDIT | BALANCE |
|------|-------------|----|-------|--------|---------|
|      |             |    |       |        |         |
|      |             |    |       |        |         |

## Prepaid Insurance     ACCOUNT NO. 128

| DATE | EXPLANATION | PR | DEBIT | CREDIT | BALANCE |
|------|-------------|----|-------|--------|---------|
|      |             |    |       |        |         |
|      |             |    |       |        |         |

## Prepaid Rent     ACCOUNT NO. 131

| DATE | EXPLANATION | PR | DEBIT | CREDIT | BALANCE |
|------|-------------|----|-------|--------|---------|
|      |             |    |       |        |         |
|      |             |    |       |        |         |

## Office Equipment     ACCOUNT NO. 163

| DATE | EXPLANATION | PR | DEBIT | CREDIT | BALANCE |
|------|-------------|----|-------|--------|---------|
|      |             |    |       |        |         |
|      |             |    |       |        |         |
|      |             |    |       |        |         |

## Accounts Payable     ACCOUNT NO. 201

| DATE | EXPLANATION | PR | DEBIT | CREDIT | BALANCE |
|------|-------------|----|-------|--------|---------|
|      |             |    |       |        |         |
|      |             |    |       |        |         |
|      |             |    |       |        |         |
|      |             |    |       |        |         |

## Claude Flynne, Capital     ACCOUNT NO. 301

| DATE | EXPLANATION | PR | DEBIT | CREDIT | BALANCE |
|------|-------------|----|-------|--------|---------|
|      |             |    |       |        |         |
|      |             |    |       |        |         |

## Claude Flynne, Withdrawals     ACCOUNT NO. 302

| DATE | EXPLANATION | PR | DEBIT | CREDIT | BALANCE |
|------|-------------|----|-------|--------|---------|
|      |             |    |       |        |         |
|      |             |    |       |        |         |

### Accounting Fees Earned                           ACCOUNT NO. 401

| DATE | EXPLANATION | PR | DEBIT | CREDIT | BALANCE |
|------|-------------|----|-------|--------|---------|
|      |             |    |       |        |         |
|      |             |    |       |        |         |
|      |             |    |       |        |         |
|      |             |    |       |        |         |

### Utilities Expense                                ACCOUNT NO. 690

| DATE | EXPLANATION | PR | DEBIT | CREDIT | BALANCE |
|------|-------------|----|-------|--------|---------|
|      |             |    |       |        |         |
|      |             |    |       |        |         |

## Part 3

### Trial Balance

|  |  |  |
|--|--|--|
|  |  |  |
|  |  |  |
|  |  |  |
|  |  |  |
|  |  |  |
|  |  |  |
|  |  |  |
|  |  |  |
|  |  |  |
|  |  |  |
|  |  |  |
|  |  |  |
|  |  |  |
|  |  |  |
|  |  |  |
|  |  |  |
|  |  |  |
|  |  |  |

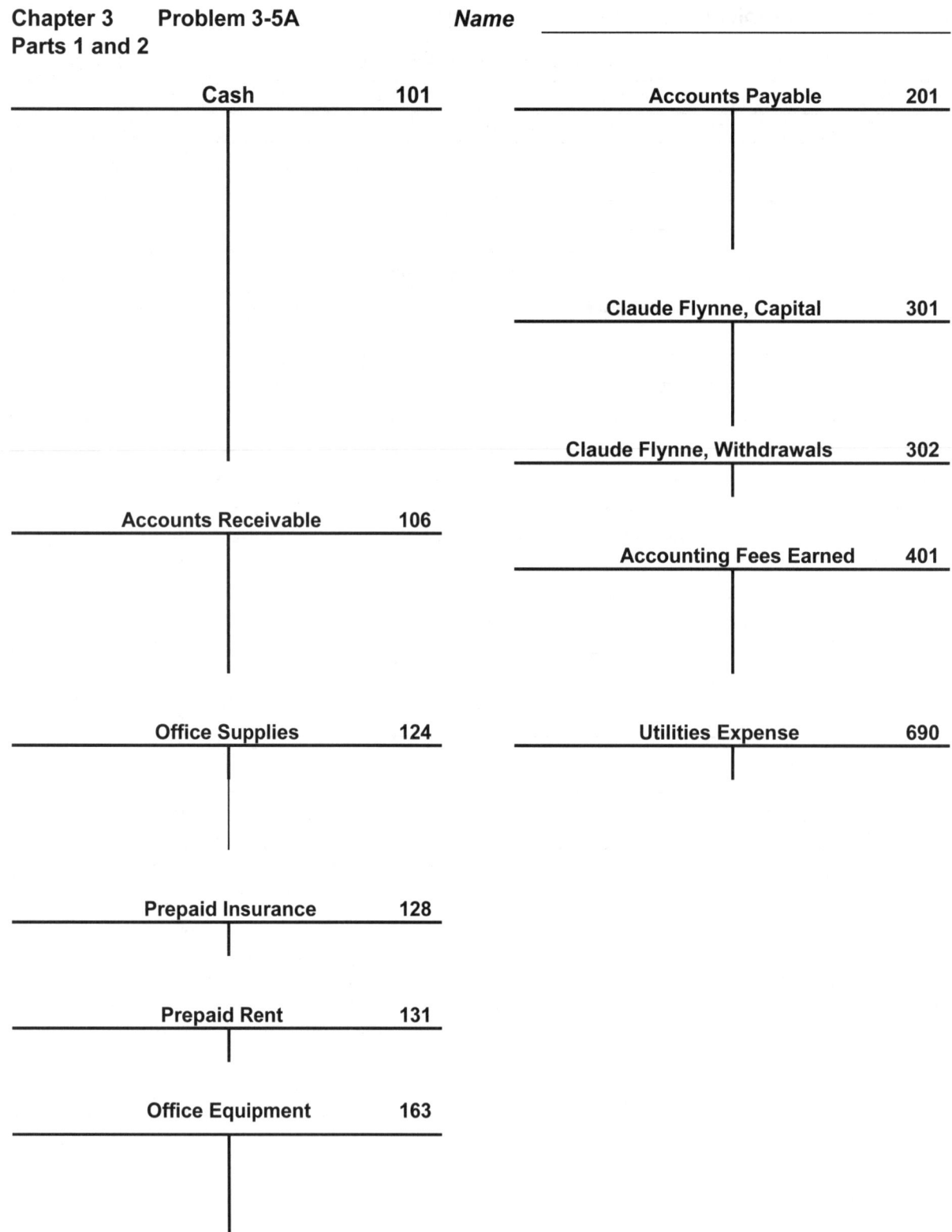

| Cash | 101 | | Accounts Payable | 201 |
|---|---|---|---|---|

| Accounts Receivable | 106 | | Claude Flynne, Capital | 301 |
|---|---|---|---|---|

| | | | Claude Flynne, Withdrawals | 302 |
|---|---|---|---|---|

| | | | Accounting Fees Earned | 401 |
|---|---|---|---|---|

| Office Supplies | 124 | | Utilities Expense | 690 |
|---|---|---|---|---|

| Prepaid Insurance | 128 |
|---|---|

| Prepaid Rent | 131 |
|---|---|

| Office Equipment | 163 |
|---|---|

**Part 3:** *Prepare the trial balance on the page provided for Part 3 of Problem 3-4A.*

*Name* _____

## GENERAL JOURNAL                                    Page ____

| Date | Account Titles and Explanation | PR | Debit | Credit |
|------|-------------------------------|----|-------|--------|
|      |                               |    |       |        |
|      |                               |    |       |        |
|      |                               |    |       |        |
|      |                               |    |       |        |
|      |                               |    |       |        |
|      |                               |    |       |        |
|      |                               |    |       |        |
|      |                               |    |       |        |
|      |                               |    |       |        |
|      |                               |    |       |        |
|      |                               |    |       |        |
|      |                               |    |       |        |
|      |                               |    |       |        |
|      |                               |    |       |        |
|      |                               |    |       |        |
|      |                               |    |       |        |
|      |                               |    |       |        |
|      |                               |    |       |        |
|      |                               |    |       |        |
|      |                               |    |       |        |
|      |                               |    |       |        |
|      |                               |    |       |        |
|      |                               |    |       |        |
|      |                               |    |       |        |
|      |                               |    |       |        |
|      |                               |    |       |        |
|      |                               |    |       |        |
|      |                               |    |       |        |
|      |                               |    |       |        |
|      |                               |    |       |        |
|      |                               |    |       |        |
|      |                               |    |       |        |
|      |                               |    |       |        |
|      |                               |    |       |        |
|      |                               |    |       |        |
|      |                               |    |       |        |
|      |                               |    |       |        |
|      |                               |    |       |        |
|      |                               |    |       |        |
|      |                               |    |       |        |

## GENERAL JOURNAL

Page ____

| Date | Account Titles and Explanation | PR | Debit | Credit |
|------|-------------------------------|----|-------|--------|
| | | | | |
| | | | | |
| | | | | |
| | | | | |
| | | | | |
| | | | | |
| | | | | |
| | | | | |
| | | | | |
| | | | | |
| | | | | |
| | | | | |
| | | | | |
| | | | | |
| | | | | |
| | | | | |
| | | | | |
| | | | | |
| | | | | |
| | | | | |
| | | | | |
| | | | | |
| | | | | |
| | | | | |
| | | | | |
| | | | | |
| | | | | |
| | | | | |
| | | | | |
| | | | | |

## Parts 2 and 3

### GENERAL LEDGER

Cash                                          ACCOUNT NO. 101

| DATE | EXPLANATION | PR | DEBIT | CREDIT | BALANCE |
|------|-------------|----|-------|--------|---------|
| | | | | | |
| | | | | | |
| | | | | | |
| | | | | | |
| | | | | | |
| | | | | | |
| | | | | | |
| | | | | | |
| | | | | | |

### Accounts Receivable                                    ACCOUNT NO. 106

| DATE | EXPLANATION | PR | DEBIT | CREDIT | BALANCE |
|------|-------------|----|-------|--------|---------|
|      |             |    |       |        |         |
|      |             |    |       |        |         |
|      |             |    |       |        |         |
|      |             |    |       |        |         |

### Office Supplies                                    ACCOUNT NO. 124

| DATE | EXPLANATION | PR | DEBIT | CREDIT | BALANCE |
|------|-------------|----|-------|--------|---------|
|      |             |    |       |        |         |
|      |             |    |       |        |         |
|      |             |    |       |        |         |

### Prepaid Insurance                                    ACCOUNT NO. 128

| DATE | EXPLANATION | PR | DEBIT | CREDIT | BALANCE |
|------|-------------|----|-------|--------|---------|
|      |             |    |       |        |         |
|      |             |    |       |        |         |

### Prepaid Rent                                    ACCOUNT NO. 131

| DATE | EXPLANATION | PR | DEBIT | CREDIT | BALANCE |
|------|-------------|----|-------|--------|---------|
|      |             |    |       |        |         |
|      |             |    |       |        |         |

### Office Equipment                                    ACCOUNT NO. 163

| DATE | EXPLANATION | PR | DEBIT | CREDIT | BALANCE |
|------|-------------|----|-------|--------|---------|
|      |             |    |       |        |         |
|      |             |    |       |        |         |
|      |             |    |       |        |         |

### Accounts Payable                                    ACCOUNT NO. 201

| DATE | EXPLANATION | PR | DEBIT | CREDIT | BALANCE |
|------|-------------|----|-------|--------|---------|
|      |             |    |       |        |         |
|      |             |    |       |        |         |
|      |             |    |       |        |         |
|      |             |    |       |        |         |

### Marilyn Og, Capital                                    ACCOUNT NO. 301

| DATE | EXPLANATION | PR | DEBIT | CREDIT | BALANCE |
|------|-------------|----|-------|--------|---------|
|      |             |    |       |        |         |
|      |             |    |       |        |         |

### Marilyn Og, Withdrawals                                    ACCOUNT NO. 302

| DATE | EXPLANATION | PR | DEBIT | CREDIT | BALANCE |
|------|-------------|----|-------|--------|---------|
|      |             |    |       |        |         |
|      |             |    |       |        |         |

### Services Revenue                                    ACCOUNT NO. 403

| DATE | EXPLANATION | PR | DEBIT | CREDIT | BALANCE |
|------|-------------|----|-------|--------|---------|
|      |             |    |       |        |         |
|      |             |    |       |        |         |
|      |             |    |       |        |         |
|      |             |    |       |        |         |

### Utilities Expense                                    ACCOUNT NO. 690

| DATE | EXPLANATION | PR | DEBIT | CREDIT | BALANCE |
|------|-------------|----|-------|--------|---------|
|      |             |    |       |        |         |
|      |             |    |       |        |         |

## Part 4

### Trial Balance

|  |  |  |
|--|--|--|
|  |  |  |
|  |  |  |
|  |  |  |
|  |  |  |
|  |  |  |
|  |  |  |
|  |  |  |
|  |  |  |
|  |  |  |
|  |  |  |
|  |  |  |
|  |  |  |
|  |  |  |
|  |  |  |
|  |  |  |

*Analysis component:* _____

_____

_____

_____

_____

_____

_____

_____

_____

_____

_____

_____

**Part 1:** *Journalize the entries on the Journal page provided in Part 1 of Problem 3-6A.*

**Part 2**

| Cash | 101 | | Accounts Payable | 201 |
| --- | --- | --- | --- | --- |

| Accounts Receivable | 106 | | Marilyn Og, Capital | 301 |
| --- | --- | --- | --- | --- |

| | | | Marilyn Og, Withdrawals | 302 |

| | | | Services Revenue | 401 |

| Office Supplies | 124 | | Utilities Expense | 690 |
| --- | --- | --- | --- | --- |

| Prepaid Insurance | 128 |
| --- | --- |

| Prepaid Rent | 131 |
| --- | --- |

| Office Equipment | 163 |
| --- | --- |

**Part 4 and Analysis component:** *Prepare on the page provided in Part 4 of Problem 3-6A.*

## Income Statement

| | | |
|---|---|---|
| | | |
| | | |
| | | |
| | | |
| | | |
| | | |
| | | |
| | | |
| | | |
| | | |
| | | |

## Statement of Owner's Equity

| | | |
|---|---|---|
| | | |
| | | |
| | | |
| | | |
| | | |
| | | |
| | | |
| | | |
| | | |

## Balance Sheet

| | | | |
|---|---|---|---|
| | | | |
| | | | |
| | | | |
| | | | |
| | | | |
| | | | |
| | | | |
| | | | |
| | | | |
| | | | |
| | | | |

*Analysis component:*    **GENERAL JOURNAL**    Page____

| Date | Account Titles and Explanation | PR | Debit | Credit |
|------|-------------------------------|----|-------|--------|
|      |                               |    |       |        |
|      |                               |    |       |        |
|      |                               |    |       |        |
|      |                               |    |       |        |
|      |                               |    |       |        |
|      |                               |    |       |        |
|      |                               |    |       |        |
|      |                               |    |       |        |
|      |                               |    |       |        |
|      |                               |    |       |        |
|      |                               |    |       |        |

**Problem 3-9A**

**GENERAL JOURNAL**    Page____

| Date | Account Titles and Explanation | PR | Debit | Credit |
|------|-------------------------------|----|-------|--------|
|      |                               |    |       |        |
|      |                               |    |       |        |
|      |                               |    |       |        |
|      |                               |    |       |        |
|      |                               |    |       |        |
|      |                               |    |       |        |
|      |                               |    |       |        |
|      |                               |    |       |        |
|      |                               |    |       |        |
|      |                               |    |       |        |
|      |                               |    |       |        |
|      |                               |    |       |        |
|      |                               |    |       |        |
|      |                               |    |       |        |
|      |                               |    |       |        |
|      |                               |    |       |        |
|      |                               |    |       |        |
|      |                               |    |       |        |
|      |                               |    |       |        |
|      |                               |    |       |        |
|      |                               |    |       |        |
|      |                               |    |       |        |
|      |                               |    |       |        |
|      |                               |    |       |        |
|      |                               |    |       |        |
|      |                               |    |       |        |

## GENERAL JOURNAL    Page____

| Date | Account Titles and Explanation | PR | Debit | Credit |
|------|-------------------------------|----|-------|--------|
|      |                               |    |       |        |
|      |                               |    |       |        |
|      |                               |    |       |        |
|      |                               |    |       |        |
|      |                               |    |       |        |
|      |                               |    |       |        |
|      |                               |    |       |        |
|      |                               |    |       |        |
|      |                               |    |       |        |
|      |                               |    |       |        |
|      |                               |    |       |        |
|      |                               |    |       |        |
|      |                               |    |       |        |
|      |                               |    |       |        |
|      |                               |    |       |        |
|      |                               |    |       |        |
|      |                               |    |       |        |
|      |                               |    |       |        |
|      |                               |    |       |        |
|      |                               |    |       |        |
|      |                               |    |       |        |
|      |                               |    |       |        |
|      |                               |    |       |        |
|      |                               |    |       |        |
|      |                               |    |       |        |
|      |                               |    |       |        |
|      |                               |    |       |        |
|      |                               |    |       |        |
|      |                               |    |       |        |
|      |                               |    |       |        |
|      |                               |    |       |        |
|      |                               |    |       |        |
|      |                               |    |       |        |
|      |                               |    |       |        |
|      |                               |    |       |        |
|      |                               |    |       |        |
|      |                               |    |       |        |
|      |                               |    |       |        |
|      |                               |    |       |        |
|      |                               |    |       |        |

## GENERAL JOURNAL                    Page____

| Date | Account Titles and Explanation | PR | Debit | Credit |
|---|---|---|---|---|
|  |  |  |  |  |
|  |  |  |  |  |
|  |  |  |  |  |
|  |  |  |  |  |
|  |  |  |  |  |
|  |  |  |  |  |
|  |  |  |  |  |
|  |  |  |  |  |
|  |  |  |  |  |
|  |  |  |  |  |
|  |  |  |  |  |
|  |  |  |  |  |
|  |  |  |  |  |
|  |  |  |  |  |
|  |  |  |  |  |
|  |  |  |  |  |
|  |  |  |  |  |
|  |  |  |  |  |
|  |  |  |  |  |
|  |  |  |  |  |
|  |  |  |  |  |
|  |  |  |  |  |
|  |  |  |  |  |
|  |  |  |  |  |
|  |  |  |  |  |

**Parts 2 and 3**

## GENERAL LEDGER

Cash                                                ACCOUNT NO. 101

| DATE | EXPLANATION | PR | DEBIT | CREDIT | BALANCE |
|---|---|---|---|---|---|
| 2011 |  |  |  |  |  |
| Jun. 30 | Beginning balance |  |  |  | 26,000 |
|  |  |  |  |  |  |
|  |  |  |  |  |  |
|  |  |  |  |  |  |
|  |  |  |  |  |  |
|  |  |  |  |  |  |
|  |  |  |  |  |  |
|  |  |  |  |  |  |
|  |  |  |  |  |  |
|  |  |  |  |  |  |
|  |  |  |  |  |  |
|  |  |  |  |  |  |
|  |  |  |  |  |  |
|  |  |  |  |  |  |
|  |  |  |  |  |  |

### Accounts Receivable                                     ACCOUNT NO. 106

| DATE | EXPLANATION | PR | DEBIT | CREDIT | BALANCE |
|------|-------------|----|-------|--------|---------|
| 2011 | | | | | |
| Jun. 30 | Beginning balance | | | | 3,000 |
| | | | | | |
| | | | | | |
| | | | | | |

### Prepaid Insurance                                     ACCOUNT NO. 128

| DATE | EXPLANATION | PR | DEBIT | CREDIT | BALANCE |
|------|-------------|----|-------|--------|---------|
| 2011 | | | | | |
| Jun. 30 | Beginning balance | | | | 500 |
| | | | | | |

### Office Equipment                                     ACCOUNT NO. 163

| DATE | EXPLANATION | PR | DEBIT | CREDIT | BALANCE |
|------|-------------|----|-------|--------|---------|
| 2011 | | | | | |
| Jun. 30 | Beginning balance | | | | 1,700 |
| | | | | | |
| | | | | | |

### Drafting Equipment                                     ACCOUNT NO. 167

| DATE | EXPLANATION | PR | DEBIT | CREDIT | BALANCE |
|------|-------------|----|-------|--------|---------|
| 2011 | | | | | |
| Jun. 30 | Beginning balance | | | | 1,200 |
| | | | | | |
| | | | | | |

### Building                                     ACCOUNT NO. 173

| DATE | EXPLANATION | PR | DEBIT | CREDIT | BALANCE |
|------|-------------|----|-------|--------|---------|
| 2011 | | | | | |
| Jun. 30 | Beginning balance | | | | 42,000 |
| | | | | | |

### Land                                     ACCOUNT NO. 183

| DATE | EXPLANATION | PR | DEBIT | CREDIT | BALANCE |
|------|-------------|----|-------|--------|---------|
| 2011 | | | | | |
| Jun. 30 | Beginning balance | | | | 28,000 |
| | | | | | |

### Accounts Payable                                            ACCOUNT NO. 201

| DATE | EXPLANATION | PR | DEBIT | CREDIT | BALANCE |
|------|-------------|----|-------|--------|---------|
| 2011 | | | | | |
| Jun. 30 | Beginning balance | | | | 1,740 |
| | | | | | |
| | | | | | |
| | | | | | |

### Long-Term Notes Payable                                     ACCOUNT NO. 251

| DATE | EXPLANATION | PR | DEBIT | CREDIT | BALANCE |
|------|-------------|----|-------|--------|---------|
| 2011 | | | | | |
| Jun. 30 | Beginning balance | | | | 24,000 |
| | | | | | |
| | | | | | |

### Bishr Binbutti, Capital                                      ACCOUNT NO. 301

| DATE | EXPLANATION | PR | DEBIT | CREDIT | BALANCE |
|------|-------------|----|-------|--------|---------|
| 2011 | | | | | |
| Jun. 30 | Beginning balance | | | | 54,000 |
| | | | | | |

### Bishr Binbutti, Withdrawals                                  ACCOUNT NO. 302

| DATE | EXPLANATION | PR | DEBIT | CREDIT | BALANCE |
|------|-------------|----|-------|--------|---------|
| 2011 | | | | | |
| Jun. 30 | Beginning balance | | | | 1,000 |
| | | | | | |

### Engineering Fees Earned                                      ACCOUNT NO. 401

| DATE | EXPLANATION | PR | DEBIT | CREDIT | BALANCE |
|------|-------------|----|-------|--------|---------|
| 2011 | | | | | |
| Jun. 30 | Beginning balance | | | | 29,600 |
| | | | | | |
| | | | | | |
| | | | | | |

### Wages Expense                                                ACCOUNT NO. 623

| DATE | EXPLANATION | PR | DEBIT | CREDIT | BALANCE |
|------|-------------|----|-------|--------|---------|
| 2011 | | | | | |
| Jun. 30 | Beginning balance | | | | 4,000 |
| | | | | | |
| | | | | | |

### Equipment Rental Expense

ACCOUNT NO. 645

| DATE | EXPLANATION | PR | DEBIT | CREDIT | BALANCE |
|------|-------------|----|-------|--------|---------|
| 2011 | | | | | |
| Jun. 30 | Beginning balance | | | | 1,000 |
| | | | | | |

### Advertising Expense

ACCOUNT NO. 655

| DATE | EXPLANATION | PR | DEBIT | CREDIT | BALANCE |
|------|-------------|----|-------|--------|---------|
| 2011 | | | | | |
| Jun. 30 | Beginning balance | | | | 640 |
| | | | | | |

### Repairs Expense

ACCOUNT NO. 684

| DATE | EXPLANATION | PR | DEBIT | CREDIT | BALANCE |
|------|-------------|----|-------|--------|---------|
| 2011 | | | | | |
| Jun. 30 | Beginning balance | | | | 300 |
| | | | | | |

## Parts 4

### Trial Balance

| | | |
|---|---|---|
| | | |
| | | |
| | | |
| | | |
| | | |
| | | |
| | | |
| | | |
| | | |
| | | |
| | | |
| | | |
| | | |
| | | |
| | | |
| | | |
| | | |
| | | |
| | | |
| | | |
| | | |
| | | |
| | | |

Part 1:  *Journalize the entries in the general journal pages provided for Problem 3-9A.*

Parts 2 and 3

| Cash | | 101 |
|---|---|---|
| Bal. | 26,000 | |

| Drafting Equipment | | 167 |
|---|---|---|
| Bal. | 1,200 | |

| Building | | 173 |
|---|---|---|
| Bal. | 42,000 | |

| Land | | 183 |
|---|---|---|
| Bal. | 28,000 | |

| Accounts Receivable | | 106 |
|---|---|---|
| Bal. | 3,000 | |

| Accounts Payable | | 201 |
|---|---|---|
| | 1,740 | Bal. |

| Prepaid Insurance | | 128 |
|---|---|---|
| Bal. | 500 | |

| Long-Term Notes Payable | | 251 |
|---|---|---|
| | 24,000 | Bal. |

| Office Equipment | | 163 |
|---|---|---|
| Bal. | 1,700 | |

| Bishr Binbutti, Capital | | 301 |
|---|---|---|
| | 54,000 | Bal. |

| Bishr Binbutti, Withdrawals | 302 |
|---|---|
| Bal. | 1,000 | | |

| Equipment Rental Expense | 645 |
|---|---|
| Bal. | 1,000 | | |

| Engineering Fees Earned | 401 |
|---|---|
| | 29,600 | Bal. |

| Advertising Expense | 655 |
|---|---|
| Bal. | 640 | | |

| Repairs Expense | 684 |
|---|---|
| Bal. | 300 | | |

| Wages Expense | 623 |
|---|---|
| Bal. | 4,000 | | |

**Part 4:** *Prepare the trial balance on the page provided for Part 4 of Problem 3-9A.*

**Problem 3-11A      Part 1**

### GENERAL JOURNAL                          Page____

| Date | Account Titles and Explanation | PR | Debit | Credit |
|---|---|---|---|---|
| | | | | |
| | | | | |
| | | | | |
| | | | | |
| | | | | |
| | | | | |
| | | | | |
| | | | | |
| | | | | |
| | | | | |
| | | | | |
| | | | | |
| | | | | |
| | | | | |
| | | | | |
| | | | | |
| | | | | |
| | | | | |

## GENERAL JOURNAL

| Date | Account Titles and Explanation | PR | Debit | Credit |
|------|-------------------------------|----|-------|--------|
|  |  |  |  |  |
|  |  |  |  |  |
|  |  |  |  |  |
|  |  |  |  |  |
|  |  |  |  |  |
|  |  |  |  |  |
|  |  |  |  |  |
|  |  |  |  |  |
|  |  |  |  |  |
|  |  |  |  |  |
|  |  |  |  |  |
|  |  |  |  |  |
|  |  |  |  |  |
|  |  |  |  |  |
|  |  |  |  |  |
|  |  |  |  |  |
|  |  |  |  |  |
|  |  |  |  |  |
|  |  |  |  |  |
|  |  |  |  |  |
|  |  |  |  |  |
|  |  |  |  |  |
|  |  |  |  |  |
|  |  |  |  |  |

## Parts 2 and 3

| Cash | | 101 |
|------|--|-----|
| Bal. | 6,000 | |

| Supplies | | 126 |
|----------|--|-----|
| Bal. | 950 | |

| Furniture | | 161 |
|-----------|--|-----|
| Bal. | 8,000 | |

| Accounts Payable | | 201 |
|---|---|---|
| | 1,500 | Bal. |

| Unearned Teaching Revenue | | 233 |
|---|---|---|
| | 9,800 | Bal. |

| Ted Ng, Capital | | 301 |
|---|---|---|
| | 3,000 | Bal. |

| Ted Ng, Withdrawals | | 302 |
|---|---|---|
| Bal. | 13,000 | |

| Teaching Revenue | | 401 |
|---|---|---|
| | 46,000 | Bal. |

| Wages Expense | | 623 |
|---|---|---|
| Bal. | 26,350 | |

| Rent Expense | | 640 |
|---|---|---|
| Bal. | 6,000 | |

## Part 4

### Trial Balance

| | | |
|---|---|---|
| | | |
| | | |
| | | |
| | | |
| | | |
| | | |
| | | |
| | | |
| | | |
| | | |
| | | |
| | | |
| | | |
| | | |
| | | |
| | | |
| | | |

## Income Statement

| | | |
|---|---|---|
| | | |
| | | |
| | | |
| | | |
| | | |
| | | |
| | | |
| | | |
| | | |
| | | |
| | | |
| | | |

## Statement of Owner's Equity

| | | |
|---|---|---|
| | | |
| | | |
| | | |
| | | |
| | | |
| | | |
| | | |
| | | |
| | | |
| | | |
| | | |

## Balance Sheet

| | | | |
|---|---|---|---|
| | | | |
| | | | |
| | | | |
| | | | |
| | | | |
| | | | |
| | | | |
| | | | |
| | | | |
| | | | |
| | | | |
| | | | |
| | | | |
| | | | |

## Income Statement

| | | |
|---|---|---|
| | | |
| | | |
| | | |
| | | |
| | | |
| | | |
| | | |
| | | |
| | | |
| | | |

## Statement of Owner's Equity

| | | |
|---|---|---|
| | | |
| | | |
| | | |
| | | |
| | | |
| | | |
| | | |
| | | |
| | | |
| | | |

## Balance Sheet

| | | | |
|---|---|---|---|
| | | | |
| | | | |
| | | | |
| | | | |
| | | | |
| | | | |
| | | | |
| | | | |
| | | | |
| | | | |
| | | | |
| | | | |

## Analysis component:

### GENERAL JOURNAL                                         Page____

| Date | Account Titles and Explanation | PR | Debit | Credit |
|------|-------------------------------|----|-------|--------|
|  |  |  |  |  |
|  |  |  |  |  |
|  |  |  |  |  |
|  |  |  |  |  |
|  |  |  |  |  |
|  |  |  |  |  |
|  |  |  |  |  |
|  |  |  |  |  |

## Problem 3-13A

### Trial Balance

|  |  |  |
|--|--|--|
|  |  |  |
|  |  |  |
|  |  |  |
|  |  |  |
|  |  |  |
|  |  |  |
|  |  |  |
|  |  |  |
|  |  |  |
|  |  |  |
|  |  |  |
|  |  |  |
|  |  |  |
|  |  |  |
|  |  |  |
|  |  |  |
|  |  |  |
|  |  |  |

## Calculations:

**Name** _____

| Cash | Land |
|------|------|

| | Accounts Payable |
|--|------------------|

| | Long-Term Notes Payable |
|--|-------------------------|

| Accounts Receivable | Susan West, Capital |
|---------------------|---------------------|

| Office Supplies | Susan West, Withdrawals |
|-----------------|-------------------------|

| Automobiles | Fees Earned |
|-------------|-------------|

| Office Equipment | Salaries Expense |
|------------------|------------------|

| | Utilities Expense |
|--|-------------------|

| Building | |
|----------|--|

Name _____

## GENERAL JOURNAL

Page ____

| Date | | Account Titles and Explanation | PR | Debit | Credit |
|---|---|---|---|---|---|
| | | | | | |
| | | | | | |
| | | | | | |
| | | | | | |
| | | | | | |
| | | | | | |
| | | | | | |
| | | | | | |
| | | | | | |
| | | | | | |
| | | | | | |
| | | | | | |
| | | | | | |
| | | | | | |
| | | | | | |
| | | | | | |
| | | | | | |
| | | | | | |
| | | | | | |
| | | | | | |
| | | | | | |
| | | | | | |
| | | | | | |
| | | | | | |
| | | | | | |
| | | | | | |
| | | | | | |
| | | | | | |
| | | | | | |
| | | | | | |
| | | | | | |
| | | | | | |
| | | | | | |
| | | | | | |
| | | | | | |
| | | | | | |
| | | | | | |
| | | | | | |
| | | | | | |
| | | | | | |
| | | | | | |
| | | | | | |

## GENERAL JOURNAL

Page ____

| Date | | Account Titles and Explanation | PR | Debit | Credit |
|---|---|---|---|---|---|
| | | | | | |
| | | | | | |
| | | | | | |
| | | | | | |
| | | | | | |
| | | | | | |
| | | | | | |
| | | | | | |
| | | | | | |

## Problem 3-3B

## GENERAL JOURNAL

Page ____

| Date | | Account Titles and Explanation | PR | Debit | Credit |
|---|---|---|---|---|---|
| | | | | | |
| | | | | | |
| | | | | | |
| | | | | | |
| | | | | | |
| | | | | | |
| | | | | | |
| | | | | | |
| | | | | | |
| | | | | | |
| | | | | | |
| | | | | | |
| | | | | | |
| | | | | | |
| | | | | | |
| | | | | | |
| | | | | | |
| | | | | | |
| | | | | | |
| | | | | | |
| | | | | | |
| | | | | | |
| | | | | | |
| | | | | | |
| | | | | | |
| | | | | | |
| | | | | | |
| | | | | | |

## GENERAL JOURNAL                          Page ____

| Date | Account Titles and Explanation | PR | Debit | Credit |
|------|-------------------------------|----|-------|--------|
|      |                               |    |       |        |
|      |                               |    |       |        |
|      |                               |    |       |        |
|      |                               |    |       |        |
|      |                               |    |       |        |
|      |                               |    |       |        |
|      |                               |    |       |        |
|      |                               |    |       |        |
|      |                               |    |       |        |
|      |                               |    |       |        |
|      |                               |    |       |        |
|      |                               |    |       |        |
|      |                               |    |       |        |
|      |                               |    |       |        |
|      |                               |    |       |        |
|      |                               |    |       |        |
|      |                               |    |       |        |
|      |                               |    |       |        |
|      |                               |    |       |        |
|      |                               |    |       |        |
|      |                               |    |       |        |
|      |                               |    |       |        |
|      |                               |    |       |        |
|      |                               |    |       |        |
|      |                               |    |       |        |
|      |                               |    |       |        |
|      |                               |    |       |        |
|      |                               |    |       |        |
|      |                               |    |       |        |
|      |                               |    |       |        |
|      |                               |    |       |        |
|      |                               |    |       |        |
|      |                               |    |       |        |
|      |                               |    |       |        |
|      |                               |    |       |        |
|      |                               |    |       |        |
|      |                               |    |       |        |
|      |                               |    |       |        |
|      |                               |    |       |        |
|      |                               |    |       |        |
|      |                               |    |       |        |
|      |                               |    |       |        |

**Problem 3-4B**

**Parts 1 and 2**

## GENERAL LEDGER

### Cash                                 ACCOUNT NO. 101

| DATE | EXPLANATION | PR | DEBIT | CREDIT | BALANCE |
|------|-------------|----|-------|--------|---------|
| | | | | | |
| | | | | | |
| | | | | | |
| | | | | | |
| | | | | | |
| | | | | | |
| | | | | | |
| | | | | | |
| | | | | | |
| | | | | | |
| | | | | | |
| | | | | | |

### Accounts Receivable                       ACCOUNT NO. 106

| DATE | EXPLANATION | PR | DEBIT | CREDIT | BALANCE |
|------|-------------|----|-------|--------|---------|
| | | | | | |
| | | | | | |
| | | | | | |
| | | | | | |

### Office Supplies                             ACCOUNT NO. 124

| DATE | EXPLANATION | PR | DEBIT | CREDIT | BALANCE |
|------|-------------|----|-------|--------|---------|
| | | | | | |
| | | | | | |
| | | | | | |

### Prepaid Insurance                        ACCOUNT NO. 128

| DATE | EXPLANATION | PR | DEBIT | CREDIT | BALANCE |
|------|-------------|----|-------|--------|---------|
| | | | | | |
| | | | | | |

### Prepaid Rent                               ACCOUNT NO. 131

| DATE | EXPLANATION | PR | DEBIT | CREDIT | BALANCE |
|------|-------------|----|-------|--------|---------|
| | | | | | |
| | | | | | |

### Office Equipment                           ACCOUNT NO. 163

| DATE | EXPLANATION | PR | DEBIT | CREDIT | BALANCE |
|------|-------------|----|-------|--------|---------|
| | | | | | |
| | | | | | |
| | | | | | |

### Accounts Payable    ACCOUNT NO. 210

| DATE | EXPLANATION | PR | DEBIT | CREDIT | BALANCE |
|------|-------------|----|-------|--------|---------|
|      |             |    |       |        |         |
|      |             |    |       |        |         |
|      |             |    |       |        |         |
|      |             |    |       |        |         |

### Adam Uppe, Capital    ACCOUNT NO. 301

| DATE | EXPLANATION | PR | DEBIT | CREDIT | BALANCE |
|------|-------------|----|-------|--------|---------|
|      |             |    |       |        |         |
|      |             |    |       |        |         |

### Adam Uppe, Withdrawals    ACCOUNT NO. 302

| DATE | EXPLANATION | PR | DEBIT | CREDIT | BALANCE |
|------|-------------|----|-------|--------|---------|
|      |             |    |       |        |         |
|      |             |    |       |        |         |

### Accounting Fees Earned    ACCOUNT NO. 401

| DATE | EXPLANATION | PR | DEBIT | CREDIT | BALANCE |
|------|-------------|----|-------|--------|---------|
|      |             |    |       |        |         |
|      |             |    |       |        |         |
|      |             |    |       |        |         |
|      |             |    |       |        |         |

### Professional Development Expense    ACCOUNT NO. 680

| DATE | EXPLANATION | PR | DEBIT | CREDIT | BALANCE |
|------|-------------|----|-------|--------|---------|
|      |             |    |       |        |         |
|      |             |    |       |        |         |

### Utilities Expense    ACCOUNT NO. 690

| DATE | EXPLANATION | PR | DEBIT | CREDIT | BALANCE |
|------|-------------|----|-------|--------|---------|
|      |             |    |       |        |         |
|      |             |    |       |        |         |

## Trial Balance

|  |  |  |
|---|---|---|
|  |  |  |
|  |  |  |
|  |  |  |
|  |  |  |
|  |  |  |
|  |  |  |
|  |  |  |
|  |  |  |
|  |  |  |
|  |  |  |
|  |  |  |
|  |  |  |
|  |  |  |
|  |  |  |
|  |  |  |
|  |  |  |
|  |  |  |
|  |  |  |
|  |  |  |
|  |  |  |
|  |  |  |
|  |  |  |

**Part 1:** *Journalize the entries on the journal pages provided in Part 1 of Problem 3-4B.*

**Part 2**

| Cash | 101 | | Accounts Payable | 201 |
|---|---|---|---|---|

| Accounts Receivable | 106 | | Adam Uppe, Capital | 301 |
|---|---|---|---|---|

| | | | Adam Uppe, Withdrawals | 302 |
|---|---|---|---|---|

| | | | Accounting Fees Earned | 401 |
|---|---|---|---|---|

| Office Supplies | 124 | | Professional Development Expense | 680 |
|---|---|---|---|---|

| Prepaid Insurance | 128 | | Utilities Expense | 690 |
|---|---|---|---|---|

| Prepaid Rent | 131 |
|---|---|

| Office Equipment | 163 |
|---|---|

**Part 3:** *Prepare the trial balance on the page provided for Part 3 of Problem 3-4B.*

**Part 1**

GENERAL JOURNAL                              Page____

| Date | Account Titles and Explanation | PR | Debit | Credit |
|------|-------------------------------|----|-------|--------|
|      |                               |    |       |        |
|      |                               |    |       |        |
|      |                               |    |       |        |
|      |                               |    |       |        |
|      |                               |    |       |        |
|      |                               |    |       |        |
|      |                               |    |       |        |
|      |                               |    |       |        |
|      |                               |    |       |        |
|      |                               |    |       |        |
|      |                               |    |       |        |
|      |                               |    |       |        |
|      |                               |    |       |        |
|      |                               |    |       |        |
|      |                               |    |       |        |
|      |                               |    |       |        |
|      |                               |    |       |        |
|      |                               |    |       |        |
|      |                               |    |       |        |
|      |                               |    |       |        |
|      |                               |    |       |        |
|      |                               |    |       |        |
|      |                               |    |       |        |
|      |                               |    |       |        |
|      |                               |    |       |        |
|      |                               |    |       |        |
|      |                               |    |       |        |
|      |                               |    |       |        |
|      |                               |    |       |        |
|      |                               |    |       |        |
|      |                               |    |       |        |
|      |                               |    |       |        |
|      |                               |    |       |        |
|      |                               |    |       |        |
|      |                               |    |       |        |
|      |                               |    |       |        |
|      |                               |    |       |        |
|      |                               |    |       |        |
|      |                               |    |       |        |
|      |                               |    |       |        |
|      |                               |    |       |        |
|      |                               |    |       |        |

## GENERAL JOURNAL                                    Page____

| Date | Account Titles and Explanation | PR | Debit | Credit |
|------|-------------------------------|----|-------|--------|
|      |                               |    |       |        |
|      |                               |    |       |        |
|      |                               |    |       |        |
|      |                               |    |       |        |
|      |                               |    |       |        |
|      |                               |    |       |        |
|      |                               |    |       |        |
|      |                               |    |       |        |
|      |                               |    |       |        |
|      |                               |    |       |        |
|      |                               |    |       |        |
|      |                               |    |       |        |
|      |                               |    |       |        |
|      |                               |    |       |        |
|      |                               |    |       |        |
|      |                               |    |       |        |
|      |                               |    |       |        |
|      |                               |    |       |        |
|      |                               |    |       |        |
|      |                               |    |       |        |
|      |                               |    |       |        |
|      |                               |    |       |        |

**Parts 2 and 3**

## GENERAL LEDGER

### Cash                                               ACCOUNT NO. 101

| DATE | EXPLANATION | PR | DEBIT | CREDIT | BALANCE |
|------|-------------|----|-------|--------|---------|
|      |             |    |       |        |         |
|      |             |    |       |        |         |
|      |             |    |       |        |         |
|      |             |    |       |        |         |
|      |             |    |       |        |         |
|      |             |    |       |        |         |
|      |             |    |       |        |         |
|      |             |    |       |        |         |
|      |             |    |       |        |         |
|      |             |    |       |        |         |

### Accounts Receivable                                ACCOUNT NO. 106

| DATE | EXPLANATION | PR | DEBIT | CREDIT | BALANCE |
|------|-------------|----|-------|--------|---------|
|      |             |    |       |        |         |
|      |             |    |       |        |         |
|      |             |    |       |        |         |
|      |             |    |       |        |         |

### Office Supplies                                                    ACCOUNT NO. 124

| DATE | EXPLANATION | PR | DEBIT | CREDIT | BALANCE |
|------|-------------|----|-------|--------|---------|
|      |             |    |       |        |         |
|      |             |    |       |        |         |
|      |             |    |       |        |         |

### Prepaid Insurance                                                  ACCOUNT NO. 128

| DATE | EXPLANATION | PR | DEBIT | CREDIT | BALANCE |
|------|-------------|----|-------|--------|---------|
|      |             |    |       |        |         |
|      |             |    |       |        |         |

### Prepaid Rent                                                       ACCOUNT NO. 131

| DATE | EXPLANATION | PR | DEBIT | CREDIT | BALANCE |
|------|-------------|----|-------|--------|---------|
|      |             |    |       |        |         |
|      |             |    |       |        |         |

### Office Equipment                                                   ACCOUNT NO. 163

| DATE | EXPLANATION | PR | DEBIT | CREDIT | BALANCE |
|------|-------------|----|-------|--------|---------|
|      |             |    |       |        |         |
|      |             |    |       |        |         |
|      |             |    |       |        |         |

### Accounts Payable                                                   ACCOUNT NO. 201

| DATE | EXPLANATION | PR | DEBIT | CREDIT | BALANCE |
|------|-------------|----|-------|--------|---------|
|      |             |    |       |        |         |
|      |             |    |       |        |         |
|      |             |    |       |        |         |
|      |             |    |       |        |         |
|      |             |    |       |        |         |

### Arthur Leonard, Capital                                            ACCOUNT NO. 301

| DATE | EXPLANATION | PR | DEBIT | CREDIT | BALANCE |
|------|-------------|----|-------|--------|---------|
|      |             |    |       |        |         |
|      |             |    |       |        |         |

### Arthur Leonard, Withdrawals                                        ACCOUNT NO. 302

| DATE | EXPLANATION | PR | DEBIT | CREDIT | BALANCE |
|------|-------------|----|-------|--------|---------|
|      |             |    |       |        |         |
|      |             |    |       |        |         |

### Service Fees Earned                                                ACCOUNT NO. 401

| DATE | EXPLANATION | PR | DEBIT | CREDIT | BALANCE |
|------|-------------|----|-------|--------|---------|
|      |             |    |       |        |         |
|      |             |    |       |        |         |
|      |             |    |       |        |         |
|      |             |    |       |        |         |

### Wages Expense                                          ACCOUNT NO. 680

| DATE | EXPLANATION | PR | DEBIT | CREDIT | BALANCE |
|------|-------------|----|-------|--------|---------|
|      |             |    |       |        |         |
|      |             |    |       |        |         |

### Utilities Expense                                       ACCOUNT NO. 690

| DATE | EXPLANATION | PR | DEBIT | CREDIT | BALANCE |
|------|-------------|----|-------|--------|---------|
|      |             |    |       |        |         |
|      |             |    |       |        |         |

## Part 4

### Trial Balance

|  |  |  |
|--|--|--|
|  |  |  |
|  |  |  |
|  |  |  |
|  |  |  |
|  |  |  |
|  |  |  |
|  |  |  |
|  |  |  |
|  |  |  |
|  |  |  |
|  |  |  |
|  |  |  |
|  |  |  |
|  |  |  |
|  |  |  |
|  |  |  |
|  |  |  |
|  |  |  |
|  |  |  |

## *Analysis component:*

_____
_____
_____
_____
_____
_____
_____
_____
_____
_____
_____

**Part 1:** *Journalize the entries on the Journal page provided in Part 1 of Problem 3-6B.*

**Parts 2 and 3**

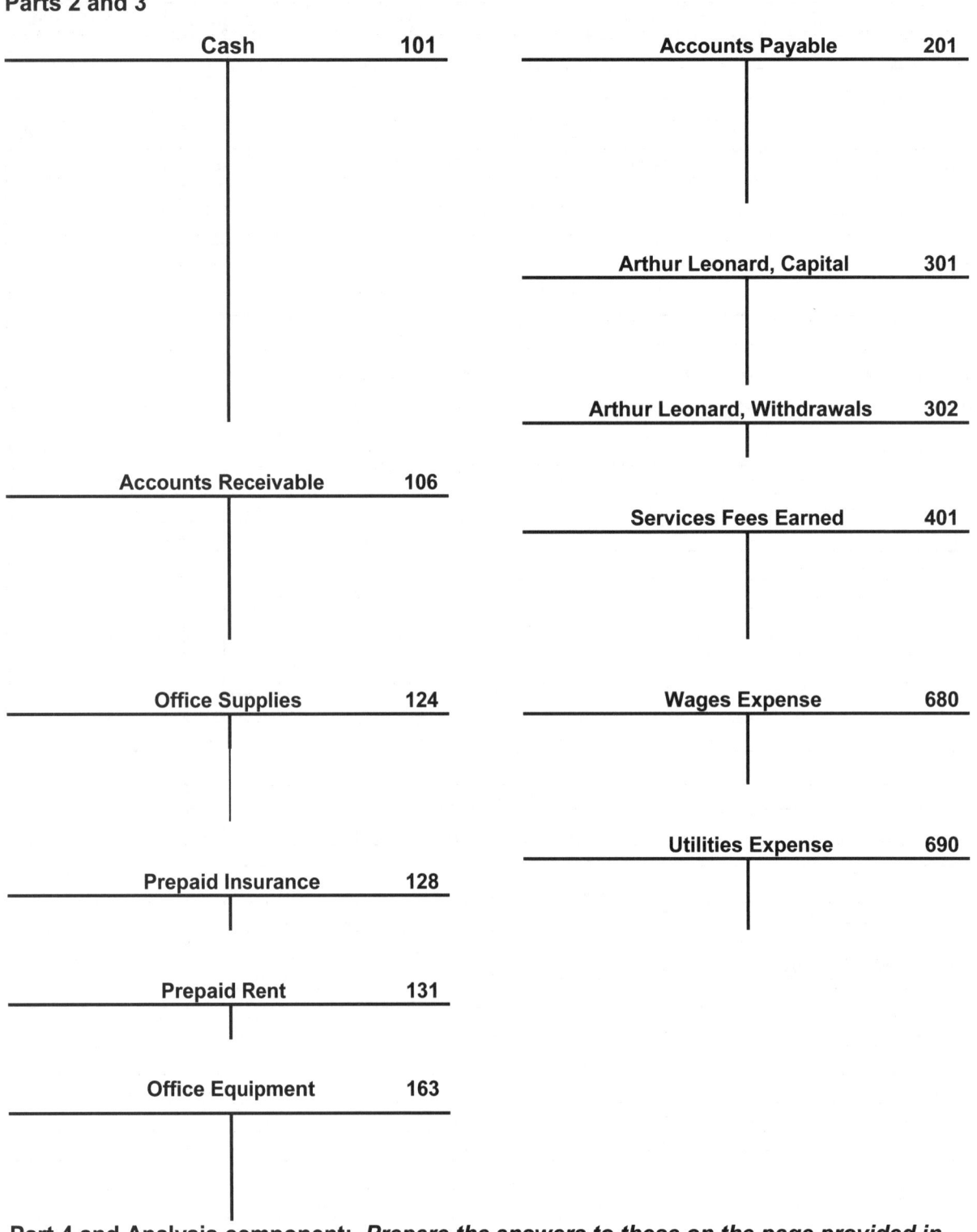

| Cash | 101 |
| Accounts Payable | 201 |
| Arthur Leonard, Capital | 301 |
| Arthur Leonard, Withdrawals | 302 |
| Accounts Receivable | 106 |
| Services Fees Earned | 401 |
| Office Supplies | 124 |
| Wages Expense | 680 |
| Prepaid Insurance | 128 |
| Utilities Expense | 690 |
| Prepaid Rent | 131 |
| Office Equipment | 163 |

**Part 4 and Analysis component:** *Prepare the answers to these on the page provided in Part 4 and the analysis component in Problem 3-6B.*

## Income Statement

| | | |
|---|---|---|
| | | |
| | | |
| | | |
| | | |
| | | |
| | | |
| | | |
| | | |
| | | |
| | | |
| | | |
| | | |

## Statement of Owner's Equity

| | | |
|---|---|---|
| | | |
| | | |
| | | |
| | | |
| | | |
| | | |
| | | |
| | | |

## Balance Sheet

| | | | |
|---|---|---|---|
| | | | |
| | | | |
| | | | |
| | | | |
| | | | |
| | | | |
| | | | |
| | | | |
| | | | |
| | | | |
| | | | |
| | | | |
| | | | |
| | | | |
| | | | |
| | | | |

## GENERAL JOURNAL                                              Page ____

| Date | Account Titles and Explanation | PR | Debit | Credit |
|------|-------------------------------|----|-------|--------|
|      |                               |    |       |        |
|      |                               |    |       |        |
|      |                               |    |       |        |
|      |                               |    |       |        |
|      |                               |    |       |        |
|      |                               |    |       |        |
|      |                               |    |       |        |
|      |                               |    |       |        |
|      |                               |    |       |        |
|      |                               |    |       |        |
|      |                               |    |       |        |

**Problem 3-9B     Part 1**

## GENERAL JOURNAL                                              Page ____

| Date | Account Titles and Explanation | PR | Debit | Credit |
|------|-------------------------------|----|-------|--------|
|      |                               |    |       |        |
|      |                               |    |       |        |
|      |                               |    |       |        |
|      |                               |    |       |        |
|      |                               |    |       |        |
|      |                               |    |       |        |
|      |                               |    |       |        |
|      |                               |    |       |        |
|      |                               |    |       |        |
|      |                               |    |       |        |
|      |                               |    |       |        |
|      |                               |    |       |        |
|      |                               |    |       |        |
|      |                               |    |       |        |
|      |                               |    |       |        |
|      |                               |    |       |        |
|      |                               |    |       |        |
|      |                               |    |       |        |
|      |                               |    |       |        |
|      |                               |    |       |        |
|      |                               |    |       |        |
|      |                               |    |       |        |
|      |                               |    |       |        |
|      |                               |    |       |        |
|      |                               |    |       |        |
|      |                               |    |       |        |
|      |                               |    |       |        |

## GENERAL JOURNAL                                    Page ____

| Date | Account Titles and Explanation | PR | Debit | Credit |
|------|-------------------------------|----|-------|--------|
|      |                               |    |       |        |
|      |                               |    |       |        |
|      |                               |    |       |        |
|      |                               |    |       |        |
|      |                               |    |       |        |
|      |                               |    |       |        |
|      |                               |    |       |        |
|      |                               |    |       |        |
|      |                               |    |       |        |
|      |                               |    |       |        |
|      |                               |    |       |        |
|      |                               |    |       |        |
|      |                               |    |       |        |
|      |                               |    |       |        |
|      |                               |    |       |        |
|      |                               |    |       |        |
|      |                               |    |       |        |
|      |                               |    |       |        |
|      |                               |    |       |        |
|      |                               |    |       |        |
|      |                               |    |       |        |
|      |                               |    |       |        |
|      |                               |    |       |        |
|      |                               |    |       |        |
|      |                               |    |       |        |
|      |                               |    |       |        |
|      |                               |    |       |        |
|      |                               |    |       |        |
|      |                               |    |       |        |
|      |                               |    |       |        |
|      |                               |    |       |        |
|      |                               |    |       |        |
|      |                               |    |       |        |
|      |                               |    |       |        |
|      |                               |    |       |        |
|      |                               |    |       |        |
|      |                               |    |       |        |
|      |                               |    |       |        |
|      |                               |    |       |        |
|      |                               |    |       |        |

**Parts 2 and 3**

## GENERAL LEDGER

**Cash**  **ACCOUNT NO. 101**

| DATE | EXPLANATION | PR | DEBIT | CREDIT | BALANCE |
|------|-------------|----|----|------|-------|
| 2011 | | | | | |
| Jun. 30 | Beginning balance | | | | 51,175 |
| | | | | | |
| | | | | | |
| | | | | | |
| | | | | | |
| | | | | | |
| | | | | | |
| | | | | | |
| | | | | | |
| | | | | | |
| | | | | | |
| | | | | | |
| | | | | | |
| | | | | | |
| | | | | | |
| | | | | | |
| | | | | | |
| | | | | | |

**Accounts Receivable**  **ACCOUNT NO. 106**

| DATE | EXPLANATION | PR | DEBIT | CREDIT | BALANCE |
|------|-------------|----|----|------|-------|
| 2011 | | | | | |
| Jun. 30 | Beginning balance | | | | 950 |
| | | | | | |
| | | | | | |
| | | | | | |

**Prepaid Insurance**  **ACCOUNT NO. 128**

| DATE | EXPLANATION | PR | DEBIT | CREDIT | BALANCE |
|------|-------------|----|----|------|-------|
| 2011 | | | | | |
| Jun. 30 | Beginning balance | | | | 275 |
| | | | | | |

**Office Equipment**  **ACCOUNT NO. 163**

| DATE | EXPLANATION | PR | DEBIT | CREDIT | BALANCE |
|------|-------------|----|----|------|-------|
| 2011 | | | | | |
| Jun. 30 | Beginning balance | | | | 1,200 |
| | | | | | |
| | | | | | |

### Computer Equipment                    ACCOUNT NO. 167

| DATE | EXPLANATION | PR | DEBIT | CREDIT | BALANCE |
|---|---|---|---|---|---|
| 2011 | | | | | |
| Jun. 30 | Beginning balance | | | | 800 |
| | | | | | |
| | | | | | |

### Building                    ACCOUNT NO. 173

| DATE | EXPLANATION | PR | DEBIT | CREDIT | BALANCE |
|---|---|---|---|---|---|
| 2011 | | | | | |
| Jun. 30 | Beginning balance | | | | 14,000 |
| | | | | | |

### Land                    ACCOUNT NO. 183

| DATE | EXPLANATION | PR | DEBIT | CREDIT | BALANCE |
|---|---|---|---|---|---|
| 2011 | | | | | |
| Jun. 30 | Beginning balance | | | | 6,000 |
| | | | | | |

### Accounts Payable                    ACCOUNT NO. 201

| DATE | EXPLANATION | PR | DEBIT | CREDIT | BALANCE |
|---|---|---|---|---|---|
| 2011 | | | | | |
| Jun. 30 | Beginning balance | | | | 725 |
| | | | | | |
| | | | | | |
| | | | | | |
| | | | | | |

### Unearned Fees                    ACCOUNT NO. 233

| DATE | EXPLANATION | PR | DEBIT | CREDIT | BALANCE |
|---|---|---|---|---|---|
| 2011 | | | | | |
| Jun. 30 | Beginning balance | | | | 0 |
| | | | | | |

### Long-Term Notes Payable                    ACCOUNT NO. 251

| DATE | EXPLANATION | PR | DEBIT | CREDIT | BALANCE |
|---|---|---|---|---|---|
| 2011 | | | | | |
| Jun. 30 | Beginning balance | | | | 7,000 |
| | | | | | |
| | | | | | |

### Avery Wilson, Capital                    ACCOUNT NO. 301

| DATE | EXPLANATION | PR | DEBIT | CREDIT | BALANCE |
|------|-------------|----|-------|--------|---------|
| 2011 | | | | | |
| Jun. 30 | Beginning balance | | | | 60,000 |
| | | | | | |

### Avery Wilson, Withdrawals                ACCOUNT NO. 302

| DATE | EXPLANATION | PR | DEBIT | CREDIT | BALANCE |
|------|-------------|----|-------|--------|---------|
| 2011 | | | | | |
| Jun. 30 | Beginning balance | | | | 600 |
| | | | | | |

### Fees Earned                             ACCOUNT NO. 401

| DATE | EXPLANATION | PR | DEBIT | CREDIT | BALANCE |
|------|-------------|----|-------|--------|---------|
| 2011 | | | | | |
| Jun. 30 | Beginning balance | | | | 8,400 |
| | | | | | |
| | | | | | |
| | | | | | |

### Wages Expense                           ACCOUNT NO. 623

| DATE | EXPLANATION | PR | DEBIT | CREDIT | BALANCE |
|------|-------------|----|-------|--------|---------|
| 2011 | | | | | |
| Jun. 30 | Beginning balance | | | | 780 |
| | | | | | |
| | | | | | |

### Computer Rental Expense                 ACCOUNT NO. 645

| DATE | EXPLANATION | PR | DEBIT | CREDIT | BALANCE |
|------|-------------|----|-------|--------|---------|
| 2011 | | | | | |
| Jun. 30 | Beginning balance | | | | 230 |
| | | | | | |

### Advertising Expense                     ACCOUNT NO. 655

| DATE | EXPLANATION | PR | DEBIT | CREDIT | BALANCE |
|------|-------------|----|-------|--------|---------|
| 2011 | | | | | |
| Jun. 30 | Beginning balance | | | | 75 |
| | | | | | |

### Repairs Expense                         ACCOUNT NO. 684

| DATE | EXPLANATION | PR | DEBIT | CREDIT | BALANCE |
|------|-------------|----|-------|--------|---------|
| 2011 | | | | | |
| Jun. 30 | Beginning balance | | | | 40 |
| | | | | | |

## Trial Balance

| | | |
|---|---|---|
| | | |
| | | |
| | | |
| | | |
| | | |
| | | |
| | | |
| | | |
| | | |
| | | |
| | | |
| | | |
| | | |
| | | |
| | | |
| | | |
| | | |
| | | |
| | | |
| | | |
| | | |
| | | |
| | | |
| | | |
| | | |
| | | |
| | | |

**Part 1:** *Journalize the entries in the journal pages provided in Part 1 of Problem 3-9B.*

**Parts 2 and 3**

| Cash | 101 |
|---|---|
| Bal.    51,175 | |

| Computer Equipment | 167 |
|---|---|
| Bal.    800 | |

| Building | 173 |
|---|---|
| Bal.    14,000 | |

| Land | 183 |
|---|---|
| Bal.    6,000 | |

| Accounts Receivable | 106 |
|---|---|
| Bal.    950 | |

| Accounts Payable | 201 |
|---|---|
| | 725    Bal. |

| Prepaid Insurance | 128 |
|---|---|
| Bal.    275 | |

| Unearned Fees | 233 |
|---|---|
| | -0-    Bal. |

| Office Equipment | 163 |
|---|---|
| Bal.    1,200 | |

| Long-Term Notes Payable | 251 |
|---|---|
| | 7,000    Bal. |

| Avery Wilson, Capital | 301 | | Wages Expense | 623 |
|---|---|---|---|---|
| | 60,000 | Bal. | Bal. | 780 | |

| Avery Wilson, Withdrawals | 302 |
|---|---|
| Bal. | 600 | |

| Computer Rental Expense | 645 |
|---|---|
| Bal. | 230 | |

| Advertising Expense | 655 |
|---|---|
| Bal. | 75 | |

| Fees Earned | 401 |
|---|---|
| | 8,400 | Bal. |

| Repairs Expense | 684 |
|---|---|
| Bal. | 40 | |

**Part 4 and analysis component:** *Prepare these on the page provided for Part 4 and Analysis Component of Problem 3-9B.*

**Problem 3-11B     Part 1**

### GENERAL JOURNAL                                    Page____

| Date | Account Titles and Explanation | PR | Debit | Credit |
|---|---|---|---|---|
| | | | | |
| | | | | |
| | | | | |
| | | | | |
| | | | | |
| | | | | |
| | | | | |
| | | | | |
| | | | | |
| | | | | |
| | | | | |
| | | | | |
| | | | | |
| | | | | |
| | | | | |
| | | | | |

## GENERAL JOURNAL      Page____

| Date | Account Titles and Explanation | PR | Debit | Credit |
|------|-------------------------------|----|-------|--------|
|      |                               |    |       |        |
|      |                               |    |       |        |
|      |                               |    |       |        |
|      |                               |    |       |        |
|      |                               |    |       |        |
|      |                               |    |       |        |
|      |                               |    |       |        |
|      |                               |    |       |        |
|      |                               |    |       |        |
|      |                               |    |       |        |
|      |                               |    |       |        |
|      |                               |    |       |        |
|      |                               |    |       |        |
|      |                               |    |       |        |
|      |                               |    |       |        |
|      |                               |    |       |        |
|      |                               |    |       |        |
|      |                               |    |       |        |
|      |                               |    |       |        |
|      |                               |    |       |        |
|      |                               |    |       |        |
|      |                               |    |       |        |
|      |                               |    |       |        |
|      |                               |    |       |        |
|      |                               |    |       |        |
|      |                               |    |       |        |
|      |                               |    |       |        |

**Parts 2 and 3**

|          | Cash | 101   |   |          | Office Supplies | 126 |
|----------|------|-------|---|----------|-----------------|-----|
| Bal.     | 13,000 |     |   | Bal.     | 450             |     |

|   |   |   |   |          | Office Furniture | 161 |
|---|---|---|---|----------|------------------|-----|
|   |   |   |   | Bal.     | 18,000           |     |

| Accounts Payable | | 201 |
|---|---|---|
| | 23,500 | Bal. |

| Notes Payable | | 233 |
|---|---|---|
| | 10,000 | Bal. |

| Ivy Tran, Capital | | 301 |
|---|---|---|
| | 4,000 | Bal. |

| Ivy Tran, Withdrawals | | 302 |
|---|---|---|
| Bal. | 4,000 | |

| Travel Revenue | | 401 |
|---|---|---|
| | 17,000 | Bal. |

| Wages Expense | | 623 |
|---|---|---|
| Bal. | 19,000 | |

| Interest Expense | | 633 |
|---|---|---|
| Bal. | 50 | |

## Part 4

### Trial Balance

| | | |
|---|---|---|
| | | |
| | | |
| | | |
| | | |
| | | |
| | | |
| | | |
| | | |
| | | |
| | | |
| | | |
| | | |
| | | |
| | | |
| | | |
| | | |
| | | |
| | | |
| | | |

## Income Statement

| | | |
|---|---|---|
| | | |
| | | |
| | | |
| | | |
| | | |
| | | |
| | | |
| | | |
| | | |
| | | |
| | | |
| | | |

## Statement of Owner's Equity

| | | |
|---|---|---|
| | | |
| | | |
| | | |
| | | |
| | | |
| | | |
| | | |
| | | |
| | | |
| | | |

## Balance Sheet

| | | | |
|---|---|---|---|
| | | | |
| | | | |
| | | | |
| | | | |
| | | | |
| | | | |
| | | | |
| | | | |
| | | | |
| | | | |
| | | | |
| | | | |
| | | | |
| | | | |

*Analysis component:*

_____

_____

_____

_____

_____

_____

_____

_____

_____


**Problem 3-12B**

<table>
<tr><td colspan="3" align="center">Income Statement</td></tr>
<tr><td></td><td></td><td></td></tr>
<tr><td></td><td></td><td></td></tr>
<tr><td></td><td></td><td></td></tr>
<tr><td></td><td></td><td></td></tr>
<tr><td></td><td></td><td></td></tr>
<tr><td></td><td></td><td></td></tr>
<tr><td></td><td></td><td></td></tr>
<tr><td></td><td></td><td></td></tr>
<tr><td></td><td></td><td></td></tr>
<tr><td></td><td></td><td></td></tr>
<tr><td></td><td></td><td></td></tr>
<tr><td></td><td></td><td></td></tr>
<tr><td></td><td></td><td></td></tr>
<tr><td></td><td></td><td></td></tr>
<tr><td></td><td></td><td></td></tr>
<tr><td></td><td></td><td></td></tr>
<tr><td></td><td></td><td></td></tr>
</table>

## Statement of Owner's Equity

| | | |
|---|---|---|
| | | |
| | | |
| | | |
| | | |
| | | |
| | | |
| | | |
| | | |
| | | |
| | | |
| | | |
| | | |
| | | |

## Balance Sheet

| | | | |
|---|---|---|---|
| | | | |
| | | | |
| | | | |
| | | | |
| | | | |
| | | | |
| | | | |
| | | | |
| | | | |
| | | | |
| | | | |
| | | | |
| | | | |
| | | | |
| | | | |
| | | | |
| | | | |
| | | | |
| | | | |
| | | | |

## Trial Balance

| | | |
|---|---|---|
| | | |
| | | |
| | | |
| | | |
| | | |
| | | |
| | | |
| | | |
| | | |
| | | |
| | | |
| | | |
| | | |
| | | |
| | | |
| | | |
| | | |
| | | |

**Calculations:**

Parts 2 and 6:  October/November Transactions

## GENERAL JOURNAL

| Date | Account Titles and Explanation | PR | Debit | Credit |
|------|-------------------------------|----|-------|--------|
|      |                               |    |       |        |
|      |                               |    |       |        |
|      |                               |    |       |        |
|      |                               |    |       |        |
|      |                               |    |       |        |
|      |                               |    |       |        |
|      |                               |    |       |        |
|      |                               |    |       |        |
|      |                               |    |       |        |
|      |                               |    |       |        |
|      |                               |    |       |        |
|      |                               |    |       |        |
|      |                               |    |       |        |
|      |                               |    |       |        |
|      |                               |    |       |        |
|      |                               |    |       |        |
|      |                               |    |       |        |
|      |                               |    |       |        |
|      |                               |    |       |        |
|      |                               |    |       |        |
|      |                               |    |       |        |
|      |                               |    |       |        |
|      |                               |    |       |        |
|      |                               |    |       |        |
|      |                               |    |       |        |
|      |                               |    |       |        |
|      |                               |    |       |        |
|      |                               |    |       |        |
|      |                               |    |       |        |
|      |                               |    |       |        |
|      |                               |    |       |        |
|      |                               |    |       |        |
|      |                               |    |       |        |
|      |                               |    |       |        |
|      |                               |    |       |        |
|      |                               |    |       |        |
|      |                               |    |       |        |
|      |                               |    |       |        |
|      |                               |    |       |        |
|      |                               |    |       |        |

| Date | Account Titles and Explanation | PR | Debit | Credit |
|------|-------------------------------|----|-------|--------|
|      |                               |    |       |        |
|      |                               |    |       |        |
|      |                               |    |       |        |
|      |                               |    |       |        |
|      |                               |    |       |        |
|      |                               |    |       |        |
|      |                               |    |       |        |
|      |                               |    |       |        |
|      |                               |    |       |        |
|      |                               |    |       |        |
|      |                               |    |       |        |
|      |                               |    |       |        |
|      |                               |    |       |        |
|      |                               |    |       |        |
|      |                               |    |       |        |
|      |                               |    |       |        |
|      |                               |    |       |        |
|      |                               |    |       |        |
|      |                               |    |       |        |
|      |                               |    |       |        |
|      |                               |    |       |        |
|      |                               |    |       |        |
|      |                               |    |       |        |
|      |                               |    |       |        |
|      |                               |    |       |        |
|      |                               |    |       |        |
|      |                               |    |       |        |
|      |                               |    |       |        |
|      |                               |    |       |        |
|      |                               |    |       |        |
|      |                               |    |       |        |
|      |                               |    |       |        |
|      |                               |    |       |        |
|      |                               |    |       |        |
|      |                               |    |       |        |
|      |                               |    |       |        |
|      |                               |    |       |        |
|      |                               |    |       |        |
|      |                               |    |       |        |
|      |                               |    |       |        |
|      |                               |    |       |        |
|      |                               |    |       |        |
|      |                               |    |       |        |
|      |                               |    |       |        |
|      |                               |    |       |        |
|      |                               |    |       |        |

Name _____

| Date | Account Titles and Explanation | PR | Debit | Credit |
|------|-------------------------------|----|----|----|
|      |                               |    |    |    |
|      |                               |    |    |    |
|      |                               |    |    |    |
|      |                               |    |    |    |
|      |                               |    |    |    |
|      |                               |    |    |    |
|      |                               |    |    |    |
|      |                               |    |    |    |
|      |                               |    |    |    |
|      |                               |    |    |    |
|      |                               |    |    |    |
|      |                               |    |    |    |
|      |                               |    |    |    |
|      |                               |    |    |    |
|      |                               |    |    |    |
|      |                               |    |    |    |
|      |                               |    |    |    |
|      |                               |    |    |    |
|      |                               |    |    |    |
|      |                               |    |    |    |
|      |                               |    |    |    |
|      |                               |    |    |    |
|      |                               |    |    |    |
|      |                               |    |    |    |
|      |                               |    |    |    |
|      |                               |    |    |    |
|      |                               |    |    |    |
|      |                               |    |    |    |
|      |                               |    |    |    |
|      |                               |    |    |    |
|      |                               |    |    |    |
|      |                               |    |    |    |
|      |                               |    |    |    |
|      |                               |    |    |    |
|      |                               |    |    |    |
|      |                               |    |    |    |
|      |                               |    |    |    |
|      |                               |    |    |    |
|      |                               |    |    |    |

Parts 1, 3, and 7                        GENERAL LEDGER

### Cash                                                    ACCOUNT NO. 101

| DATE | EXPLANATION | PR | DEBIT | CREDIT | BALANCE |
|------|-------------|----|-------|--------|---------|
|  |  |  |  |  |  |
|  |  |  |  |  |  |
|  |  |  |  |  |  |
|  |  |  |  |  |  |
|  |  |  |  |  |  |
|  |  |  |  |  |  |
|  |  |  |  |  |  |
|  |  |  |  |  |  |
|  |  |  |  |  |  |
|  |  |  |  |  |  |
|  |  |  |  |  |  |
|  |  |  |  |  |  |
|  |  |  |  |  |  |
|  |  |  |  |  |  |
|  |  |  |  |  |  |
|  |  |  |  |  |  |
|  |  |  |  |  |  |
|  |  |  |  |  |  |

### Accounts Receivable                                     ACCOUNT NO. 106

| DATE | EXPLANATION | PR | DEBIT | CREDIT | BALANCE |
|------|-------------|----|-------|--------|---------|
|  |  |  |  |  |  |
|  |  |  |  |  |  |
|  |  |  |  |  |  |
|  |  |  |  |  |  |
|  |  |  |  |  |  |
|  |  |  |  |  |  |
|  |  |  |  |  |  |
|  |  |  |  |  |  |

### Computer Supplies                                       ACCOUNT NO. 126

| DATE | EXPLANATION | PR | DEBIT | CREDIT | BALANCE |
|------|-------------|----|-------|--------|---------|
|  |  |  |  |  |  |
|  |  |  |  |  |  |
|  |  |  |  |  |  |

### Office Equipment                                        ACCOUNT NO. 163

| DATE | EXPLANATION | PR | DEBIT | CREDIT | BALANCE |
|------|-------------|----|-------|--------|---------|
|  |  |  |  |  |  |
|  |  |  |  |  |  |
|  |  |  |  |  |  |

## Computer Equipment                    ACCOUNT NO. 167

| DATE | EXPLANATION | PR | DEBIT | CREDIT | BALANCE |
|------|-------------|----|-------|--------|---------|
|      |             |    |       |        |         |
|      |             |    |       |        |         |
|      |             |    |       |        |         |

## Accounts Payable                      ACCOUNT NO. 201

| DATE | EXPLANATION | PR | DEBIT | CREDIT | BALANCE |
|------|-------------|----|-------|--------|---------|
|      |             |    |       |        |         |
|      |             |    |       |        |         |
|      |             |    |       |        |         |

## Mary Graham, Capital                  ACCOUNT NO. 301

| DATE | EXPLANATION | PR | DEBIT | CREDIT | BALANCE |
|------|-------------|----|-------|--------|---------|
|      |             |    |       |        |         |
|      |             |    |       |        |         |
|      |             |    |       |        |         |

## Mary Graham, Withdrawals              ACCOUNT NO. 302

| DATE | EXPLANATION | PR | DEBIT | CREDIT | BALANCE |
|------|-------------|----|-------|--------|---------|
|      |             |    |       |        |         |
|      |             |    |       |        |         |
|      |             |    |       |        |         |

## Computer Services Revenue             ACCOUNT NO. 403

| DATE | EXPLANATION | PR | DEBIT | CREDIT | BALANCE |
|------|-------------|----|-------|--------|---------|
|      |             |    |       |        |         |
|      |             |    |       |        |         |
|      |             |    |       |        |         |
|      |             |    |       |        |         |

## Wages Expense                         ACCOUNT NO. 623

| DATE | EXPLANATION | PR | DEBIT | CREDIT | BALANCE |
|------|-------------|----|-------|--------|---------|
|      |             |    |       |        |         |
|      |             |    |       |        |         |
|      |             |    |       |        |         |

## Advertising Expense                   ACCOUNT NO. 655

| DATE | EXPLANATION | PR | DEBIT | CREDIT | BALANCE |
|------|-------------|----|-------|--------|---------|
|      |             |    |       |        |         |
|      |             |    |       |        |         |
|      |             |    |       |        |         |

### Mileage Expense                    ACCOUNT NO. 676

| DATE | EXPLANATION | PR | DEBIT | CREDIT | BALANCE |
|------|-------------|----|-------|--------|---------|
|      |             |    |       |        |         |
|      |             |    |       |        |         |
|      |             |    |       |        |         |

### Repairs Expense, Computer          ACCOUNT NO. 684

| DATE | EXPLANATION | PR | DEBIT | CREDIT | BALANCE |
|------|-------------|----|-------|--------|---------|
|      |             |    |       |        |         |
|      |             |    |       |        |         |
|      |             |    |       |        |         |

### Charitable Donations Expense        ACCOUNT NO. 699

| DATE | EXPLANATION | PR | DEBIT | CREDIT | BALANCE |
|------|-------------|----|-------|--------|---------|
|      |             |    |       |        |         |
|      |             |    |       |        |         |
|      |             |    |       |        |         |

**Part 4**

### ECHO SYSTMES
### Trial Balance
### October 31, 2011

| | Debit | Credit |
|---|---|---|
| | | |
| | | |
| | | |
| | | |
| | | |
| | | |
| | | |
| | | |
| | | |
| | | |
| | | |
| | | |
| | | |
| | | |
| | | |
| | | |
| | | |
| | | |
| | | |
| | | |
| | | |
| | | |
| | | |
| | | |
| | | |
| | | |
| | | |

**Part 5**

### ECHO SYSTEMS
### Income Statement
### Month Ended October 31, 2011

| | | |
|---|---|---|
| | | |
| | | |
| | | |
| | | |
| | | |
| | | |
| | | |
| | | |
| | | |
| | | |
| | | |
| | | |
| | | |

### ECHO SYSTMES
### Statement of Owner's Equity
### Month Ended October 31, 2011

| | | |
|---|---|---|
| | | |
| | | |
| | | |
| | | |
| | | |
| | | |
| | | |
| | | |
| | | |

### ECHO SYSTEMS
### Balance Sheet
### October 31, 2011

| | | | |
|---|---|---|---|
| | | | |
| | | | |
| | | | |
| | | | |
| | | | |
| | | | |
| | | | |
| | | | |
| | | | |
| | | | |
| | | | |
| | | | |
| | | | |
| | | | |
| | | | |

**Part 8**

<table>
<tr><td colspan="3" align="center">ECHO SYSTMES</td></tr>
<tr><td colspan="3" align="center">Trial Balance</td></tr>
<tr><td colspan="3" align="center">November 30, 2011</td></tr>
<tr><td></td><td align="center">Debit</td><td align="center">Credit</td></tr>
<tr><td></td><td></td><td></td></tr>
<tr><td></td><td></td><td></td></tr>
<tr><td></td><td></td><td></td></tr>
<tr><td></td><td></td><td></td></tr>
<tr><td></td><td></td><td></td></tr>
<tr><td></td><td></td><td></td></tr>
<tr><td></td><td></td><td></td></tr>
<tr><td></td><td></td><td></td></tr>
<tr><td></td><td></td><td></td></tr>
<tr><td></td><td></td><td></td></tr>
<tr><td></td><td></td><td></td></tr>
<tr><td></td><td></td><td></td></tr>
<tr><td></td><td></td><td></td></tr>
<tr><td></td><td></td><td></td></tr>
<tr><td></td><td></td><td></td></tr>
<tr><td></td><td></td><td></td></tr>
<tr><td></td><td></td><td></td></tr>
<tr><td></td><td></td><td></td></tr>
<tr><td></td><td></td><td></td></tr>
</table>

**Part 9**

<table>
<tr><td colspan="3" align="center">ECHO SYSTEMS</td></tr>
<tr><td colspan="3" align="center">Income Statement</td></tr>
<tr><td colspan="3" align="center">For Two Months Ended November 30, 2011</td></tr>
<tr><td></td><td></td><td></td></tr>
<tr><td></td><td></td><td></td></tr>
<tr><td></td><td></td><td></td></tr>
<tr><td></td><td></td><td></td></tr>
<tr><td></td><td></td><td></td></tr>
<tr><td></td><td></td><td></td></tr>
<tr><td></td><td></td><td></td></tr>
<tr><td></td><td></td><td></td></tr>
<tr><td></td><td></td><td></td></tr>
<tr><td></td><td></td><td></td></tr>
<tr><td></td><td></td><td></td></tr>
</table>

## ECHO SYSTMES
### Statement of Owner's Equity
### For Two Months Ended November 30, 2011

| | | |
|---|---|---|
| | | |
| | | |
| | | |
| | | |
| | | |
| | | |
| | | |
| | | |
| | | |
| | | |
| | | |

## ECHO SYSTEMS
### Balance Sheet
### November 30, 2011

| | | | |
|---|---|---|---|
| | | | |
| | | | |
| | | | |
| | | | |
| | | | |
| | | | |
| | | | |
| | | | |
| | | | |
| | | | |
| | | | |
| | | | |
| | | | |
| | | | |
| | | | |
| | | | |
| | | | |
| | | | |
| | | | |
| | | | |

1. _____
   _____
   _____

2. _____
   _____
   _____

3. _____
   _____
   _____

4. _____
   _____
   _____

## Quick Study 4-2

**Cash Basis:** _____
_____
_____
_____

**Accrual Basis:** _____
_____
_____
_____
_____

## Quick Study 4-3

**GENERAL JOURNAL**                         Page____

| Date | Account Titles and Explanation | PR | Debit | Credit |
|------|-------------------------------|----|-------|--------|
| a. | | | | |
| | | | | |
| | | | | |
| b. | | | | |
| | | | | |
| | | | | |
| c. | | | | |
| | | | | |
| | | | | |
| | | | | |

d. _____

## GENERAL JOURNAL                                    Page____

| Date | | Account Titles and Explanation | PR | Debit | Credit |
|------|--|-------------------------------|----|-------|--------|
|  |  |  |  |  |  |
|  |  |  |  |  |  |
|  |  |  |  |  |  |
|  |  |  |  |  |  |
|  |  |  |  |  |  |
|  |  |  |  |  |  |
|  |  |  |  |  |  |
|  |  |  |  |  |  |
|  |  |  |  |  |  |
|  |  |  |  |  |  |
|  |  |  |  |  |  |
|  |  |  |  |  |  |
|  |  |  |  |  |  |
|  |  |  |  |  |  |
|  |  |  |  |  |  |
|  |  |  |  |  |  |
|  |  |  |  |  |  |
|  |  |  |  |  |  |

## Quick Study 4-5

## GENERAL JOURNAL                                    Page____

| Date | | Account Titles and Explanation | PR | Debit | Credit |
|------|--|-------------------------------|----|-------|--------|
|  |  |  |  |  |  |
|  |  |  |  |  |  |
|  |  |  |  |  |  |
|  |  |  |  |  |  |
|  |  |  |  |  |  |
|  |  |  |  |  |  |
|  |  |  |  |  |  |
|  |  |  |  |  |  |
|  |  |  |  |  |  |
|  |  |  |  |  |  |
|  |  |  |  |  |  |

## GENERAL JOURNAL                                   Page____

| Date | Account Titles and Explanation | PR | Debit | Credit |
|------|-------------------------------|----|-------|--------|
|      |                               |    |       |        |
|      |                               |    |       |        |
|      |                               |    |       |        |
|      |                               |    |       |        |
|      |                               |    |       |        |
|      |                               |    |       |        |
|      |                               |    |       |        |
|      |                               |    |       |        |
|      |                               |    |       |        |
|      |                               |    |       |        |
|      |                               |    |       |        |

### Quick Study 4-7

## GENERAL JOURNAL                                   Page____

| Date | Account Titles and Explanation | PR | Debit | Credit |
|------|-------------------------------|----|-------|--------|
|      |                               |    |       |        |
|      |                               |    |       |        |
|      |                               |    |       |        |
|      |                               |    |       |        |
|      |                               |    |       |        |
|      |                               |    |       |        |
|      |                               |    |       |        |
|      |                               |    |       |        |
|      |                               |    |       |        |
|      |                               |    |       |        |
|      |                               |    |       |        |
|      |                               |    |       |        |

### Quick Study 4-8

| Debit | Credit | |
|-------|--------|--|
| a. _____ | _____ | Accrual of unpaid and unrecorded advertising that was used by Stark Company. |
| b. _____ | _____ | Adjustment of Unearned Services Revenue to recognize earned revenue. |
| c. _____ | _____ | Recorded revenue for work completed this accounting period; the cash will be received in the next period. |
| d. _____ | _____ | The cost of Equipment was matched to the time periods benefited. |
| e. _____ | _____ | Adjustment of Prepaid Advertising to recognize the portion used. |

| | Dr./Cr. | Account Titles | Statement |
|---|---|---|---|
| (a) | Debit | | |
| | Credit | | |
| (b) | Debit | | |
| | Credit | | |
| (c) | Debit | | |
| | Credit | | |
| (d) | Debit | | |
| | Credit | | |
| (e) | Debit | | |
| | Credit | | |

**Quick Study 4-10**

| | Type of Adjustment | Net income will be overstated, understated, or no effect | Assets will be overstated, understated, or no effect | Liabilities will be overstated, understated, or no effect | Owner's Equity will be overstated, understated, or no effect |
|---|---|---|---|---|---|
| a. | Prepaid Expenses | | | | |
| b. | Amortization | | | | |
| c. | Unearned Revenues | | | | |
| d. | Accrued Expenses | | | | |
| e. | Accrued Revenues | | | | |

*If adjustment is not recorded:*

**Quick Study 4-11**

GENERAL JOURNAL                    Page____

| Date | Account Titles and Explanation | PR | Debit | Credit |
|---|---|---|---|---|
| | | | | |
| | | | | |
| | | | | |
| | | | | |
| | | | | |
| | | | | |
| | | | | |
| | | | | |
| | | | | |
| | | | | |
| | | | | |
| | | | | |

## GENERAL JOURNAL                                    Page____

| Date | Account Titles and Explanation | PR | Debit | Credit |
|------|-------------------------------|----|-------|--------|
|      |                               |    |       |        |
|      |                               |    |       |        |
|      |                               |    |       |        |
|      |                               |    |       |        |
|      |                               |    |       |        |
|      |                               |    |       |        |
|      |                               |    |       |        |
|      |                               |    |       |        |
|      |                               |    |       |        |
|      |                               |    |       |        |
|      |                               |    |       |        |

## *Quick Study 4-13

## GENERAL JOURNAL                                    Page____

| Date | Account Titles and Explanation | PR | Debit | Credit |
|------|-------------------------------|----|-------|--------|
|      |                               |    |       |        |
|      |                               |    |       |        |
|      |                               |    |       |        |
|      |                               |    |       |        |
|      |                               |    |       |        |
|      |                               |    |       |        |
|      |                               |    |       |        |
|      |                               |    |       |        |
|      |                               |    |       |        |
|      |                               |    |       |        |
|      |                               |    |       |        |

## GENERAL JOURNAL                    Page____

| Date | Account Titles and Explanation | PR | Debit | Credit |
|------|-------------------------------|----|-------|--------|
| a. | | | | |
| | | | | |
| | | | | |
| b. | | | | |
| | | | | |
| | | | | |
| c. | | | | |
| | | | | |
| | | | | |
| d. | | | | |
| | | | | |
| | | | | |
| | | | | |

*Name* _____

| 1. _____ | 7. _____ |
| 2. _____ | 8. _____ |
| 3. _____ | 9. _____ |
| 4. _____ | 10. _____ |
| 5. _____ | 11. _____ |
| 6. _____ | 12. _____ |

## Exercise 4-2

### GENERAL JOURNAL                                    Page____

| Date | Account Titles and Explanation | PR | Debit | Credit |
|------|-------------------------------|----|-------|--------|
| a. | | | | |
| | | | | |
| | | | | |
| | | | | |
| b. | | | | |
| | | | | |
| | | | | |
| | | | | |
| c. | | | | |
| | | | | |
| | | | | |
| | | | | |
| d. | | | | |
| | | | | |
| | | | | |
| | | | | |
| e. | | | | |
| | | | | |
| | | | | |
| | | | | |
| f. | | | | |
| | | | | |
| | | | | |
| | | | | |
| g. | | | | |
| | | | | |
| | | | | |
| | | | | |

## GENERAL JOURNAL    Page____

| Date | Account Titles and Explanation | PR | Debit | Credit |
|------|-------------------------------|-----|-------|--------|
| a. | | | | |
| | | | | |
| | | | | |
| | | | | |
| b. | | | | |
| | | | | |
| | | | | |
| | | | | |
| c. | | | | |
| | | | | |
| | | | | |
| | | | | |
| d. | | | | |
| | | | | |
| | | | | |
| | | | | |
| e. | | | | |
| | | | | |
| | | | | |
| | | | | |
| f. | | | | |
| | | | | |
| | | | | |
| | | | | |
| g. | | | | |
| | | | | |
| | | | | |
| | | | | |
| | | | | |

## GENERAL JOURNAL                                    Page____

| Date | Account Titles and Explanation | PR | Debit | Credit |
|------|-------------------------------|-----|-------|--------|
| a. | | | | |
| | | | | |
| | | | | |
| | | | | |
| b. | | | | |
| | | | | |
| | | | | |
| | | | | |
| c. | | | | |
| | | | | |
| | | | | |
| | | | | |
| d. | | | | |
| | | | | |
| | | | | |
| | | | | |
| e. | | | | |
| | | | | |
| | | | | |
| | | | | |
| f. | | | | |
| | | | | |
| | | | | |
| | | | | |
| g. | | | | |
| | | | | |
| | | | | |
| | | | | |
| | | | | |

## GENERAL JOURNAL          Page____

| Date | | Account Titles and Explanation | PR | Debit | Credit |
|---|---|---|---|---|---|
| a. | | | | | |
| | | | | | |
| | | | | | |
| | | | | | |
| b. | | | | | |
| | | | | | |
| | | | | | |
| | | | | | |
| c. | | | | | |
| | | | | | |
| | | | | | |
| | | | | | |
| | | | | | |

## Exercise 4-6

### GENERAL JOURNAL          Page____

| Date | | Account Titles and Explanation | PR | Debit | Credit |
|---|---|---|---|---|---|
| a. | | | | | |
| | | | | | |
| | | | | | |
| b. | | | | | |
| | | | | | |
| | | | | | |
| c. | | | | | |
| | | | | | |
| | | | | | |
| d. | | | | | |
| | | | | | |
| | | | | | |
| e. | | | | | |
| | | | | | |
| | | | | | |
| | | | | | |

**a.** _____

_____

_____

_____

**b.** _____

_____

_____

_____

**c.** _____

_____

_____

_____

**d.** _____

_____

_____

_____

## Exercise 4-8

**Adjusting Entry:**

### GENERAL JOURNAL                          Page____

| Date | Account Titles and Explanation | PR | Debit | Credit |
|------|-------------------------------|----|-------|--------|
|      |                               |    |       |        |
|      |                               |    |       |        |
|      |                               |    |       |        |
|      |                               |    |       |        |
|      |                               |    |       |        |

**Payday Entry:**

### GENERAL JOURNAL                          Page____

| Date | Account Titles and Explanation | PR | Debit | Credit |
|------|-------------------------------|----|-------|--------|
|      |                               |    |       |        |
|      |                               |    |       |        |
|      |                               |    |       |        |
|      |                               |    |       |        |
|      |                               |    |       |        |

**(a)**
**Adjusting Entry:**

GENERAL JOURNAL    Page____

| Date | Account Titles and Explanation | PR | Debit | Credit |
|------|-------------------------------|----|-------|--------|
|      |                               |    |       |        |
|      |                               |    |       |        |
|      |                               |    |       |        |
|      |                               |    |       |        |
|      |                               |    |       |        |

**Journal Entry (Next Period):**

GENERAL JOURNAL    Page____

| Date | Account Titles and Explanation | PR | Debit | Credit |
|------|-------------------------------|----|-------|--------|
|      |                               |    |       |        |
|      |                               |    |       |        |
|      |                               |    |       |        |
|      |                               |    |       |        |
|      |                               |    |       |        |

**(b)**
**Adjusting Entry:**

GENERAL JOURNAL    Page____

| Date | Account Titles and Explanation | PR | Debit | Credit |
|------|-------------------------------|----|-------|--------|
|      |                               |    |       |        |
|      |                               |    |       |        |
|      |                               |    |       |        |
|      |                               |    |       |        |
|      |                               |    |       |        |

**Journal Entry (Next Period):**

GENERAL JOURNAL    Page____

| Date | Account Titles and Explanation | PR | Debit | Credit |
|------|-------------------------------|----|-------|--------|
|      |                               |    |       |        |
|      |                               |    |       |        |
|      |                               |    |       |        |
|      |                               |    |       |        |
|      |                               |    |       |        |

**(c)**
**Adjusting Entry:**

GENERAL JOURNAL                                    Page____

| Date | Account Titles and Explanation | PR | Debit | Credit |
|------|-------------------------------|----|-------|--------|
|      |                               |    |       |        |
|      |                               |    |       |        |
|      |                               |    |       |        |
|      |                               |    |       |        |
|      |                               |    |       |        |

**Journal Entry (Next Period):**

GENERAL JOURNAL                                    Page____

| Date | Account Titles and Explanation | PR | Debit | Credit |
|------|-------------------------------|----|-------|--------|
|      |                               |    |       |        |
|      |                               |    |       |        |
|      |                               |    |       |        |
|      |                               |    |       |        |
|      |                               |    |       |        |

**Exercise 4-10**

GENERAL JOURNAL                                    Page____

| Date | Account Titles and Explanation | PR | Debit | Credit |
|------|-------------------------------|----|-------|--------|
|      |                               |    |       |        |
|      |                               |    |       |        |
|      |                               |    |       |        |
|      |                               |    |       |        |
|      |                               |    |       |        |
|      |                               |    |       |        |
|      |                               |    |       |        |
|      |                               |    |       |        |
|      |                               |    |       |        |
|      |                               |    |       |        |
|      |                               |    |       |        |
|      |                               |    |       |        |
|      |                               |    |       |        |
|      |                               |    |       |        |
|      |                               |    |       |        |
|      |                               |    |       |        |
|      |                               |    |       |        |

## GENERAL JOURNAL                                Page____

| Date | Account Titles and Explanation | PR | Debit | Credit |
|------|-------------------------------|----|----|----|
|      |                               |    |    |    |
|      |                               |    |    |    |
|      |                               |    |    |    |
|      |                               |    |    |    |
|      |                               |    |    |    |
|      |                               |    |    |    |
|      |                               |    |    |    |
|      |                               |    |    |    |
|      |                               |    |    |    |
|      |                               |    |    |    |
|      |                               |    |    |    |
|      |                               |    |    |    |
|      |                               |    |    |    |
|      |                               |    |    |    |
|      |                               |    |    |    |
|      |                               |    |    |    |
|      |                               |    |    |    |
|      |                               |    |    |    |
|      |                               |    |    |    |
|      |                               |    |    |    |
|      |                               |    |    |    |

*Analysis component:*

_____

_____

_____

_____

_____

_____

_____

| ACCOUNT | UNADJUSTED TRIAL BALANCE | | ADJUSTMENTS | | ADJUSTED TRIAL BALANCE | |
|---|---|---|---|---|---|---|
| | Debit | Credit | Debit | Credit | Debit | Credit |
| Cash | 5,000 | | | | | |
| Accounts receivable | 4,500 | | | | | |
| Prepaid insurance | 700 | | | | | |
| Equipment | 12,000 | | | | | |
| Accum. amort., equipment | | 6,000 | | | | |
| Accounts payable | | 1,200 | | | | |
| Jane Adams, capital | | 9,000 | | | | |
| Jane Adams, withdrawals | 3,000 | | | | | |
| Revenues | | 45,000 | | | | |
| Amort. exp., equipment | -0- | | | | | |
| Salaries expense | 29,000 | | | | | |
| Insurance expense | 7,000 | | | | | |
| Totals | 61,200 | 61,200 | | | | |

## Exercise 4-12

### Income Statement

| | | |
|---|---|---|
| | | |
| | | |
| | | |
| | | |
| | | |
| | | |
| | | |
| | | |
| | | |

### Statement of Owner's Equity

| | | |
|---|---|---|
| | | |
| | | |
| | | |
| | | |
| | | |
| | | |
| | | |

## Balance Sheet

| | | | |
|---|---|---|---|
| | | | |
| | | | |
| | | | |
| | | | |
| | | | |
| | | | |
| | | | |
| | | | |
| | | | |
| | | | |
| | | | |

*Analysis component:* _____

_____

_____

_____

_____

## *Exercise 4-13

### GENERAL JOURNAL                    Page____

| Date | Account Titles and Explanation | PR | Debit | Credit |
|---|---|---|---|---|
| a. | | | | |
| | | | | |
| | | | | |
| | | | | |
| | | | | |
| | | | | |
| | | | | |
| | | | | |
| b. | | | | |
| | | | | |
| | | | | |
| | | | | |
| | | | | |
| | | | | |
| | | | | |
| | | | | |
| | | | | |
| | | | | |

### GENERAL JOURNAL                              Page____

| Date | Account Titles and Explanation | PR | Debit | Credit |
|------|-------------------------------|----|-------|--------|
| c.   |                               |    |       |        |
|      |                               |    |       |        |
|      |                               |    |       |        |
|      |                               |    |       |        |
|      |                               |    |       |        |
|      |                               |    |       |        |
|      |                               |    |       |        |
|      |                               |    |       |        |
|      |                               |    |       |        |
| d.   |                               |    |       |        |
|      |                               |    |       |        |
|      |                               |    |       |        |
|      |                               |    |       |        |
|      |                               |    |       |        |
|      |                               |    |       |        |
|      |                               |    |       |        |
|      |                               |    |       |        |
|      |                               |    |       |        |
|      |                               |    |       |        |

*Analysis component:*

_____
_____
_____
_____
_____
_____

*Name* _____

## GENERAL JOURNAL                    Page____

| Date | Account Titles and Explanation | PR | Debit | Credit |
|------|-------------------------------|----|-------|--------|
| a. | | | | |
| | | | | |
| | | | | |
| | | | | |
| | | | | |
| | | | | |
| b. | | | | |
| | | | | |
| | | | | |
| | | | | |
| | | | | |
| | | | | |
| c. | | | | |
| | | | | |
| | | | | |
| | | | | |
| | | | | |
| | | | | |
| d. | | | | |
| | | | | |
| | | | | |
| | | | | |
| | | | | |
| | | | | |
| e. | | | | |
| | | | | |
| | | | | |
| | | | | |
| | | | | |
| | | | | |
| f. | | | | |
| | | | | |
| | | | | |
| | | | | |
| | | | | |
| | | | | |

a. Initial credit recorded in Unearned Fees account:

**GENERAL JOURNAL**                                    Page____

| Date | Account Titles and Explanation | PR | Debit | Credit |
|------|-------------------------------|----|----|----|
|  |  |  |  |  |
|  |  |  |  |  |
|  |  |  |  |  |
|  |  |  |  |  |
|  |  |  |  |  |
|  |  |  |  |  |
|  |  |  |  |  |
|  |  |  |  |  |
|  |  |  |  |  |
|  |  |  |  |  |
|  |  |  |  |  |
|  |  |  |  |  |
|  |  |  |  |  |
|  |  |  |  |  |
|  |  |  |  |  |
|  |  |  |  |  |
|  |  |  |  |  |
|  |  |  |  |  |
|  |  |  |  |  |
|  |  |  |  |  |
|  |  |  |  |  |
|  |  |  |  |  |
|  |  |  |  |  |
|  |  |  |  |  |
|  |  |  |  |  |
|  |  |  |  |  |
|  |  |  |  |  |
|  |  |  |  |  |
|  |  |  |  |  |
|  |  |  |  |  |
|  |  |  |  |  |
|  |  |  |  |  |
|  |  |  |  |  |
|  |  |  |  |  |
|  |  |  |  |  |
|  |  |  |  |  |
|  |  |  |  |  |
|  |  |  |  |  |
|  |  |  |  |  |
|  |  |  |  |  |

b. Initial credit recorded in Fees Earned account:

GENERAL JOURNAL                    Page____

| Date | Account Titles and Explanation | PR | Debit | Credit |
|---|---|---|---|---|
|  |  |  |  |  |
|  |  |  |  |  |
|  |  |  |  |  |
|  |  |  |  |  |
|  |  |  |  |  |
|  |  |  |  |  |
|  |  |  |  |  |
|  |  |  |  |  |
|  |  |  |  |  |
|  |  |  |  |  |
|  |  |  |  |  |
|  |  |  |  |  |
|  |  |  |  |  |
|  |  |  |  |  |
|  |  |  |  |  |
|  |  |  |  |  |
|  |  |  |  |  |
|  |  |  |  |  |
|  |  |  |  |  |
|  |  |  |  |  |
|  |  |  |  |  |
|  |  |  |  |  |
|  |  |  |  |  |
|  |  |  |  |  |
|  |  |  |  |  |
|  |  |  |  |  |
|  |  |  |  |  |
|  |  |  |  |  |
|  |  |  |  |  |
|  |  |  |  |  |
|  |  |  |  |  |
|  |  |  |  |  |
|  |  |  |  |  |
|  |  |  |  |  |

c.

_____
_____
_____
_____
_____
_____
_____
_____
_____

## GENERAL JOURNAL      Page____

| Date | Account Titles and Explanation | PR | Debit | Credit |
|---|---|---|---|---|
| a. | | | | |
| | | | | |
| | | | | |
| b. | | | | |
| | | | | |
| | | | | |
| c. | | | | |
| | | | | |
| | | | | |
| d. | | | | |
| | | | | |
| | | | | |
| | | | | |

*Analysis component:*

_____

_____

_____

## Problem 4-2A

### GENERAL JOURNAL      Page____

| Date | Account Titles and Explanation | PR | Debit | Credit |
|---|---|---|---|---|
| a. | | | | |
| | | | | |
| | | | | |
| | | | | |
| b. | | | | |
| | | | | |
| | | | | |
| | | | | |
| c. | | | | |
| | | | | |
| | | | | |
| | | | | |

*Analysis component:*

_____
_____
_____
_____
_____
_____
_____
_____
_____
_____
_____

## Problem 4-3A

**GENERAL JOURNAL**                    Page____

| Date | Account Titles and Explanation | PR | Debit | Credit |
|------|-------------------------------|----|-------|--------|
| a. | | | | |
| | | | | |
| | | | | |
| | | | | |
| b. | | | | |
| | | | | |
| | | | | |
| | | | | |
| c. | | | | |
| | | | | |
| | | | | |
| | | | | |
| d. | | | | |
| | | | | |
| | | | | |
| | | | | |

*Analysis component:*

_____
_____
_____
_____
_____
_____
_____
_____

**Adjusting Entries:**          **GENERAL JOURNAL**          Page____

| Date | Account Titles and Explanation | PR | Debit | Credit |
|---|---|---|---|---|
| a. | | | | |
| | | | | |
| | | | | |
| | | | | |
| b. | | | | |
| | | | | |
| | | | | |
| | | | | |
| c. | | | | |
| | | | | |
| | | | | |
| | | | | |
| d. | | | | |
| | | | | |
| | | | | |
| | | | | |
| e. | | | | |
| | | | | |
| | | | | |
| | | | | |

Subsequent Entries:    **GENERAL JOURNAL**    Page____

| Date | Account Titles and Explanation | PR | Debit | Credit |
|------|-------------------------------|----|-------|--------|
| a. | | | | |
| | | | | |
| | | | | |
| | | | | |
| b. | | | | |
| | | | | |
| | | | | |
| | | | | |
| c. | | | | |
| | | | | |
| | | | | |
| | | | | |
| d. | | | | |
| | | | | |
| | | | | |
| | | | | |
| e. | | | | |
| | | | | |
| | | | | |
| | | | | |
| | | | | |

**Adjusting Entries:**            GENERAL JOURNAL                    Page____

| Date | | Account Titles and Explanation | PR | Debit | Credit |
|---|---|---|---|---|---|
| a. | | | | | |
| | | | | | |
| | | | | | |
| b. | | | | | |
| | | | | | |
| | | | | | |
| c. | | | | | |
| | | | | | |
| | | | | | |
| d. | | | | | |
| | | | | | |
| | | | | | |
| | | | | | |

**Subsequent Entries:**            GENERAL JOURNAL                    Page____

| Date | | Account Titles and Explanation | PR | Debit | Credit |
|---|---|---|---|---|---|
| a. | | | | | |
| | | | | | |
| | | | | | |
| b. | | | | | |
| | | | | | |
| | | | | | |
| c. | | | | | |
| | | | | | |
| | | | | | |
| d. | | | | | |
| | | | | | |
| | | | | | |
| | | | | | |

Subsequent Entries:              **GENERAL JOURNAL**                    Page____

| Date | Account Titles and Explanation | PR | Debit | Credit |
|------|-------------------------------|----|-------|--------|
| a. | | | | |
| | | | | |
| | | | | |
| b. | | | | |
| | | | | |
| | | | | |
| c. | | | | |
| | | | | |
| | | | | |
| d. | | | | |
| | | | | |
| | | | | |
| e. | | | | |
| | | | | |
| | | | | |
| f. | | | | |
| | | | | |
| | | | | |
| g. | | | | |
| | | | | |
| | | | | |
| h. | | | | |
| | | | | |
| | | | | |

**Part 2:**  *See next page for Part 2 working paper.*
  **Part 3:** _____
_____
_____

  **Part 4:** _____
_____
_____
_____

## Part 2

| ACCOUNT | UNADJUSTED TRIAL BALANCE | | ADJUSTMENTS | | ADJUSTED TRIAL BALANCE | |
|---|---|---|---|---|---|---|
| | Debit | Credit | Debit | Credit | Debit | Credit |
| Cash | 52,000 | | | | | |
| Accounts receivable | -0- | | | | | |
| Teaching supplies | 20,000 | | | | | |
| Prepaid insurance | 30,000 | | | | | |
| Prepaid rent | 4,000 | | | | | |
| Professional library | 60,000 | | | | | |
| Accum. amort., library | | 18,000 | | | | |
| Equipment | 140,000 | | | | | |
| Accum. amort., equipment | | 32,000 | | | | |
| Accounts payable | | 72,000 | | | | |
| Salaries payable | | -0- | | | | |
| Unearned extension fees | | 22,000 | | | | |
| Sheila Carr, capital | | 127,200 | | | | |
| Sheila Carr, withdrawals | 80,000 | | | | | |
| Tuition fees earned | | 204,000 | | | | |
| Extension fees earned | | 76,000 | | | | |
| Amort. exp., equipment | -0- | | | | | |
| Amort. exp., library | -0- | | | | | |
| Salaries expense | 96,000 | | | | | |
| Insurance expense | -0- | | | | | |
| Rent expense | 44,000 | | | | | |
| Teaching supplies expense | -0- | | | | | |
| Advertising expense | 14,000 | | | | | |
| Utilities expense | 11,200 | | | | | |
| Totals | 551,200 | 551,200 | | | | |

## Problem 4-7A
**Subsequent Entries:**          **GENERAL JOURNAL**          Page_____

| Date | | Account Titles and Explanation | PR | Debit | Credit |
|---|---|---|---|---|---|
| a. | | | | | |
| | | | | | |
| | | | | | |
| | | | | | |
| b. | | | | | |
| | | | | | |
| | | | | | |
| | | | | | |
| | | | | | |
| | | | | | |

## GENERAL JOURNAL                                    Page____

| Date | | Account Titles and Explanation | PR | Debit | Credit |
|---|---|---|---|---|---|
| c. | | | | | |
| | | | | | |
| | | | | | |
| | | | | | |
| d. | | | | | |
| | | | | | |
| | | | | | |
| | | | | | |
| e. | | | | | |
| | | | | | |
| | | | | | |
| | | | | | |
| f. | | | | | |
| | | | | | |
| | | | | | |
| | | | | | |
| g. | | | | | |
| | | | | | |
| | | | | | |
| | | | | | |
| h. | | | | | |
| | | | | | |
| | | | | | |
| | | | | | |
| i. | | | | | |
| | | | | | |
| | | | | | |
| | | | | | |
| j. | | | | | |
| | | | | | |
| | | | | | |
| | | | | | |
| | | | | | |

| Date | Account Titles and Explanation | PR | Debit | Credit |
|------|-------------------------------|----|-------|--------|
|  |  |  |  |  |
|  |  |  |  |  |
|  |  |  |  |  |
|  |  |  |  |  |
|  |  |  |  |  |
|  |  |  |  |  |
|  |  |  |  |  |
|  |  |  |  |  |
|  |  |  |  |  |
|  |  |  |  |  |
|  |  |  |  |  |
|  |  |  |  |  |
|  |  |  |  |  |
|  |  |  |  |  |
|  |  |  |  |  |
|  |  |  |  |  |
|  |  |  |  |  |
|  |  |  |  |  |
|  |  |  |  |  |
|  |  |  |  |  |
|  |  |  |  |  |
|  |  |  |  |  |
|  |  |  |  |  |
|  |  |  |  |  |
|  |  |  |  |  |
|  |  |  |  |  |
|  |  |  |  |  |
|  |  |  |  |  |
|  |  |  |  |  |
|  |  |  |  |  |
|  |  |  |  |  |
|  |  |  |  |  |
|  |  |  |  |  |
|  |  |  |  |  |
|  |  |  |  |  |
|  |  |  |  |  |

GENERAL JOURNAL                         Page____

| Date | Account Titles and Explanation | PR | Debit | Credit |
|------|-------------------------------|----|----|----|
|      |                               |    |    |    |
|      |                               |    |    |    |
|      |                               |    |    |    |
|      |                               |    |    |    |
|      |                               |    |    |    |
|      |                               |    |    |    |
|      |                               |    |    |    |
|      |                               |    |    |    |
|      |                               |    |    |    |
|      |                               |    |    |    |
|      |                               |    |    |    |
|      |                               |    |    |    |
|      |                               |    |    |    |
|      |                               |    |    |    |
|      |                               |    |    |    |
|      |                               |    |    |    |
|      |                               |    |    |    |
|      |                               |    |    |    |

Chapter 4    Problem 4-9A

GENERAL JOURNAL                         Page____

| Date | Account Titles and Explanation | PR | Debit | Credit |
|------|-------------------------------|----|----|----|
| a.   |                               |    |    |    |
|      |                               |    |    |    |
|      |                               |    |    |    |
|      |                               |    |    |    |
| b.   |                               |    |    |    |
|      |                               |    |    |    |
|      |                               |    |    |    |
| c.   |                               |    |    |    |
|      |                               |    |    |    |
|      |                               |    |    |    |
|      |                               |    |    |    |
| d.   |                               |    |    |    |
|      |                               |    |    |    |
|      |                               |    |    |    |
|      |                               |    |    |    |
|      |                               |    |    |    |
|      |                               |    |    |    |

## GENERAL JOURNAL                                          Page____

| Date | Account Titles and Explanation | PR | Debit | Credit |
|---|---|---|---|---|
| **e.** | | | | |
| | | | | |
| | | | | |
| | | | | |
| | | | | |
| **f.** | | | | |
| | | | | |
| | | | | |
| | | | | |
| | | | | |
| **g.** | | | | |
| | | | | |
| | | | | |
| | | | | |
| | | | | |
| **h.** | | | | |
| | | | | |
| | | | | |
| | | | | |
| | | | | |
| **i.** | | | | |
| | | | | |
| | | | | |
| | | | | |
| | | | | |

## Problem 4-10A    Parts 1 and 2

### GENERAL LEDGER

Cash                                          **ACCOUNT NO. 101**

| DATE | EXPLANATION | PR | DEBIT | CREDIT | BALANCE |
|---|---|---|---|---|---|
| 2011 | | | | | |
| Oct 31 | Balance | | | | 28,000 |

Accounts Receivable                           **ACCOUNT NO. 106**

| DATE | EXPLANATION | PR | DEBIT | CREDIT | BALANCE |
|---|---|---|---|---|---|
| 2011 | | | | | |
| Oct 31 | Balance | | | | 56,000 |
| | | | | | |

### Interest Receivable                                                           ACCOUNT NO. 109

| DATE | EXPLANATION | PR | DEBIT | CREDIT | BALANCE |
|------|-------------|----|-------|--------|---------|
| 2011 |             |    |       |        |         |
|      |             |    |       |        |         |

### Notes Receivable                                                            ACCOUNT NO. 111

| DATE | EXPLANATION | PR | DEBIT | CREDIT | BALANCE |
|------|-------------|----|-------|--------|---------|
| 2011 |             |    |       |        |         |
| Oct 31 | Balance   |    |       |        | 30,000  |

### Supplies                                                                          ACCOUNT NO. 126

| DATE | EXPLANATION | PR | DEBIT | CREDIT | BALANCE |
|------|-------------|----|-------|--------|---------|
| 2011 |             |    |       |        |         |
| Oct 31 | Balance   |    |       |        | 4,600   |
|      |             |    |       |        |         |

### Prepaid Insurance                                                         ACCOUNT NO. 128

| DATE | EXPLANATION | PR | DEBIT | CREDIT | BALANCE |
|------|-------------|----|-------|--------|---------|
| 2011 |             |    |       |        |         |
| Oct 31 | Balance   |    |       |        | 9,350   |
|      |             |    |       |        |         |

### Prepaid Rent                                                                  ACCOUNT NO. 131

| DATE | EXPLANATION | PR | DEBIT | CREDIT | BALANCE |
|------|-------------|----|-------|--------|---------|
| 2011 |             |    |       |        |         |
| Oct 31 | Balance   |    |       |        | 21,000  |
|      |             |    |       |        |         |

### Office Furniture                                                            ACCOUNT NO. 161

| DATE | EXPLANATION | PR | DEBIT | CREDIT | BALANCE |
|------|-------------|----|-------|--------|---------|
| 2011 |             |    |       |        |         |
| Oct 31 | Balance   |    |       |        | 61,440  |

### Accumulated Amortization, Office Furniture                    ACCOUNT NO. 162

| DATE | EXPLANATION | PR | DEBIT | CREDIT | BALANCE |
|------|-------------|----|-------|--------|---------|
| 2011 |             |    |       |        |         |
| Oct 31 | Balance   |    |       |        | 20,480  |
|      |             |    |       |        |         |

## Accounts Payable                                                         ACCOUNT NO. 201

| DATE | EXPLANATION | PR | DEBIT | CREDIT | BALANCE |
|------|-------------|----|----|------|------|
| 2011 | | | | | |
| Oct 31 | Balance | | | | 35,000 |

## Wages Payable                                                            ACCOUNT NO. 210

| DATE | EXPLANATION | PR | DEBIT | CREDIT | BALANCE |
|------|-------------|----|----|------|------|
| 2011 | | | | | |
| | | | | | |

## Unearned Consulting Fees                                                 ACCOUNT NO. 233

| DATE | EXPLANATION | PR | DEBIT | CREDIT | BALANCE |
|------|-------------|----|----|------|------|
| 2011 | | | | | |
| Oct 31 | Balance | | | | 13,160 |
| | | | | | |
| | | | | | |

## Jeff Moore, Capital                                                      ACCOUNT NO. 301

| DATE | EXPLANATION | PR | DEBIT | CREDIT | BALANCE |
|------|-------------|----|----|------|------|
| 2011 | | | | | |
| Oct 31 | Balance | | | | 60,000 |

## Jeff Moore, Withdrawals                                                  ACCOUNT NO. 302

| DATE | EXPLANATION | PR | DEBIT | CREDIT | BALANCE |
|------|-------------|----|----|------|------|
| 2011 | | | | | |
| Oct 31 | Balance | | | | 16,450 |

## Consulting Fees Earned                                                   ACCOUNT NO. 401

| DATE | EXPLANATION | PR | DEBIT | CREDIT | BALANCE |
|------|-------------|----|----|------|------|
| 2011 | | | | | |
| Oct 31 | Balance | | | | 314,600 |
| | | | | | |
| | | | | | |
| | | | | | |

### Interest Revenue — ACCOUNT NO. 409

| DATE | EXPLANATION | PR | DEBIT | CREDIT | BALANCE |
|------|-------------|----|-------|--------|---------|
| 2011 | | | | | |
| Oct 31 | Balance | | | | 1,400 |
| | | | | | |

### Amortization Expense, Office Furniture — ACCOUNT NO. 601

| DATE | EXPLANATION | PR | DEBIT | CREDIT | BALANCE |
|------|-------------|----|-------|--------|---------|
| 2011 | | | | | |
| | | | | | |

### Wages Expense — ACCOUNT NO. 622

| DATE | EXPLANATION | PR | DEBIT | CREDIT | BALANCE |
|------|-------------|----|-------|--------|---------|
| 2011 | | | | | |
| Oct 31 | Balance | | | | 147,000 |
| | | | | | |

### Insurance Expense — ACCOUNT NO. 637

| DATE | EXPLANATION | PR | DEBIT | CREDIT | BALANCE |
|------|-------------|----|-------|--------|---------|
| 2011 | | | | | |
| | | | | | |

### Rent Expense — ACCOUNT NO. 640

| DATE | EXPLANATION | PR | DEBIT | CREDIT | BALANCE |
|------|-------------|----|-------|--------|---------|
| 2011 | | | | | |
| Oct 31 | Balance | | | | 64,000 |
| | | | | | |

### Supplies Expense — ACCOUNT NO. 650

| DATE | EXPLANATION | PR | DEBIT | CREDIT | BALANCE |
|------|-------------|----|-------|--------|---------|
| 2011 | | | | | |
| Oct 31 | Balance | | | | 6,800 |
| | | | | | |

## Adjusted Trial Balance

| | | | |
|---|---|---|---|
| | | | |
| | | | |
| | | | |
| | | | |
| | | | |
| | | | |
| | | | |
| | | | |
| | | | |
| | | | |
| | | | |
| | | | |
| | | | |
| | | | |
| | | | |
| | | | |
| | | | |
| | | | |
| | | | |
| | | | |
| | | | |
| | | | |
| | | | |
| | | | |
| | | | |
| | | | |

## Part 4

## Income Statement

| | | |
|---|---|---|
| | | |
| | | |
| | | |
| | | |
| | | |
| | | |
| | | |
| | | |
| | | |
| | | |
| | | |
| | | |
| | | |
| | | |

## Statement of Owner's Equity

|  |  |  |
|---|---|---|
|  |  |  |
|  |  |  |
|  |  |  |
|  |  |  |
|  |  |  |
|  |  |  |
|  |  |  |

## Balance Sheet

|  |  |  |  |
|---|---|---|---|
|  |  |  |  |
|  |  |  |  |
|  |  |  |  |
|  |  |  |  |
|  |  |  |  |
|  |  |  |  |
|  |  |  |  |
|  |  |  |  |
|  |  |  |  |
|  |  |  |  |
|  |  |  |  |
|  |  |  |  |
|  |  |  |  |
|  |  |  |  |
|  |  |  |  |
|  |  |  |  |
|  |  |  |  |
|  |  |  |  |
|  |  |  |  |
|  |  |  |  |
|  |  |  |  |

*Analysis component:*

_____

_____

_____

_____

_____

_____

## GENERAL JOURNAL                                    Page____

| Date | Account Titles and Explanation | PR | Debit | Credit |
|------|-------------------------------|----|-------|--------|
| a. | | | | |
| | | | | |
| | | | | |
| | | | | |
| b. | | | | |
| | | | | |
| | | | | |
| | | | | |
| c. | | | | |
| | | | | |
| | | | | |
| | | | | |
| d. | | | | |
| | | | | |
| | | | | |
| | | | | |
| e. | | | | |
| | | | | |
| | | | | |
| | | | | |
| f. | | | | |
| | | | | |
| | | | | |
| | | | | |
| g. | | | | |
| | | | | |
| | | | | |
| | | | | |
| | | | | |

| ACCOUNT | UNADJUSTED TRIAL BALANCE | | ADJUSTMENTS | | ADJUSTED TRIAL BALANCE | |
|---|---|---|---|---|---|---|
| | Debit | Credit | Debit | Credit | Debit | Credit |
| Cash | 6,000 | | | | | |
| Accounts receivable | 11,200 | | | | | |
| Repair supplies | 2,200 | | | | | |
| Prepaid rent | 14,000 | | | | | |
| Office furniture | 26,000 | | | | | |
| Accounts payable | | 8,000 | | | | |
| Notes payable | | 21,600 | | | | |
| Al Zink, capital | | 67,758 | | | | |
| Al Zink, withdrawals | 5,000 | | | | | |
| Hospitality revenues | | 128,000 | | | | |
| Salaries expense | 142,200 | | | | | |
| Repair supplies expense | 15,500 | | | | | |
| Interest expense | 1,458 | | | | | |
| Internet expenses | 1,800 | | | | | |
| Totals | 225,358 | 225,358 | | | | |
| | | | | | | |
| | | | | | | |
| | | | | | | |
| | | | | | | |
| | | | | | | |
| | | | | | | |
| | | | | | | |
| | | | | | | |

Part 2

## Income Statement

| | | |
|---|---|---|
| | | |
| | | |
| | | |
| | | |
| | | |
| | | |
| | | |
| | | |
| | | |
| | | |
| | | |
| | | |
| | | |

---

### Statement of Owner's Equity

| | | |
|---|---|---|
| | | |
| | | |
| | | |
| | | |
| | | |
| | | |
| | | |

---

### Balance Sheet

| | | | |
|---|---|---|---|
| | | | |
| | | | |
| | | | |
| | | | |
| | | | |
| | | | |
| | | | |
| | | | |
| | | | |
| | | | |
| | | | |
| | | | |
| | | | |
| | | | |
| | | | |
| | | | |
| | | | |
| | | | |

*Analysis component:*

_____
_____
_____
_____
_____
_____
_____
_____

## Income Statement

|  |  |  |
|---|---|---|
|  |  |  |
|  |  |  |
|  |  |  |
|  |  |  |
|  |  |  |
|  |  |  |
|  |  |  |
|  |  |  |
|  |  |  |
|  |  |  |
|  |  |  |
|  |  |  |
|  |  |  |
|  |  |  |
|  |  |  |
|  |  |  |
|  |  |  |
|  |  |  |
|  |  |  |
|  |  |  |
|  |  |  |

## Statement of Owner's Equity

|  |  |  |
|---|---|---|
|  |  |  |
|  |  |  |
|  |  |  |
|  |  |  |
|  |  |  |
|  |  |  |
|  |  |  |
|  |  |  |

## Balance Sheet

| | | | |
|---|---|---|---|
| | | | |
| | | | |
| | | | |
| | | | |
| | | | |
| | | | |
| | | | |
| | | | |
| | | | |
| | | | |
| | | | |
| | | | |
| | | | |
| | | | |
| | | | |
| | | | |
| | | | |
| | | | |
| | | | |
| | | | |
| | | | |
| | | | |
| | | | |
| | | | |
| | | | |
| | | | |
| | | | |
| | | | |
| | | | |
| | | | |
| | | | |

### *Analysis component:*

_____
_____
_____
_____
_____
_____
_____
_____
_____
_____

## GENERAL JOURNAL

Page____

| Date | Account Titles and Explanation | PR | Debit | Credit |
|------|-------------------------------|----|----|----|
| | | | | |
| | | | | |
| | | | | |
| | | | | |
| | | | | |
| | | | | |
| | | | | |
| | | | | |
| | | | | |
| | | | | |
| | | | | |
| | | | | |
| | | | | |
| | | | | |
| | | | | |
| | | | | |
| | | | | |
| | | | | |
| | | | | |
| | | | | |
| | | | | |
| | | | | |
| | | | | |
| | | | | |
| | | | | |
| | | | | |
| | | | | |
| | | | | |
| | | | | |
| | | | | |
| | | | | |
| | | | | |
| | | | | |
| | | | | |
| | | | | |
| | | | | |
| | | | | |
| | | | | |
| | | | | |
| | | | | |
| | | | | |
| | | | | |
| | | | | |
| | | | | |
| | | | | |
| | | | | |

| Cash | 101 | | Prepaid Rent | 131 |
|---|---|---|---|---|

| Office Furniture | 161 | | Accum. Amort., Office Furn. | 162 |
|---|---|---|---|---|

| Accounts Payable | 201 | | Unearned Revenue | 233 |
|---|---|---|---|---|

| Delanie Tugut, Capital | 301 | | Delanie Tugut, Withdrawals | 302 |
|---|---|---|---|---|

| Revenue 401 | | | Amort. Exp., Office Furniture | 602 |
|---|---|---|---|---|

| Wages Expense | 623 | | Rent Expense | 640 |
|---|---|---|---|---|

| Telephone Expense | 688 | | Hotel Expenses | 696 |
|---|---|---|---|---|

## Trial Balance

|  | Debit | Credit |
|---|---|---|
|  |  |  |
|  |  |  |
|  |  |  |
|  |  |  |
|  |  |  |
|  |  |  |
|  |  |  |
|  |  |  |
|  |  |  |
|  |  |  |
|  |  |  |
|  |  |  |
|  |  |  |
|  |  |  |
|  |  |  |

## Part 5 – Adjusting entries

### GENERAL JOURNAL                                    Page____

| Date | | Account Titles and Explanation | PR | Debit | Credit |
|---|---|---|---|---|---|
|  |  |  |  |  |  |
|  |  |  |  |  |  |
|  |  |  |  |  |  |
|  |  |  |  |  |  |
|  |  |  |  |  |  |
|  |  |  |  |  |  |
|  |  |  |  |  |  |
|  |  |  |  |  |  |
|  |  |  |  |  |  |
|  |  |  |  |  |  |
|  |  |  |  |  |  |
|  |  |  |  |  |  |
|  |  |  |  |  |  |
|  |  |  |  |  |  |
|  |  |  |  |  |  |
|  |  |  |  |  |  |
|  |  |  |  |  |  |
|  |  |  |  |  |  |
|  |  |  |  |  |  |
|  |  |  |  |  |  |
|  |  |  |  |  |  |

## Trial Balance

| | Debit | Credit |
|---|---|---|
| | | |
| | | |
| | | |
| | | |
| | | |
| | | |
| | | |
| | | |
| | | |
| | | |
| | | |
| | | |
| | | |
| | | |
| | | |
| | | |
| | | |
| | | |
| | | |
| | | |
| | | |

**Part 7**

## Income Statement

| | | |
|---|---|---|
| | | |
| | | |
| | | |
| | | |
| | | |
| | | |
| | | |
| | | |
| | | |
| | | |
| | | |
| | | |
| | | |
| | | |
| | | |

## Statement of Owner's Equity

| | | |
|---|---|---|
| | | |
| | | |
| | | |
| | | |
| | | |
| | | |
| | | |

## Balance Sheet

| | | | |
|---|---|---|---|
| | | | |
| | | | |
| | | | |
| | | | |
| | | | |
| | | | |
| | | | |
| | | | |
| | | | |
| | | | |
| | | | |
| | | | |
| | | | |
| | | | |
| | | | |
| | | | |
| | | | |
| | | | |
| | | | |
| | | | |

*Analysis component:*

_____

_____

_____

_____

_____

_____

_____

## GENERAL JOURNAL

| Date | Account Titles and Explanation | PR | Debit | Credit |
|------|-------------------------------|----|-------|--------|
|      |                               |    |       |        |
|      |                               |    |       |        |
|      |                               |    |       |        |
|      |                               |    |       |        |
|      |                               |    |       |        |
|      |                               |    |       |        |
|      |                               |    |       |        |
|      |                               |    |       |        |
|      |                               |    |       |        |
|      |                               |    |       |        |
|      |                               |    |       |        |
|      |                               |    |       |        |
|      |                               |    |       |        |
|      |                               |    |       |        |
|      |                               |    |       |        |
|      |                               |    |       |        |
|      |                               |    |       |        |
|      |                               |    |       |        |
|      |                               |    |       |        |
|      |                               |    |       |        |
|      |                               |    |       |        |
|      |                               |    |       |        |
|      |                               |    |       |        |
|      |                               |    |       |        |
|      |                               |    |       |        |
|      |                               |    |       |        |
|      |                               |    |       |        |
|      |                               |    |       |        |
|      |                               |    |       |        |
|      |                               |    |       |        |
|      |                               |    |       |        |
|      |                               |    |       |        |

*Analysis component:* _____

_____

_____

_____

_____

_____

_____

_____

_____

| ACCOUNT | UNADJUSTED TRIAL BALANCE | | ADJUSTMENTS | | ADJUSTED TRIAL BALANCE | |
|---|---|---|---|---|---|---|
| | Debit | Credit | Debit | Credit | Debit | Credit |
| Cash | 20,000 | | | | | |
| Accounts receivable | 49,700 | | | | | |
| Prepaid rent | -0- | | | | | |
| Prepaid insurance | -0- | | | | | |
| Accounts payable | | 2,500 | | | | |
| Unearned consulting fees | | -0- | | | | |
| Bruce Willis, capital | | 15,600 | | | | |
| Consulting fees earned | | 82,000 | | | | |
| Rent expense | 28,000 | | | | | |
| Insurance expense | 2,400 | | | | | |
| Totals | 100,100 | 100,100 | | | | |

*Problem 4-17A

Part 1 - Entries that initially recognize assets and liabilities:

## GENERAL JOURNAL                                    Page____

| Date | Account Titles and Explanation | PR | Debit | Credit |
|---|---|---|---|---|
| | | | | |
| | | | | |
| | | | | |
| | | | | |
| | | | | |
| | | | | |
| | | | | |
| | | | | |
| | | | | |
| | | | | |
| | | | | |
| | | | | |
| | | | | |
| | | | | |
| | | | | |
| | | | | |
| | | | | |
| | | | | |
| | | | | |
| | | | | |
| | | | | |
| | | | | |
| | | | | |

GENERAL JOURNAL                                      Page____

| Date | Account Titles and Explanation | PR | Debit | Credit |
|------|-------------------------------|----|-------|--------|
|  |  |  |  |  |
|  |  |  |  |  |
|  |  |  |  |  |
|  |  |  |  |  |
|  |  |  |  |  |
|  |  |  |  |  |
|  |  |  |  |  |
|  |  |  |  |  |
|  |  |  |  |  |
|  |  |  |  |  |
|  |  |  |  |  |
|  |  |  |  |  |
|  |  |  |  |  |
|  |  |  |  |  |
|  |  |  |  |  |
|  |  |  |  |  |
|  |  |  |  |  |
|  |  |  |  |  |
|  |  |  |  |  |
|  |  |  |  |  |

**Part 2 – Entries that initially recognize expenses and revenues:**

GENERAL JOURNAL                                      Page____

| Date | Account Titles and Explanation | PR | Debit | Credit |
|------|-------------------------------|----|-------|--------|
|  |  |  |  |  |
|  |  |  |  |  |
|  |  |  |  |  |
|  |  |  |  |  |
|  |  |  |  |  |
|  |  |  |  |  |
|  |  |  |  |  |
|  |  |  |  |  |
|  |  |  |  |  |
|  |  |  |  |  |
|  |  |  |  |  |
|  |  |  |  |  |
|  |  |  |  |  |
|  |  |  |  |  |
|  |  |  |  |  |
|  |  |  |  |  |
|  |  |  |  |  |
|  |  |  |  |  |
|  |  |  |  |  |
|  |  |  |  |  |
|  |  |  |  |  |
|  |  |  |  |  |

## GENERAL JOURNAL                                                Page____

| Date | Account Titles and Explanation | PR | Debit | Credit |
|------|-------------------------------|----|----|----|
|  |  |  |  |  |
|  |  |  |  |  |
|  |  |  |  |  |
|  |  |  |  |  |
|  |  |  |  |  |
|  |  |  |  |  |
|  |  |  |  |  |
|  |  |  |  |  |
|  |  |  |  |  |
|  |  |  |  |  |
|  |  |  |  |  |
|  |  |  |  |  |
|  |  |  |  |  |
|  |  |  |  |  |
|  |  |  |  |  |
|  |  |  |  |  |
|  |  |  |  |  |
|  |  |  |  |  |
|  |  |  |  |  |
|  |  |  |  |  |
|  |  |  |  |  |
|  |  |  |  |  |
|  |  |  |  |  |
|  |  |  |  |  |

*Analysis component:*

_____
_____
_____
_____
_____
_____
_____
_____
_____
_____
_____
_____
_____
_____
_____
_____
_____

**Name** _____

## GENERAL JOURNAL                                              Page____

| Date | Account Titles and Explanation | PR | Debit | Credit |
|------|-------------------------------|----|-------|--------|
| **a.** | | | | |
| | | | | |
| | | | | |
| **b.** | | | | |
| | | | | |
| | | | | |
| **c.** | | | | |
| | | | | |
| | | | | |
| **d.** | | | | |
| | | | | |
| | | | | |
| | | | | |

*Analysis component:* _____
_____
_____
_____

## Problem 4-2B

## GENERAL JOURNAL                                              Page____

| Date | Account Titles and Explanation | PR | Debit | Credit |
|------|-------------------------------|----|-------|--------|
| **a.** | | | | |
| | | | | |
| | | | | |
| | | | | |
| **b.** | | | | |
| | | | | |
| | | | | |
| | | | | |
| **c.** | | | | |
| | | | | |
| | | | | |
| | | | | |

*Analysis component:*

_____
_____
_____
_____
_____
_____
_____
_____
_____
_____

## Problem 4-3B

### GENERAL JOURNAL                                        Page____

| Date | Account Titles and Explanation | PR | Debit | Credit |
|------|-------------------------------|-----|-------|--------|
| a. | | | | |
| | | | | |
| | | | | |
| | | | | |
| b. | | | | |
| | | | | |
| | | | | |
| | | | | |
| c. | | | | |
| | | | | |
| | | | | |
| | | | | |
| d. | | | | |
| | | | | |
| | | | | |

*Analysis component:*

_____
_____
_____
_____
_____
_____
_____
_____

**Adjusting Entries:**      **GENERAL JOURNAL**      Page____

| Date | Account Titles and Explanation | PR | Debit | Credit |
|---|---|---|---|---|
| a. | | | | |
| | | | | |
| | | | | |
| | | | | |
| | | | | |
| b. | | | | |
| | | | | |
| | | | | |
| | | | | |
| | | | | |
| c. | | | | |
| | | | | |
| | | | | |
| | | | | |
| | | | | |
| d. | | | | |
| | | | | |
| | | | | |
| | | | | |
| | | | | |
| e. | | | | |
| | | | | |
| | | | | |

**Subsequent Entries:**          **GENERAL JOURNAL**          Page____

| Date | Account Titles and Explanation | PR | Debit | Credit |
|------|-------------------------------|----|-------|--------|
| a. | | | | |
| | | | | |
| | | | | |
| | | | | |
| b. | | | | |
| | | | | |
| | | | | |
| | | | | |
| c. | | | | |
| | | | | |
| | | | | |
| | | | | |
| d. | | | | |
| | | | | |
| | | | | |
| | | | | |
| e. | | | | |
| | | | | |
| | | | | |
| | | | | |
| | | | | |

*Name* _____

## Adjusting Entries:    GENERAL JOURNAL    Page____

| Date | | Account Titles and Explanation | PR | Debit | Credit |
|---|---|---|---|---|---|
| a. | | | | | |
| | | | | | |
| | | | | | |
| b. | | | | | |
| | | | | | |
| | | | | | |
| c. | | | | | |
| | | | | | |
| | | | | | |
| d. | | | | | |
| | | | | | |
| | | | | | |
| | | | | | |

## Subsequent Entries:    GENERAL JOURNAL    Page____

| Date | | Account Titles and Explanation | PR | Debit | Credit |
|---|---|---|---|---|---|
| a. | | | | | |
| | | | | | |
| | | | | | |
| b. | | | | | |
| | | | | | |
| | | | | | |
| c. | | | | | |
| | | | | | |
| | | | | | |
| d. | | | | | |
| | | | | | |
| | | | | | |
| | | | | | |

Subsequent Entries:              **GENERAL JOURNAL**              Page____

| Date | Account Titles and Explanation | PR | Debit | Credit |
|------|-------------------------------|----|-------|--------|
| a. | | | | |
| | | | | |
| | | | | |
| b. | | | | |
| | | | | |
| | | | | |
| c. | | | | |
| | | | | |
| | | | | |
| d. | | | | |
| | | | | |
| | | | | |
| e. | | | | |
| | | | | |
| | | | | |
| f. | | | | |
| | | | | |
| | | | | |
| g. | | | | |
| | | | | |
| | | | | |
| h. | | | | |
| | | | | |
| | | | | |

Part 2: *See next page for Part 2 working paper.*
  Part 3: _____

_____

_____

  Part 4: _____

_____

_____

_____

## Part 2

| ACCOUNT | UNADJUSTED TRIAL BALANCE Debit | UNADJUSTED TRIAL BALANCE Credit | ADJUSTMENTS Debit | ADJUSTMENTS Credit | ADJUSTED TRIAL BALANCE Debit | ADJUSTED TRIAL BALANCE Credit |
|---|---|---|---|---|---|---|
| Cash | 50,000 | | | | | |
| Accounts receivable | -0- | | | | | |
| Teaching supplies | 60,000 | | | | | |
| Prepaid insurance | 18,000 | | | | | |
| Prepaid rent | 2,600 | | | | | |
| Professional library | 10,000 | | | | | |
| Accum. amort., library | | 1,500 | | | | |
| Equipment | 30,000 | | | | | |
| Accum. amort., equipment | | 16,000 | | | | |
| Accounts payable | | 12,200 | | | | |
| Salaries payable | | -0- | | | | |
| Unearned extension fees | | 27,600 | | | | |
| Jay Stevens, capital | | 68,500 | | | | |
| Jay Stevens, withdrawals | 20,000 | | | | | |
| Tuition fees earned | | 105,000 | | | | |
| Extension fees earned | | 62,000 | | | | |
| Amort. exp., equipment | -0- | | | | | |
| Amort. exp., library | -0- | | | | | |
| Salaries expense | 43,200 | | | | | |
| Insurance expense | -0- | | | | | |
| Rent expense | 28,600 | | | | | |
| Teaching supplies expense | -0- | | | | | |
| Advertising expense | 18,000 | | | | | |
| Utilities expense | 12,400 | | | | | |
| Totals | 292,800 | 292,800 | | | | |

## Problem 4-7B
**Subsequent Entries:**　　　GENERAL JOURNAL　　　Page____

| Date | Account Titles and Explanation | PR | Debit | Credit |
|---|---|---|---|---|
| a. | | | | |
| | | | | |
| | | | | |
| | | | | |
| b. | | | | |
| | | | | |
| | | | | |
| | | | | |
| | | | | |
| | | | | |

## GENERAL JOURNAL                    Page____

| Date | Account Titles and Explanation | PR | Debit | Credit |
|------|-------------------------------|----|----|----|
| c. |  |  |  |  |
|  |  |  |  |  |
|  |  |  |  |  |
|  |  |  |  |  |
| d. |  |  |  |  |
|  |  |  |  |  |
|  |  |  |  |  |
|  |  |  |  |  |
| e. |  |  |  |  |
|  |  |  |  |  |
|  |  |  |  |  |
|  |  |  |  |  |
| f. |  |  |  |  |
|  |  |  |  |  |
|  |  |  |  |  |
|  |  |  |  |  |
| g. |  |  |  |  |
|  |  |  |  |  |
|  |  |  |  |  |
|  |  |  |  |  |
| h. |  |  |  |  |
|  |  |  |  |  |
|  |  |  |  |  |
|  |  |  |  |  |
| i. |  |  |  |  |
|  |  |  |  |  |
|  |  |  |  |  |
|  |  |  |  |  |
| j. |  |  |  |  |
|  |  |  |  |  |
|  |  |  |  |  |
|  |  |  |  |  |
|  |  |  |  |  |

| Date | Account Titles and Explanation | PR | Debit | Credit |
|------|-------------------------------|----|-------|--------|
|      |                               |    |       |        |
|      |                               |    |       |        |
|      |                               |    |       |        |
|      |                               |    |       |        |
|      |                               |    |       |        |
|      |                               |    |       |        |
|      |                               |    |       |        |
|      |                               |    |       |        |
|      |                               |    |       |        |
|      |                               |    |       |        |
|      |                               |    |       |        |
|      |                               |    |       |        |
|      |                               |    |       |        |
|      |                               |    |       |        |
|      |                               |    |       |        |
|      |                               |    |       |        |
|      |                               |    |       |        |
|      |                               |    |       |        |
|      |                               |    |       |        |
|      |                               |    |       |        |
|      |                               |    |       |        |
|      |                               |    |       |        |
|      |                               |    |       |        |
|      |                               |    |       |        |
|      |                               |    |       |        |
|      |                               |    |       |        |
|      |                               |    |       |        |
|      |                               |    |       |        |
|      |                               |    |       |        |
|      |                               |    |       |        |
|      |                               |    |       |        |
|      |                               |    |       |        |
|      |                               |    |       |        |
|      |                               |    |       |        |
|      |                               |    |       |        |
|      |                               |    |       |        |
|      |                               |    |       |        |
|      |                               |    |       |        |
|      |                               |    |       |        |
|      |                               |    |       |        |

Part 2                    **GENERAL JOURNAL**                    Page____

| Date | Account Titles and Explanation | PR | Debit | Credit |
|------|-------------------------------|----|-------|--------|
|      |                               |    |       |        |
|      |                               |    |       |        |
|      |                               |    |       |        |
|      |                               |    |       |        |
|      |                               |    |       |        |
|      |                               |    |       |        |
|      |                               |    |       |        |
|      |                               |    |       |        |
|      |                               |    |       |        |
|      |                               |    |       |        |
|      |                               |    |       |        |
|      |                               |    |       |        |
|      |                               |    |       |        |
|      |                               |    |       |        |

Chapter 4    Problem 4-9B

**GENERAL JOURNAL**                    Page____

| Date | Account Titles and Explanation | PR | Debit | Credit |
|------|-------------------------------|----|-------|--------|
| a.   |                               |    |       |        |
|      |                               |    |       |        |
|      |                               |    |       |        |
|      |                               |    |       |        |
| b.   |                               |    |       |        |
|      |                               |    |       |        |
|      |                               |    |       |        |
|      |                               |    |       |        |
| c.   |                               |    |       |        |
|      |                               |    |       |        |
|      |                               |    |       |        |
|      |                               |    |       |        |
| d.   |                               |    |       |        |
|      |                               |    |       |        |
|      |                               |    |       |        |
|      |                               |    |       |        |

## GENERAL JOURNAL    Page____

| Date | Account Titles and Explanation | PR | Debit | Credit |
|---|---|---|---|---|
| e. | | | | |
| | | | | |
| | | | | |
| | | | | |
| f. | | | | |
| | | | | |
| | | | | |
| | | | | |
| g. | | | | |
| | | | | |
| | | | | |
| | | | | |
| h. | | | | |
| | | | | |
| | | | | |
| | | | | |
| i. | | | | |
| | | | | |
| | | | | |
| | | | | |
| | | | | |

*Analysis component:*

_____
_____
_____
_____
_____
_____
_____
_____

*Name* _____

## Cash      ACCOUNT NO. 101

| DATE | EXPLANATION | PR | DEBIT | CREDIT | BALANCE |
|------|-------------|----|-------|--------|---------|
| 2011 | | | | | |
| Dec 31 | Balance | | | | 2,800 |

## Accounts Receivable      ACCOUNT NO. 106

| DATE | EXPLANATION | PR | DEBIT | CREDIT | BALANCE |
|------|-------------|----|-------|--------|---------|
| 2011 | | | | | |
| Dec 31 | Balance | | | | 3,955 |
| | | | | | |

## Supplies      ACCOUNT NO. 126

| DATE | EXPLANATION | PR | DEBIT | CREDIT | BALANCE |
|------|-------------|----|-------|--------|---------|
| 2011 | | | | | |
| | | | | | 320 |

## Prepaid Advertising      ACCOUNT NO. 128

| DATE | EXPLANATION | PR | DEBIT | CREDIT | BALANCE |
|------|-------------|----|-------|--------|---------|
| 2011 | | | | | |
| Dec 31 | Balance | | | | 2,800 |

## Prepaid Rent      ACCOUNT NO. 131

| DATE | EXPLANATION | PR | DEBIT | CREDIT | BALANCE |
|------|-------------|----|-------|--------|---------|
| 2011 | | | | | |
| Dec 31 | Balance | | | | 13,500 |
| | | | | | |

## Surveying Equipment      ACCOUNT NO. 167

| DATE | EXPLANATION | PR | DEBIT | CREDIT | BALANCE |
|------|-------------|----|-------|--------|---------|
| 2011 | | | | | |
| Dec 31 | Balance | | | | 29,000 |
| | | | | | |

## Accum. Amort. – Surveying Equipment      ACCOUNT NO. 168

| DATE | EXPLANATION | PR | DEBIT | CREDIT | BALANCE |
|------|-------------|----|-------|--------|---------|
| 2011 | | | | | |
| Dec 31 | Balance | | | | 3,674 |
| | | | | | |

### Accounts Payable — ACCOUNT NO. 201

| DATE | EXPLANATION | PR | DEBIT | CREDIT | BALANCE |
|---|---|---|---|---|---|
| 2011 | | | | | |
| Dec 31 | Balance | | | | 1,900 |
| | | | | | |

### Interest Payable — ACCOUNT NO. 203

| DATE | EXPLANATION | PR | DEBIT | CREDIT | BALANCE |
|---|---|---|---|---|---|
| 2011 | | | | | |
| | | | | | |

### Wages Payable — ACCOUNT NO. 210

| DATE | EXPLANATION | PR | DEBIT | CREDIT | BALANCE |
|---|---|---|---|---|---|
| 2011 | | | | | |
| | | | | | |

### Unearned Surveying Fees — ACCOUNT NO. 233

| DATE | EXPLANATION | PR | DEBIT | CREDIT | BALANCE |
|---|---|---|---|---|---|
| 2011 | | | | | |
| Dec. 31 | Balance | | | | 2,400 |
| | | | | | |

### Notes Payable — ACCOUNT NO. 251

| DATE | EXPLANATION | PR | DEBIT | CREDIT | BALANCE |
|---|---|---|---|---|---|
| 2011 | | | | | |
| Dec 31 | Balance | | | | 18,000 |

### Alissa Kay, Capital — ACCOUNT NO. 301

| DATE | EXPLANATION | PR | DEBIT | CREDIT | BALANCE |
|---|---|---|---|---|---|
| 2011 | | | | | |
| Dec 31 | Balance | | | | 14,326 |

### Alissa Kay, Withdrawals — ACCOUNT NO. 302

| DATE | EXPLANATION | PR | DEBIT | CREDIT | BALANCE |
|---|---|---|---|---|---|
| 2011 | | | | | |
| Dec 31 | Balance | | | | 2,150 |

## Surveying Fees Earned                                          ACCOUNT NO. 401

| DATE | EXPLANATION | PR | DEBIT | CREDIT | BALANCE |
|------|-------------|-----|-------|--------|---------|
| 2011 | | | | | |
| Dec 31 | Balance | | | | 67,049 |
| | | | | | |
| | | | | | |

## Amortization Expense, Surveying Furniture          ACCOUNT NO. 601

| DATE | EXPLANATION | PR | DEBIT | CREDIT | BALANCE |
|------|-------------|-----|-------|--------|---------|
| 2011 | | | | | |
| Dec. 31 | Balance | | | | 1,837 |
| | | | | | |

## Wages Expense                                          ACCOUNT NO. 622

| DATE | EXPLANATION | PR | DEBIT | CREDIT | BALANCE |
|------|-------------|-----|-------|--------|---------|
| 2011 | | | | | |
| Dec 31 | Balance | | | | 19,863 |
| | | | | | |

## Interest Expense                                          ACCOUNT NO. 633

| DATE | EXPLANATION | PR | DEBIT | CREDIT | BALANCE |
|------|-------------|-----|-------|--------|---------|
| 2011 | | | | | |
| Dec. 31 | Balance | | | | 945 |
| | | | | | |

## Supplies Expense                                          ACCOUNT NO. 650

| DATE | EXPLANATION | PR | DEBIT | CREDIT | BALANCE |
|------|-------------|-----|-------|--------|---------|
| 2011 | | | | | |
| Dec 31 | Balance | | | | 1,479 |
| | | | | | |

## Advertising Expense                                          ACCOUNT NO. 655

| DATE | EXPLANATION | PR | DEBIT | CREDIT | BALANCE |
|------|-------------|-----|-------|--------|---------|
| 2011 | | | | | |
| Dec. 31 | Balance | | | | 500 |
| | | | | | |

## Utilities Expense                                          ACCOUNT NO. 690

| DATE | EXPLANATION | PR | DEBIT | CREDIT | BALANCE |
|------|-------------|-----|-------|--------|---------|
| 2011 | | | | | |
| Dec 31 | Balance | | | | 6,200 |
| | | | | | |

## Adjusted Trial Balance

|  |  |  |  |
|---|---|---|---|
|  |  |  |  |
|  |  |  |  |
|  |  |  |  |
|  |  |  |  |
|  |  |  |  |
|  |  |  |  |
|  |  |  |  |
|  |  |  |  |
|  |  |  |  |
|  |  |  |  |
|  |  |  |  |
|  |  |  |  |
|  |  |  |  |
|  |  |  |  |
|  |  |  |  |
|  |  |  |  |
|  |  |  |  |
|  |  |  |  |
|  |  |  |  |
|  |  |  |  |
|  |  |  |  |
|  |  |  |  |
|  |  |  |  |
|  |  |  |  |
|  |  |  |  |

**Part 4**

## Income Statement

|  |  |  |
|---|---|---|
|  |  |  |
|  |  |  |
|  |  |  |
|  |  |  |
|  |  |  |
|  |  |  |
|  |  |  |
|  |  |  |
|  |  |  |
|  |  |  |
|  |  |  |
|  |  |  |
|  |  |  |

## Statement of Owner's Equity

| | | |
|---|---|---|
| | | |
| | | |
| | | |
| | | |
| | | |
| | | |
| | | |

## Balance Sheet

| | | | |
|---|---|---|---|
| | | | |
| | | | |
| | | | |
| | | | |
| | | | |
| | | | |
| | | | |
| | | | |
| | | | |
| | | | |
| | | | |
| | | | |
| | | | |
| | | | |
| | | | |
| | | | |
| | | | |
| | | | |
| | | | |
| | | | |
| | | | |
| | | | |
| | | | |
| | | | |

*Analysis component:* _____

_____

_____

_____

_____

_____

_____

## GENERAL JOURNAL                              Page____

| Date | Account Titles and Explanation | PR | Debit | Credit |
|------|-------------------------------|----|-------|--------|
| a. | | | | |
| | | | | |
| | | | | |
| | | | | |
| b. | | | | |
| | | | | |
| | | | | |
| | | | | |
| c. | | | | |
| | | | | |
| | | | | |
| | | | | |
| d. | | | | |
| | | | | |
| | | | | |
| | | | | |
| e. | | | | |
| | | | | |
| | | | | |
| | | | | |
| f. | | | | |
| | | | | |
| | | | | |
| | | | | |
| g. | | | | |
| | | | | |
| | | | | |
| | | | | |
| | | | | |

*Name*

| ACCOUNT | UNADJUSTED TRIAL BALANCE | | ADJUSTMENTS | | ADJUSTED TRIAL BALANCE | |
|---|---|---|---|---|---|---|
| | Debit | Credit | Debit | Credit | Debit | Credit |
| Cash | 56,000 | | | | | |
| Accounts receivable | 14,000 | | | | | |
| Repair supplies | 1,400 | | | | | |
| Prepaid arena rental | 91,000 | | | | | |
| Hockey equipment | 214,000 | | | | | |
| Accum. amort., hockey eq. | | 82,000 | | | | |
| Accounts payable | | 2,700 | | | | |
| Unearned ticket revenue | | 9,800 | | | | |
| Notes payable | | 80,000 | | | | |
| Ben Gibson, capital | | 225,700 | | | | |
| Ben Gibson, withdrawals | 36,000 | | | | | |
| Ticket revenue | | 275,000 | | | | |
| Salaries expense | 175,000 | | | | | |
| Arena rental expense | 84,000 | | | | | |
| Other expenses | 3,800 | | | | | |
| Totals | 675,200 | 675,200 | | | | |
| | | | | | | |
| | | | | | | |
| | | | | | | |
| | | | | | | |
| | | | | | | |
| | | | | | | |
| | | | | | | |

**Part 2**

## Income Statement

| | | |
|---|---|---|
| | | |
| | | |
| | | |
| | | |
| | | |
| | | |
| | | |
| | | |
| | | |
| | | |
| | | |
| | | |
| | | |

## Statement of Owner's Equity

| | | |
|---|---|---|
| | | |
| | | |
| | | |
| | | |
| | | |
| | | |

## Balance Sheet

| | | | |
|---|---|---|---|
| | | | |
| | | | |
| | | | |
| | | | |
| | | | |
| | | | |
| | | | |
| | | | |
| | | | |
| | | | |
| | | | |
| | | | |
| | | | |
| | | | |
| | | | |
| | | | |
| | | | |
| | | | |
| | | | |

*Analysis component:*

_____
_____
_____
_____
_____
_____
_____

## Income Statement

|  |  |  |
|---|---|---|
|  |  |  |
|  |  |  |
|  |  |  |
|  |  |  |
|  |  |  |
|  |  |  |
|  |  |  |
|  |  |  |
|  |  |  |
|  |  |  |
|  |  |  |
|  |  |  |
|  |  |  |
|  |  |  |
|  |  |  |
|  |  |  |
|  |  |  |
|  |  |  |
|  |  |  |

## Statement of Owner's Equity

|  |  |  |
|---|---|---|
|  |  |  |
|  |  |  |
|  |  |  |
|  |  |  |
|  |  |  |
|  |  |  |
|  |  |  |

## Balance Sheet

| | | | |
|---|---|---|---|
| | | | |
| | | | |
| | | | |
| | | | |
| | | | |
| | | | |
| | | | |
| | | | |
| | | | |
| | | | |
| | | | |
| | | | |
| | | | |
| | | | |
| | | | |
| | | | |
| | | | |
| | | | |
| | | | |
| | | | |
| | | | |
| | | | |
| | | | |
| | | | |
| | | | |
| | | | |
| | | | |
| | | | |
| | | | |
| | | | |
| | | | |
| | | | |
| | | | |
| | | | |
| | | | |
| | | | |
| | | | |
| | | | |
| | | | |
| | | | |
| | | | |

## GENERAL JOURNAL                                    Page____

| Date | Account Titles and Explanation | PR | Debit | Credit |
|------|-------------------------------|----|-------|--------|
|      |                               |    |       |        |
|      |                               |    |       |        |
|      |                               |    |       |        |
|      |                               |    |       |        |
|      |                               |    |       |        |
|      |                               |    |       |        |
|      |                               |    |       |        |
|      |                               |    |       |        |
|      |                               |    |       |        |
|      |                               |    |       |        |
|      |                               |    |       |        |
|      |                               |    |       |        |
|      |                               |    |       |        |
|      |                               |    |       |        |
|      |                               |    |       |        |
|      |                               |    |       |        |
|      |                               |    |       |        |
|      |                               |    |       |        |
|      |                               |    |       |        |
|      |                               |    |       |        |
|      |                               |    |       |        |
|      |                               |    |       |        |
|      |                               |    |       |        |
|      |                               |    |       |        |
|      |                               |    |       |        |
|      |                               |    |       |        |
|      |                               |    |       |        |
|      |                               |    |       |        |
|      |                               |    |       |        |
|      |                               |    |       |        |
|      |                               |    |       |        |
|      |                               |    |       |        |
|      |                               |    |       |        |
|      |                               |    |       |        |
|      |                               |    |       |        |
|      |                               |    |       |        |
|      |                               |    |       |        |
|      |                               |    |       |        |
|      |                               |    |       |        |
|      |                               |    |       |        |

| Cash | 101 |
|---|---|
| Bal. 3,200 | |

| Repair Supplies | 131 |
|---|---|
| Bal. 1,500 | |

| Tools | 161 |
|---|---|
| Bal. 8,400 | |

| Accum. Amort., Tools | 162 |
|---|---|
| | 280 Bal. |

| Accounts Payable | 201 |
|---|---|
| | 1,600 Bal. |

| Unearned Revenue | 233 |
|---|---|
| | 350 Bal. |

| Melanie Thornhill, Capital | 301 |
|---|---|
| | 4,580 Bal. |

| Melanie Thornhill, Withdrawals | 302 |
|---|---|
| Bal. -0- | |

| Revenue 401 |
|---|
| 12,900 Bal. |

| Amort. Exp., Tools | 602 |
|---|---|
| Bal. 280 | |

| Wages Expense | 623 |
|---|---|
| Bal. 980 | |

| Rent Expense | 640 |
|---|---|
| Bal. 4,000 | |

| Repairs Supplies Expense | 696 |
|---|---|
| Bal. 1,350 | |

## Trial Balance

|  | Debit | Credit |
|---|---|---|
|  |  |  |
|  |  |  |
|  |  |  |
|  |  |  |
|  |  |  |
|  |  |  |
|  |  |  |
|  |  |  |
|  |  |  |
|  |  |  |
|  |  |  |
|  |  |  |
|  |  |  |
|  |  |  |

## Part 5 – Adjusting entries

### GENERAL JOURNAL                                              Page____

| Date | Account Titles and Explanation | PR | Debit | Credit |
|---|---|---|---|---|
|  |  |  |  |  |
|  |  |  |  |  |
|  |  |  |  |  |
|  |  |  |  |  |
|  |  |  |  |  |
|  |  |  |  |  |
|  |  |  |  |  |
|  |  |  |  |  |
|  |  |  |  |  |
|  |  |  |  |  |
|  |  |  |  |  |
|  |  |  |  |  |
|  |  |  |  |  |
|  |  |  |  |  |
|  |  |  |  |  |
|  |  |  |  |  |
|  |  |  |  |  |
|  |  |  |  |  |
|  |  |  |  |  |
|  |  |  |  |  |
|  |  |  |  |  |
|  |  |  |  |  |
|  |  |  |  |  |

## Trial Balance

|  | Debit | Credit |
|---|---|---|
|  |  |  |
|  |  |  |
|  |  |  |
|  |  |  |
|  |  |  |
|  |  |  |
|  |  |  |
|  |  |  |
|  |  |  |
|  |  |  |
|  |  |  |
|  |  |  |
|  |  |  |
|  |  |  |
|  |  |  |
|  |  |  |
|  |  |  |
|  |  |  |
|  |  |  |
|  |  |  |
|  |  |  |

Part 7

## Income Statement

|  |  |  |
|---|---|---|
|  |  |  |
|  |  |  |
|  |  |  |
|  |  |  |
|  |  |  |
|  |  |  |
|  |  |  |
|  |  |  |
|  |  |  |
|  |  |  |
|  |  |  |
|  |  |  |
|  |  |  |
|  |  |  |
|  |  |  |

## Statement of Owner's Equity

| | | |
|---|---|---|
| | | |
| | | |
| | | |
| | | |
| | | |
| | | |
| | | |

## Balance Sheet

| | | | |
|---|---|---|---|
| | | | |
| | | | |
| | | | |
| | | | |
| | | | |
| | | | |
| | | | |
| | | | |
| | | | |
| | | | |
| | | | |
| | | | |
| | | | |
| | | | |
| | | | |
| | | | |
| | | | |
| | | | |
| | | | |
| | | | |

## *Analysis component:*

_____

_____

_____

_____

_____

_____

_____

## GENERAL JOURNAL

| Date | Account Titles and Explanation | PR | Debit | Credit |
|------|-------------------------------|----|-------|--------|
|      |                               |    |       |        |
|      |                               |    |       |        |
|      |                               |    |       |        |
|      |                               |    |       |        |
|      |                               |    |       |        |
|      |                               |    |       |        |
|      |                               |    |       |        |
|      |                               |    |       |        |
|      |                               |    |       |        |
|      |                               |    |       |        |
|      |                               |    |       |        |
|      |                               |    |       |        |
|      |                               |    |       |        |
|      |                               |    |       |        |
|      |                               |    |       |        |
|      |                               |    |       |        |
|      |                               |    |       |        |
|      |                               |    |       |        |
|      |                               |    |       |        |
|      |                               |    |       |        |
|      |                               |    |       |        |
|      |                               |    |       |        |
|      |                               |    |       |        |
|      |                               |    |       |        |
|      |                               |    |       |        |
|      |                               |    |       |        |
|      |                               |    |       |        |
|      |                               |    |       |        |
|      |                               |    |       |        |
|      |                               |    |       |        |
|      |                               |    |       |        |
|      |                               |    |       |        |
|      |                               |    |       |        |
|      |                               |    |       |        |
|      |                               |    |       |        |
|      |                               |    |       |        |
|      |                               |    |       |        |

*Analysis component:*

_____
_____
_____
_____
_____
_____
_____
_____

| ACCOUNT | UNADJUSTED TRIAL BALANCE | | ADJUSTMENTS | | ADJUSTED TRIAL BALANCE | |
|---|---|---|---|---|---|---|
| | Debit | Credit | Debit | Credit | Debit | Credit |
| Cash | 29,000 | | | | | |
| Accounts receivable | 18,000 | | | | | |
| Prepaid advertising | -0- | | | | | |
| Cleaning supplies | -0- | | | | | |
| Equipment | 62,000 | | | | | |
| Accum. amort., equipment | | 3,000 | | | | |
| Unearned window washing fees | | -0- | | | | |
| Unearned office cleaning fees | | -0- | | | | |
| Joel Meli, capital | | 18,300 | | | | |
| Window washing fees earned | | 76,000 | | | | |
| Office cleaning fees earned | | 138,000 | | | | |
| Advertising expense | 7,300 | | | | | |
| Salaries expense | 97,000 | | | | | |
| Amortization expense, equip. | -0- | | | | | |
| Cleaning supplies expense | 22,000 | | | | | |
| Totals | 235,300 | 235,300 | | | | |

*Problem 4-17B

Part 1 - Entries that initially recognize assets and liabilities:

### GENERAL JOURNAL                                    Page____

| Date | Account Titles and Explanation | PR | Debit | Credit |
|---|---|---|---|---|
| | | | | |
| | | | | |
| | | | | |
| | | | | |
| | | | | |
| | | | | |
| | | | | |
| | | | | |
| | | | | |
| | | | | |
| | | | | |
| | | | | |
| | | | | |
| | | | | |
| | | | | |
| | | | | |
| | | | | |
| | | | | |
| | | | | |
| | | | | |
| | | | | |
| | | | | |

## GENERAL JOURNAL                                      Page____

| Date | Account Titles and Explanation | PR | Debit | Credit |
|------|-------------------------------|----|-------|--------|
|      |                               |    |       |        |
|      |                               |    |       |        |
|      |                               |    |       |        |
|      |                               |    |       |        |
|      |                               |    |       |        |
|      |                               |    |       |        |
|      |                               |    |       |        |
|      |                               |    |       |        |
|      |                               |    |       |        |
|      |                               |    |       |        |
|      |                               |    |       |        |
|      |                               |    |       |        |
|      |                               |    |       |        |
|      |                               |    |       |        |
|      |                               |    |       |        |
|      |                               |    |       |        |
|      |                               |    |       |        |
|      |                               |    |       |        |
|      |                               |    |       |        |
|      |                               |    |       |        |
|      |                               |    |       |        |
|      |                               |    |       |        |
|      |                               |    |       |        |
|      |                               |    |       |        |

**Part 2 – Entries that initially recognize expenses and revenues:**

## GENERAL JOURNAL                                      Page____

| Date | Account Titles and Explanation | PR | Debit | Credit |
|------|-------------------------------|----|-------|--------|
|      |                               |    |       |        |
|      |                               |    |       |        |
|      |                               |    |       |        |
|      |                               |    |       |        |
|      |                               |    |       |        |
|      |                               |    |       |        |
|      |                               |    |       |        |
|      |                               |    |       |        |
|      |                               |    |       |        |
|      |                               |    |       |        |
|      |                               |    |       |        |
|      |                               |    |       |        |
|      |                               |    |       |        |
|      |                               |    |       |        |
|      |                               |    |       |        |

## GENERAL JOURNAL                                    Page____

| Date | | Account Titles and Explanation | PR | Debit | Credit |
|---|---|---|---|---|---|
| | | | | | |
| | | | | | |
| | | | | | |
| | | | | | |
| | | | | | |
| | | | | | |
| | | | | | |
| | | | | | |
| | | | | | |
| | | | | | |
| | | | | | |
| | | | | | |
| | | | | | |
| | | | | | |
| | | | | | |
| | | | | | |
| | | | | | |
| | | | | | |
| | | | | | |
| | | | | | |
| | | | | | |
| | | | | | |
| | | | | | |
| | | | | | |
| | | | | | |
| | | | | | |

*Analysis component:*

_____
_____
_____
_____
_____
_____
_____
_____
_____
_____
_____
_____
_____
_____
_____
_____
_____
_____
_____

GENERAL JOURNAL                          Page _____

| Date | Account Titles and Explanation | PR | Debit | Credit |
|------|-------------------------------|----|-------|--------|
|      |                               |    |       |        |
|      |                               |    |       |        |
|      |                               |    |       |        |
|      |                               |    |       |        |
|      |                               |    |       |        |
|      |                               |    |       |        |
|      |                               |    |       |        |
|      |                               |    |       |        |
|      |                               |    |       |        |
|      |                               |    |       |        |
|      |                               |    |       |        |
|      |                               |    |       |        |
|      |                               |    |       |        |
|      |                               |    |       |        |
|      |                               |    |       |        |
|      |                               |    |       |        |
|      |                               |    |       |        |
|      |                               |    |       |        |
|      |                               |    |       |        |
|      |                               |    |       |        |
|      |                               |    |       |        |
|      |                               |    |       |        |
|      |                               |    |       |        |
|      |                               |    |       |        |
|      |                               |    |       |        |
|      |                               |    |       |        |
|      |                               |    |       |        |
|      |                               |    |       |        |
|      |                               |    |       |        |
|      |                               |    |       |        |
|      |                               |    |       |        |
|      |                               |    |       |        |
|      |                               |    |       |        |
|      |                               |    |       |        |
|      |                               |    |       |        |
|      |                               |    |       |        |
|      |                               |    |       |        |
|      |                               |    |       |        |
|      |                               |    |       |        |
|      |                               |    |       |        |
|      |                               |    |       |        |
|      |                               |    |       |        |

GENERAL JOURNAL                    Page ____

| Date | Account Titles and Explanation | PR | Debit | Credit |
|------|-------------------------------|----|-------|--------|
|      |                               |    |       |        |
|      |                               |    |       |        |
|      |                               |    |       |        |
|      |                               |    |       |        |
|      |                               |    |       |        |
|      |                               |    |       |        |
|      |                               |    |       |        |
|      |                               |    |       |        |
|      |                               |    |       |        |
|      |                               |    |       |        |
|      |                               |    |       |        |
|      |                               |    |       |        |
|      |                               |    |       |        |
|      |                               |    |       |        |
|      |                               |    |       |        |
|      |                               |    |       |        |
|      |                               |    |       |        |
|      |                               |    |       |        |
|      |                               |    |       |        |
|      |                               |    |       |        |
|      |                               |    |       |        |
|      |                               |    |       |        |
|      |                               |    |       |        |
|      |                               |    |       |        |
|      |                               |    |       |        |
|      |                               |    |       |        |
|      |                               |    |       |        |
|      |                               |    |       |        |
|      |                               |    |       |        |
|      |                               |    |       |        |
|      |                               |    |       |        |
|      |                               |    |       |        |
|      |                               |    |       |        |
|      |                               |    |       |        |
|      |                               |    |       |        |
|      |                               |    |       |        |
|      |                               |    |       |        |
|      |                               |    |       |        |
|      |                               |    |       |        |
|      |                               |    |       |        |
|      |                               |    |       |        |
|      |                               |    |       |        |
|      |                               |    |       |        |
|      |                               |    |       |        |

## GENERAL LEDGER

### Cash                                                    ACCOUNT NO. 101

| DATE | EXPLANATION | PR | DEBIT | CREDIT | BALANCE |
|------|-------------|----|-------|--------|---------|
| 2011 Nov. 30 | Balance | | | | 70,340 |
| | | | | | |
| | | | | | |
| | | | | | |
| | | | | | |
| | | | | | |
| | | | | | |
| | | | | | |
| | | | | | |
| | | | | | |
| | | | | | |
| | | | | | |

### Accounts Receivable                                    ACCOUNT NO. 106

| DATE | EXPLANATION | PR | DEBIT | CREDIT | BALANCE |
|------|-------------|----|-------|--------|---------|
| 2011 Nov. 30 | Balance | | | | 18,900 |
| | | | | | |
| | | | | | |
| | | | | | |

### Computer Supplies                                      ACCOUNT NO. 126

| DATE | EXPLANATION | PR | DEBIT | CREDIT | BALANCE |
|------|-------------|----|-------|--------|---------|
| 2011 Nov. 30 | Balance | | | | 4,560 |
| | | | | | |
| | | | | | |
| | | | | | |

### Prepaid Insurance                                      ACCOUNT NO. 128

| DATE | EXPLANATION | PR | DEBIT | CREDIT | BALANCE |
|------|-------------|----|-------|--------|---------|
| 2011 Nov. 30 | Balance | | | | 4,320 |
| | | | | | |

### Prepaid Rent                                           ACCOUNT NO. 131

| DATE | EXPLANATION | PR | DEBIT | CREDIT | BALANCE |
|------|-------------|----|-------|--------|---------|
| 2011 Nov. 30 | Balance | | | | 9,000 |
| | | | | | |

## Office Equipment                                          ACCOUNT NO. 163

| DATE | EXPLANATION | PR | DEBIT | CREDIT | BALANCE |
|------|-------------|----|-------|--------|---------|
| 2011<br>Nov. 30 | Balance | | | | 18,000 |
| | | | | | |

## Accumulated Amortization, Office Equipment        ACCOUNT NO. 164

| DATE | EXPLANATION | PR | DEBIT | CREDIT | BALANCE |
|------|-------------|----|-------|--------|---------|
| 2011<br>Nov. 30 | Balance | | | | -0- |
| | | | | | |

## Computer Equipment                                       ACCOUNT NO. 167

| DATE | EXPLANATION | PR | DEBIT | CREDIT | BALANCE |
|------|-------------|----|-------|--------|---------|
| 2011<br>Nov. 30 | Balance | | | | 36,000 |
| | | | | | |

## Accumulated Amortization, Computer Equipment      ACCOUNT NO. 168

| DATE | EXPLANATION | PR | DEBIT | CREDIT | BALANCE |
|------|-------------|----|-------|--------|---------|
| 2011<br>Nov. 30 | Balance | | | | -0- |
| | | | | | |

## Accounts Payable                                         ACCOUNT NO. 201

| DATE | EXPLANATION | PR | DEBIT | CREDIT | BALANCE |
|------|-------------|----|-------|--------|---------|
| 2011<br>Nov. 30 | Balance | | | | -0- |
| | | | | | |

## Wages Payable                                            ACCOUNT NO. 210

| DATE | EXPLANATION | PR | DEBIT | CREDIT | BALANCE |
|------|-------------|----|-------|--------|---------|
| 2011<br>Nov. 30 | Balance | | | | -0- |
| | | | | | |

## Unearned Computer Services Revenue                  ACCOUNT NO. 236

| DATE | EXPLANATION | PR | DEBIT | CREDIT | BALANCE |
|------|-------------|----|-------|--------|---------|
| 2011<br>Nov. 30 | Balance | | | | -0- |
| | | | | | |

## Mary Graham, Capital                                     ACCOUNT NO. 301

| DATE | EXPLANATION | PR | DEBIT | CREDIT | BALANCE |
|------|-------------|----|-------|--------|---------|
| 2011<br>Nov. 30 | Balance | | | | 144,000 |

### Mary Graham, Withdrawals                    ACCOUNT NO. 302

| DATE | EXPLANATION | PR | DEBIT | CREDIT | BALANCE |
|------|-------------|-----|-------|--------|---------|
| 2011 Nov. 30 | Balance | | | | 10,800 |
| | | | | | |

### Computer Services Revenue                   ACCOUNT NO. 403

| DATE | EXPLANATION | PR | DEBIT | CREDIT | BALANCE |
|------|-------------|-----|-------|--------|---------|
| 2011 Nov. 30 | Balance | | | | 40,950 |
| | | | | | |

### Amortization Expense, Office Equipment       ACCOUNT NO. 612

| DATE | EXPLANATION | PR | DEBIT | CREDIT | BALANCE |
|------|-------------|-----|-------|--------|---------|
| 2011 Nov. 30 | Balance | | | | -0- |
| | | | | | |

### Amortization Expense, Computer Equipment     ACCOUNT NO. 613

| DATE | EXPLANATION | PR | DEBIT | CREDIT | BALANCE |
|------|-------------|-----|-------|--------|---------|
| 2011 Nov. 30 | Balance | | | | -0- |
| | | | | | |

### Wages Expense                                ACCOUNT NO. 623

| DATE | EXPLANATION | PR | DEBIT | CREDIT | BALANCE |
|------|-------------|-----|-------|--------|---------|
| 2011 Nov. 30 | Balance | | | | 4,200 |
| | | | | | |
| | | | | | |
| | | | | | |

### Insurance Expense                            ACCOUNT NO. 637

| DATE | EXPLANATION | PR | DEBIT | CREDIT | BALANCE |
|------|-------------|-----|-------|--------|---------|
| 2011 Nov. 30 | Balance | | | | -0- |
| | | | | | |

### Rent Expense                                 ACCOUNT NO. 640

| DATE | EXPLANATION | PR | DEBIT | CREDIT | BALANCE |
|------|-------------|-----|-------|--------|---------|
| 2011 Nov. 30 | Balance | | | | -0- |
| | | | | | |

## Computer Supplies Expense                ACCOUNT NO. 652

| DATE | EXPLANATION | PR | DEBIT | CREDIT | BALANCE |
|------|-------------|----|-------|--------|---------|
| 2011<br>Nov. 30 | Balance | | | | -0- |
| | | | | | |

## Advertising Expense                ACCOUNT NO. 655

| DATE | EXPLANATION | PR | DEBIT | CREDIT | BALANCE |
|------|-------------|----|-------|--------|---------|
| 2011<br>Nov. 30 | Balance | | | | 3,720 |
| | | | | | |

## Mileage Expense                ACCOUNT NO. 676

| DATE | EXPLANATION | PR | DEBIT | CREDIT | BALANCE |
|------|-------------|----|-------|--------|---------|
| 2011<br>Nov. 30 | Balance | | | | 2,200 |
| | | | | | |

## Repairs Expense, Computer                ACCOUNT NO. 684

| DATE | EXPLANATION | PR | DEBIT | CREDIT | BALANCE |
|------|-------------|----|-------|--------|---------|
| 2011<br>Nov. 30 | Balance | | | | 1,410 |
| | | | | | |

## Charitable Donations Expense                ACCOUNT NO. 699

| DATE | EXPLANATION | PR | DEBIT | CREDIT | BALANCE |
|------|-------------|----|-------|--------|---------|
| 2011<br>Nov. 30 | Balance | | | | 1,500 |

## ECHO SYSTEMS
### Adjusted Trial Balance
### December 31, 2011

|  | Debit | Credit |
|---|---|---|
|  |  |  |
|  |  |  |
|  |  |  |
|  |  |  |
|  |  |  |
|  |  |  |
|  |  |  |
|  |  |  |
|  |  |  |
|  |  |  |
|  |  |  |
|  |  |  |
|  |  |  |
|  |  |  |
|  |  |  |
|  |  |  |
|  |  |  |
|  |  |  |
|  |  |  |
|  |  |  |
|  |  |  |
|  |  |  |
|  |  |  |
|  |  |  |
|  |  |  |
|  |  |  |
|  |  |  |
|  |  |  |
|  |  |  |
|  |  |  |
|  |  |  |
|  |  |  |
|  |  |  |
|  |  |  |
|  |  |  |
|  |  |  |

### ECHO SYSTEMS
### Income Statement
### For Three Months Ended December 31, 2011

| | | |
|---|---|---|
| | | |
| | | |
| | | |
| | | |
| | | |
| | | |
| | | |
| | | |
| | | |
| | | |
| | | |
| | | |
| | | |
| | | |
| | | |
| | | |
| | | |
| | | |
| | | |
| | | |
| | | |
| | | |
| | | |
| | | |
| | | |
| | | |
| | | |
| | | |

## Part 5

### ECHO SYSTEMS
### Statement of Owner's Equity
### For Three Months Ended December 31, 2011

| | | |
|---|---|---|
| | | |
| | | |
| | | |
| | | |
| | | |
| | | |
| | | |
| | | |
| | | |

## ECHO SYSTEMS
### Balance Sheet
### December 31, 2011

| | | | |
|---|---|---|---|
| | | | |
| | | | |
| | | | |
| | | | |
| | | | |
| | | | |
| | | | |
| | | | |
| | | | |
| | | | |
| | | | |
| | | | |
| | | | |
| | | | |
| | | | |
| | | | |
| | | | |
| | | | |
| | | | |
| | | | |
| | | | |
| | | | |
| | | | |
| | | | |
| | | | |
| | | | |
| | | | |
| | | | |
| | | | |
| | | | |
| | | | |
| | | | |
| | | | |
| | | | |
| | | | |
| | | | |
| | | | |
| | | | |
| | | | |
| | | | |
| | | | |
| | | | |

1. _____ Equipment
2. _____ Owner, withdrawals
3. _____ Insurance expense
4. _____ Prepaid insurance
5. _____ Accounts receivable
6. _____ Amortization expense, equipment

## Quick Study 5-2

- see next page for QS 5-2 working paper

## Quick Study 5-3

_____
_____
_____
_____
_____
_____
_____
_____
_____
_____
_____
_____

## Quick Study 5-4

_____
_____
_____
_____
_____
_____
_____
_____
_____
_____

## Quick Study 5-5

_____
_____
_____
_____
_____
_____
_____
_____
_____
_____
_____
_____
_____
_____

| Account Title | Unadjusted Trial Balance | | Adjustments | | Adjusted Trial Balance | | Income Statement | | |
|---|---|---|---|---|---|---|---|---|---|
| | Debit | Credit | Debit | Credit | Debit | Credit | Debit | Credit | Debit |
| Cash | 15 | | | | | | | | |
| Accounts receivable | 22 | | | | | | | | |
| Supplies | 25 | | | | | | | | |
| Ed Wolt, capital | | 40 | | | | | | | |
| Ed Wolt, withdrawals | 12 | | | | | | | | |
| Fees earned | | 48 | | | | | | | |
| Supplies expense | 14 | | | | | | | | |
| Totals | 88 | 88 | | | | | | | |
| | | | | | | | | | |
| | | | | | | | | | |
| | | | | | | | | | |
| | | | | | | | | | |

## GENERAL JOURNAL　　　　　　　　Page____

| Date | Account Titles and Explanation | PR | Debit | Credit |
|---|---|---|---|---|
| | | | | |
| | | | | |
| | | | | |
| | | | | |
| | | | | |
| | | | | |
| | | | | |
| | | | | |
| | | | | |
| | | | | |
| | | | | |
| | | | | |
| | | | | |
| | | | | |
| | | | | |
| | | | | |
| | | | | |
| | | | | |
| | | | | |
| | | | | |
| | | | | |
| | | | | |

| Assets | Liabilities |
|---|---|
| 250 | 30 |

| Capital | Withdrawals |
|---|---|
| 200 | 20 |

| Revenue | Expenses |
|---|---|
| 100 | 60 |

Income Summary

## GENERAL JOURNAL                                    Page____

| Date | Account Titles and Explanation | PR | Debit | Credit |
|------|-------------------------------|----|-------|--------|
|      |                               |    |       |        |
|      |                               |    |       |        |
|      |                               |    |       |        |
|      |                               |    |       |        |
|      |                               |    |       |        |
|      |                               |    |       |        |
|      |                               |    |       |        |
|      |                               |    |       |        |
|      |                               |    |       |        |
|      |                               |    |       |        |
|      |                               |    |       |        |
|      |                               |    |       |        |
|      |                               |    |       |        |
|      |                               |    |       |        |
|      |                               |    |       |        |
|      |                               |    |       |        |
|      |                               |    |       |        |
|      |                               |    |       |        |
|      |                               |    |       |        |
|      |                               |    |       |        |
|      |                               |    |       |        |

|        Assets        |        Liabilities        |
|----------------------|---------------------------|
| 250                  |                       110 |

|        Capital       |        Withdrawals        |
|----------------------|---------------------------|
|                  200 | 20                        |

|        Revenue       |        Expenses           |
|----------------------|---------------------------|
|                  100 | 140                       |

|                      |      Income Summary       |
|----------------------|---------------------------|

## Post-Closing Trial Balance

|  | Debit | Credit |
|---|---|---|
|  |  |  |
|  |  |  |
|  |  |  |
|  |  |  |
|  |  |  |
|  |  |  |
|  |  |  |
|  |  |  |
|  |  |  |

## Quick Study 5-9

a. _____ **Preparing the unadjusted trial balance.**
b. _____ **Preparing the post-closing trial balance.**
c. _____ **Journalizing and posting adjusting entries.**
d. _____ **Journalizing and posting closing entries.**
e. _____ **Preparing the financial statements.**
f. _____ **Journalizing transactions.**
g. _____ **Posting the transaction entries.**
h. _____ **Completing the work sheet.**

## Quick Study 5-10

1. _____ **Store equipment**
2. _____ **Wages payable**
3. _____ **Cash**
4. _____ **Notes payable (due in three years)**
5. _____ **Land not currently used in business operations**
6. _____ **Accounts receivable**
7. _____ **Trademarks**

Chapter 5    Quick Study 5-11    *Name* _____

| | | | |
|---|---|---|---|
| 1. ____ | Amortization expense, trucks | 11. ____ | Accum. amort., trucks |
| 2. ____ | Lee Hale, capital | 12. ____ | Cash |
| 3. ____ | Interest receivable | 13. ____ | Building |
| 4. ____ | Lee Hale, withdrawals | 14. ____ | Patent |
| 5. ____ | Automobiles | 15. ____ | Office equipment |
| 6. ____ | Notes payable (due in 3 years) | 16. ____ | Land (used in operations) |
| 7. ____ | Accounts payable | 17. ____ | Repairs expense |
| 8. ____ | Prepaid insurance | 18. ____ | Prepaid property taxes |
| 9. ____ | Land not currently used in business operations | 19. ____ | Current portion of long-term notes payable |
| 10. ____ | Unearned services revenue | 20. ____ | Notes receivable (due in 2 years) |

Quick Study 5-12

### Partial Balance Sheet

| | | | |
|---|---|---|---|
| | | | |
| | | | |
| | | | |
| | | | |
| | | | |
| | | | |
| | | | |
| | | | |
| | | | |
| | | | |
| | | | |
| | | | |
| | | | |

*Quick Study 5-13

### GENERAL JOURNAL                                    Page____

| Date | Account Titles and Explanation | PR | Debit | Credit |
|---|---|---|---|---|
| | | | | |
| | | | | |
| | | | | |
| | | | | |
| | | | | |
| | | | | |
| | | | | |
| | | | | |
| | | | | |

_____
_____
_____
_____
_____
_____
_____
_____
_____
_____
_____

## Exercise 5-1

| | | | | |
|---|---|---|---|---|
| 1. _____ | Roberta Jefferson, withdrawals | | 9. _____ | Cash |
| 2. _____ | Interest earned | | 10. _____ | Office supplies |
| 3. _____ | Accum. amort., machinery | | 11. _____ | Roberta Jefferson, capital |
| 4. _____ | Service fees revenue | | 12. _____ | Wages payable |
| 5. _____ | Accounts receivable | | 13. _____ | Machinery |
| 6. _____ | Rent expense | | 14. _____ | Insurance expense |
| 7. _____ | Amort. exp., machinery | | 15. _____ | Interest expense |
| 8. _____ | Accounts payable | | 16. _____ | Interest receivable |

## Exercise 5-2

| ACCOUNT | ADJUSTED TRIAL BALANCE Debit | ADJUSTED TRIAL BALANCE Credit | INCOME STATEMENT Debit | INCOME STATEMENT Credit | BALANCE SHEET AND STATEMENT OF OWNER'S EQUITY Debit | BALANCE SHEET AND STATEMENT OF OWNER'S EQUITY Credit |
|---|---|---|---|---|---|---|
| Cash | 3,000 | | | | | |
| Accounts receivable | 13,100 | | | | | |
| Trucks | 41,000 | | | | | |
| Accum. amort., trucks | | 16,500 | | | | |
| Franchise | 15,000 | | | | | |
| Accounts payable | | 7,000 | | | | |
| Salaries payable | | 1,600 | | | | |
| Unearned fees | | 1,300 | | | | |
| Bo Webber, capital | | 37,750 | | | | |
| Bo Webber, withdrls. | 7,200 | | | | | |
| Plumbing fees earned | | 49,000 | | | | |
| Amort. expense, trucks | 5,500 | | | | | |
| Salaries expense | 18,500 | | | | | |
| Rent expense | 6,000 | | | | | |
| Miscellaneous expense | 3,850 | | | | | |
| Totals | 113,150 | 113,150 | | | | |
| | | | | | | |
| | | | | | | |
| | | | | | | |

**Parts 1, 2, and 3**

Musical Sensations

Work Sheet

For Year Ended December 31, 2011

| Account Title | Unadjusted Trial Balance Debit | Unadjusted Trial Balance Credit | Adjustments Debit | Adjustments Credit | Adjusted Trial Balance Debit | Adjusted Trial Balance Credit | Income Statement Debit | Income Statement Credit | Balance Sheet and Statement of Owner's Equity Debit | Balance Sheet and Statement of Owner's Equity Credit |
|---|---|---|---|---|---|---|---|---|---|---|
| Cash | 14,000 | | | | | | | | | |
| Accounts receivable | 26,000 | | | | | | | | | |
| Office supplies | 950 | | | | | | | | | |
| Musical equipment | 212,000 | | | | | | | | | |
| Accum. amort., musical equip. | | 16,200 | | | | | | | | |
| Accounts payable | | 3,350 | | | | | | | | |
| Unearned performance rev. | | 12,400 | | | | | | | | |
| Jim Daley, capital | | 272,000 | | | | | | | | |
| Jim Daley, withdrawals | 52,000 | | | | | | | | | |
| Performance revenue | | 119,000 | | | | | | | | |
| Salaries expense | 76,000 | | | | | | | | | |
| Traveling expense | 42,000 | | | | | | | | | |
| Totals | 422,950 | 422,950 | | | | | | | | |

_____                    **Jim Daley, Capital**
_____         _____|_____
_____                              |
_____                              |
_____                              |
_____                              |

**Exercise 5-4**

1(a) _____

_____

2(a)                    **GENERAL JOURNAL**                    Page____

| Date | Account Titles and Explanation | PR | Debit | Credit |
|------|-------------------------------|----|----|----|
|  |  |  |  |  |
|  |  |  |  |  |
|  |  |  |  |  |
|  |  |  |  |  |
|  |  |  |  |  |

3(a)                                         **Owner's Capital**

_____        _____|_____
_____                              |
_____                              |
_____                              |
_____                              |

1(b) _____

_____

2(b)                    **GENERAL JOURNAL**                    Page____

| Date | Account Titles and Explanation | PR | Debit | Credit |
|------|-------------------------------|----|----|----|
|  |  |  |  |  |
|  |  |  |  |  |
|  |  |  |  |  |
|  |  |  |  |  |
|  |  |  |  |  |

3(b)                                         **Owner's Capital**

_____        _____|_____
_____                              |
_____                              |
_____                              |

|  | Debit | Credit |
|---|---|---|
| Rent earned | | 99,000 |
| Salaries expense | 35,300 | |
| Insurance expense | 4,400 | |
| Dock rental expense | 12,000 | |
| Boat supplies expense | 6,220 | |
| Amortization expense, boats | 21,500 | |
| Totals | | |
|     Net income | | |
| Totals | | |

**Closing Entries**

## GENERAL JOURNAL                                                            Page____

| Date | Account Titles and Explanation | PR | Debit | Credit |
|---|---|---|---|---|
| | | | | |
| | | | | |
| | | | | |
| | | | | |
| | | | | |
| | | | | |
| | | | | |
| | | | | |
| | | | | |
| | | | | |
| | | | | |
| | | | | |
| | | | | |
| | | | | |
| | | | | |
| | | | | |
| | | | | |
| | | | | |
| | | | | |
| | | | | |
| | | | | |
| | | | | |
| | | | | |

*Name* _____

## GENERAL JOURNAL

Page____

| Date | Account Titles and Explanation | PR | Debit | Credit |
|---|---|---|---|---|
| | | | | |
| | | | | |
| | | | | |
| | | | | |
| | | | | |
| | | | | |
| | | | | |
| | | | | |
| | | | | |
| | | | | |
| | | | | |
| | | | | |
| | | | | |
| | | | | |
| | | | | |
| | | | | |
| | | | | |
| | | | | |
| | | | | |
| | | | | |
| | | | | |
| | | | | |
| | | | | |
| | | | | |
| | | | | |
| | | | | |

## Post-Closing Trial Balance

| | Debit | Credit |
|---|---|---|
| | | |
| | | |
| | | |
| | | |
| | | |
| | | |
| | | |
| | | |
| | | |
| | | |
| | | |
| | | |
| | | |

## GENERAL JOURNAL                                    Page____

| Date | Account Titles and Explanation | PR | Debit | Credit |
|------|-------------------------------|----|----|----|
|  |  |  |  |  |
|  |  |  |  |  |
|  |  |  |  |  |
|  |  |  |  |  |
|  |  |  |  |  |
|  |  |  |  |  |
|  |  |  |  |  |
|  |  |  |  |  |
|  |  |  |  |  |
|  |  |  |  |  |
|  |  |  |  |  |
|  |  |  |  |  |
|  |  |  |  |  |
|  |  |  |  |  |
|  |  |  |  |  |
|  |  |  |  |  |
|  |  |  |  |  |
|  |  |  |  |  |
|  |  |  |  |  |
|  |  |  |  |  |

## Exercise 5-8

## GENERAL JOURNAL                                    Page____

| Date | Account Titles and Explanation | PR | Debit | Credit |
|------|-------------------------------|----|----|----|
|  |  |  |  |  |
|  |  |  |  |  |
|  |  |  |  |  |
|  |  |  |  |  |
|  |  |  |  |  |
|  |  |  |  |  |
|  |  |  |  |  |
|  |  |  |  |  |
|  |  |  |  |  |
|  |  |  |  |  |
|  |  |  |  |  |
|  |  |  |  |  |
|  |  |  |  |  |
|  |  |  |  |  |
|  |  |  |  |  |
|  |  |  |  |  |
|  |  |  |  |  |
|  |  |  |  |  |
|  |  |  |  |  |
|  |  |  |  |  |

## GENERAL JOURNAL                                    Page____

| Date | Account Titles and Explanation | PR | Debit | Credit |
|---|---|---|---|---|
| | | | | |
| | | | | |
| | | | | |
| | | | | |
| | | | | |
| | | | | |
| | | | | |
| | | | | |
| | | | | |
| | | | | |
| | | | | |
| | | | | |
| | | | | |
| | | | | |
| | | | | |
| | | | | |
| | | | | |
| | | | | |
| | | | | |
| | | | | |
| | | | | |

## Exercise 5-10

## GENERAL JOURNAL                                    Page____

| Date | Account Titles and Explanation | PR | Debit | Credit |
|---|---|---|---|---|
| | | | | |
| | | | | |
| | | | | |
| | | | | |
| | | | | |
| | | | | |
| | | | | |
| | | | | |
| | | | | |
| | | | | |
| | | | | |
| | | | | |
| | | | | |
| | | | | |
| | | | | |
| | | | | |
| | | | | |
| | | | | |
| | | | | |
| | | | | |

**Posting to Accounts:**

| Assets | | | Liabilities | |
|---|---|---|---|---|
| Bal. Dec. 31  80,000 | | | | 38,100  Bal. Dec. 31 |

| Marcy Jones, Capital | | | Marcy Jones, Withdrawals | |
|---|---|---|---|---|
| | 41,000  Bal. Dec. 31 | | Bal. Dec. 31  24,000 | |

| Services Revenue | | | Salaries Expense | |
|---|---|---|---|---|
| | 73,000  Bal. Dec. 31 | | Bal. Dec. 31  20,000 | |

| Rent Expense | | | Insurance Expense | |
|---|---|---|---|---|
| Bal. Dec. 31  8,600 | | | Bal. Dec. 31  3,500 | |

| Amortization Expense | | | Income Summary | |
|---|---|---|---|---|
| Bal. Dec. 31  16,000 | | | | |

## Exercise 5-11

### Post-Closing Trial Balance

| | Debit | Credit |
|---|---|---|
| | | |
| | | |
| | | |
| | | |
| | | |
| | | |
| | | |
| | | |

1. _____

2.                    **GENERAL JOURNAL**                    Page____

| Date | Account Titles and Explanation | PR | Debit | Credit |
|------|-------------------------------|----|----|----|
|  |  |  |  |  |
|  |  |  |  |  |
|  |  |  |  |  |
|  |  |  |  |  |
|  |  |  |  |  |
|  |  |  |  |  |
|  |  |  |  |  |

3.

_____
_____                    **Bill Duggan, Capital**
_____
_____

**Exercise 5-13**

a.                        **Account Title**

| | Account Title | Adjusted Trial Balance Debit | Credit |
|---|---|---|---|
| _____ | Accounts payable | | $ 11,000 |
| _____ | Accounts receivable | $ 59,000 | |
| _____ | Accumulated amortization, equipment | | 9,000 |
| _____ | Accumulated amortization, truck | | 21,000 |
| _____ | Amortization expense | 3,800 | |
| _____ | Cash | 29,000 | |
| _____ | Equipment | 13,000 | |
| _____ | Franchise | 17,800 | |
| _____ | Gas and oil expense | 7,500 | |
| _____ | Interest expense | 4,500 | |
| _____ | Interest payable | | 750 |
| _____ | Land not currently used in business operations | 52,000 | |
| _____ | Long-term notes payable | | 35,000 |
| _____ | Notes payable, due February 1, 2012 | | 7,000 |
| _____ | Notes receivable | 6,000 | |
| _____ | Patent | 7,000 | |
| _____ | Prepaid Rent | 14,000 | |
| _____ | Rent expense | 39,000 | |
| _____ | Repair revenue | | 247,000 |
| _____ | Repair supplies | 17,000 | |
| _____ | Repair supplies expense | 14,000 | |
| _____ | Sid Whimsly, capital | | 24,050 |
| _____ | Sid Whimsly, withdrawals | 49,000 | |
| _____ | Truck | 26,000 | |
| _____ | Unearned repair revenue | | 3,800 |
| | Totals | $358,600 | $358,600 |

**b.**

_____**Sid Whimsly, Capital**_____

*Analysis component:* _____

_____

_____

_____

_____

**Exercise 5-14**                                    **Calculations:**

a.  **Current assets =**

b.  **Property, plant and equipment =**

c.  **Intangible assets =**

d.  **Long-term investments =**

e.  **Total assets =**

f.  **Current liabilities =**

g.  **Long-term liabilities =**

h.  **Total liabilities =**

i.  **Total liabilities and owner's equity =**

## Balance Sheet

| | | | |
|---|---|---|---|
| | | | |
| | | | |
| | | | |
| | | | |
| | | | |
| | | | |
| | | | |
| | | | |
| | | | |
| | | | |
| | | | |
| | | | |
| | | | |
| | | | |
| | | | |
| | | | |
| | | | |
| | | | |
| | | | |
| | | | |
| | | | |
| | | | |
| | | | |
| | | | |
| | | | |
| | | | |
| | | | |
| | | | |
| | | | |
| | | | |
| | | | |
| | | | |
| | | | |
| | | | |
| | | | |
| | | | |
| | | | |
| | | | |
| | | | |
| | | | |
| | | | |
| | | | |
| | | | |
| | | | |
| | | | |
| | | | |
| | | | |
| | | | |

## Balance Sheet

| | | | |
|---|---|---|---|
| | | | |
| | | | |
| | | | |
| | | | |
| | | | |
| | | | |
| | | | |
| | | | |
| | | | |
| | | | |
| | | | |
| | | | |
| | | | |
| | | | |
| | | | |
| | | | |
| | | | |
| | | | |
| | | | |
| | | | |
| | | | |
| | | | |
| | | | |
| | | | |
| | | | |
| | | | |
| | | | |
| | | | |
| | | | |
| | | | |
| | | | |
| | | | |
| | | | |
| | | | |
| | | | |
| | | | |

**a.** _____
_____
_____
_____
_____

**b. Journalizing:**

### GENERAL JOURNAL                                    Page____

| Date | | Account Titles and Explanation | PR | Debit | Credit |
|---|---|---|---|---|---|
| | | | | | |
| | | | | | |
| | | | | | |
| | | | | | |
| | | | | | |
| | | | | | |
| | | | | | |
| | | | | | |
| | | | | | |
| | | | | | |
| | | | | | |
| | | | | | |
| | | | | | |
| | | | | | |
| | | | | | |
| | | | | | |
| | | | | | |
| | | | | | |
| | | | | | |
| | | | | | |
| | | | | | |
| | | | | | |

**c.** _____

### Unadjusted Trial Balance

| | Debit | Credit |
|---|---|---|
| | | |
| | | |
| | | |
| | | |
| | | |
| | | |
| | | |
| | | |
| | | |
| | | |
| | | |
| | | |

**b, d, g.  Posting journal entries in (b), adjustments in (d), and closing entries in (g):**

| Cash | | Leda Svenson, Capital | |
|---|---|---|---|
| Bal. Dec. 31/11   **2,000** | | | **17,100**  Bal. Dec. 31/11 |

| Accounts Receivable | | Leda Svenson, Withdrawals | |
|---|---|---|---|
| Bal. Dec. 31/11   **5,000** | | Bal. Dec. 31/11   **-0-** | |

| | | Tutoring Fees Earned | |
|---|---|---|---|
| | | **-0-**   Bal. Dec. 31/11 | |

| Prepaid Rent | |
|---|---|
| Bal. Dec. 31/11   **3,000** | |

| Office Equipment | | Rent Expense | |
|---|---|---|---|
| Bal. Dec. 31/11  **20,000** | | Bal. Dec. 31/11   **-0-** | |

| Accum. Amort., Office Equip. | | Amortization Expense | |
|---|---|---|---|
| | **10,000**  Bal. Dec. 31/11 | Bal. Dec. 31/11   **-0-** | |

| Unearned Fees | | Advertising Expense | |
|---|---|---|---|
| | **2,900**  Bal. Dec. 31/11 | Bal. Dec. 31/11   **-0-** | |

Income Summary

d. Journalize adjustments:

### GENERAL JOURNAL                                      Page____

| Date | Account Titles and Explanation | PR | Debit | Credit |
|------|-------------------------------|----|-------|--------|
|      |                               |    |       |        |
|      |                               |    |       |        |
|      |                               |    |       |        |
|      |                               |    |       |        |
|      |                               |    |       |        |
|      |                               |    |       |        |
|      |                               |    |       |        |
|      |                               |    |       |        |
|      |                               |    |       |        |
|      |                               |    |       |        |
|      |                               |    |       |        |
|      |                               |    |       |        |
|      |                               |    |       |        |

e.

### Adjusted Trial Balance

|  | Debit | Credit |
|--|-------|--------|
|  |       |        |
|  |       |        |
|  |       |        |
|  |       |        |
|  |       |        |
|  |       |        |
|  |       |        |
|  |       |        |
|  |       |        |
|  |       |        |
|  |       |        |
|  |       |        |
|  |       |        |
|  |       |        |

f. Financial statement preparation:

### Income Statement

| | | |
|---|---|---|
| | | |
| | | |
| | | |
| | | |
| | | |
| | | |
| | | |
| | | |
| | | |

### Statement of Owner's Equity

| | | |
|---|---|---|
| | | |
| | | |
| | | |
| | | |
| | | |
| | | |
| | | |
| | | |

### Balance Sheet

| | | | |
|---|---|---|---|
| | | | |
| | | | |
| | | | |
| | | | |
| | | | |
| | | | |
| | | | |
| | | | |
| | | | |
| | | | |
| | | | |
| | | | |
| | | | |
| | | | |
| | | | |

**g. Journalize closing entries:**

### GENERAL JOURNAL                                                          Page____

| Date | Account Titles and Explanation | PR | Debit | Credit |
|------|-------------------------------|----|-------|--------|
|      |                               |    |       |        |
|      |                               |    |       |        |
|      |                               |    |       |        |
|      |                               |    |       |        |
|      |                               |    |       |        |
|      |                               |    |       |        |
|      |                               |    |       |        |
|      |                               |    |       |        |
|      |                               |    |       |        |
|      |                               |    |       |        |
|      |                               |    |       |        |
|      |                               |    |       |        |
|      |                               |    |       |        |
|      |                               |    |       |        |
|      |                               |    |       |        |
|      |                               |    |       |        |
|      |                               |    |       |        |
|      |                               |    |       |        |
|      |                               |    |       |        |
|      |                               |    |       |        |
|      |                               |    |       |        |
|      |                               |    |       |        |
|      |                               |    |       |        |

**h.** _____

### Post-Closing Trial Balance

|  | Debit | Credit |
|--|-------|--------|
|  |       |        |
|  |       |        |
|  |       |        |
|  |       |        |
|  |       |        |
|  |       |        |
|  |       |        |
|  |       |        |
|  |       |        |
|  |       |        |
|  |       |        |
|  |       |        |
|  |       |        |
|  |       |        |

*Name* _____

## GENERAL JOURNAL                                   Page____

| Date | Account Titles and Explanation | PR | Debit | Credit |
|------|-------------------------------|-----|-------|--------|
|      |                               |     |       |        |
|      |                               |     |       |        |
|      |                               |     |       |        |
|      |                               |     |       |        |
|      |                               |     |       |        |
|      |                               |     |       |        |
|      |                               |     |       |        |
|      |                               |     |       |        |

**\*Exercise 5-19**

**1. Adjusting entries:**

## GENERAL JOURNAL                                   Page _____

| Date | Account Titles and Explanation | PR | Debit | Credit |
|------|-------------------------------|-----|-------|--------|
|      |                               |     |       |        |
|      |                               |     |       |        |
|      |                               |     |       |        |
|      |                               |     |       |        |
|      |                               |     |       |        |
|      |                               |     |       |        |
|      |                               |     |       |        |
|      |                               |     |       |        |
|      |                               |     |       |        |
|      |                               |     |       |        |

**2. Subsequent entries without reversing:**

## GENERAL JOURNAL                                   Page _____

| Date | Account Titles and Explanation | PR | Debit | Credit |
|------|-------------------------------|-----|-------|--------|
|      |                               |     |       |        |
|      |                               |     |       |        |
|      |                               |     |       |        |
|      |                               |     |       |        |
|      |                               |     |       |        |
|      |                               |     |       |        |
|      |                               |     |       |        |
|      |                               |     |       |        |
|      |                               |     |       |        |
|      |                               |     |       |        |

GENERAL JOURNAL                         Page _____

| Date | Account Titles and Explanation | PR | Debit | Credit |
|------|-------------------------------|----|----|----|
|  |  |  |  |  |
|  |  |  |  |  |
|  |  |  |  |  |
|  |  |  |  |  |
|  |  |  |  |  |
|  |  |  |  |  |
|  |  |  |  |  |
|  |  |  |  |  |
|  |  |  |  |  |
|  |  |  |  |  |
|  |  |  |  |  |

3. Reversing entries and subsequent entries:

GENERAL JOURNAL                         Page _____

| Date | Account Titles and Explanation | PR | Debit | Credit |
|------|-------------------------------|----|----|----|
|  |  |  |  |  |
|  |  |  |  |  |
|  |  |  |  |  |
|  |  |  |  |  |
|  |  |  |  |  |
|  |  |  |  |  |
|  |  |  |  |  |
|  |  |  |  |  |
|  |  |  |  |  |
|  |  |  |  |  |
|  |  |  |  |  |
|  |  |  |  |  |
|  |  |  |  |  |
|  |  |  |  |  |
|  |  |  |  |  |
|  |  |  |  |  |
|  |  |  |  |  |
|  |  |  |  |  |
|  |  |  |  |  |
|  |  |  |  |  |
|  |  |  |  |  |
|  |  |  |  |  |
|  |  |  |  |  |
|  |  |  |  |  |
|  |  |  |  |  |
|  |  |  |  |  |
|  |  |  |  |  |

**Wigger Rentals**

**Work Sheet**

**For Year Ended March 31, 2011**

| Account Title | Unadjusted Trial Balance | | Adjustments | | Adjusted Trial Balance | | Income Statement | | Balance Sheet and Statement of Owner's Equity | |
|---|---|---|---|---|---|---|---|---|---|---|
| | Debit | Credit | Debit | Credit | Debit | Credit | Debit | Credit | Debit | Credit |
| Cash | 17,000 | | | | | | | | | |
| Rent receivable | 60,000 | | | | | | | | | |
| Office supplies | 6,800 | | | | | | | | | |
| Notes receivable, due 2008 | 143,000 | | | | | | | | | |
| Furniture | 46,000 | | | | | | | | | |
| Building | 625,000 | | | | | | | | | |
| Land | 110,000 | | | | | | | | | |
| Patent | 3,000 | | | | | | | | | |
| Accounts payable | | 5,800 | | | | | | | | |
| Long-term note payable | | 375,000 | | | | | | | | |
| Joan Wigger, capital | | 499,525 | | | | | | | | |
| Joan Wigger, withdrawals | 28,000 | | | | | | | | | |
| Rent earned | | 406,200 | | | | | | | | |
| Office salaries expense | 124,000 | | | | | | | | | |
| Interest expense | 20,625 | | | | | | | | | |
| Advertising expense | 28,000 | | | | | | | | | |
| Janitorial expense | 41,000 | | | | | | | | | |
| Utilities expense | 34,100 | | | | | | | | | |
| Totals | 1,286,525 | 1,286,525 | | | | | | | | |

Trenton Consulting

Work Sheet

For Year Ended March 31, 2011

| Account Title | Unadjusted Trial Balance Debit | Unadjusted Trial Balance Credit | Adjustments Debit | Adjustments Credit | Adjusted Trial Balance Debit | Adjusted Trial Balance Credit | Income Statement Debit | Income Statement Credit | Balance Sheet and Statement of Owner's Equity Debit | Balance Sheet and Statement of Owner's Equity Credit |
|---|---|---|---|---|---|---|---|---|---|---|
| Cash | 3,440 | | | | | | | | | |
| Accounts receivable | 2,990 | | | | | | | | | |
| Prepaid rent | 6,600 | | | | | | | | | |
| Equipment | 6,400 | | | | | | | | | |
| Accounts payable | | 1,440 | | | | | | | | |
| Toni Trenton, capital | | 26,650 | | | | | | | | |
| Toni Trenton, withdrawals | 800 | | | | | | | | | |
| Consulting fees earned | | 30,200 | | | | | | | | |
| Wages expense | 28,120 | | | | | | | | | |
| Insurance expense | 1,620 | | | | | | | | | |
| Rent expense | 8,320 | | | | | | | | | |
| Totals | 58,290 | 58,290 | | | | | | | | |

**Part 4**

_____           **Toni Trenton, Capital**
_____
_____
_____

*Analysis component:* _____

_____
_____
_____
_____
_____

Challenger Construction

Work Sheet

For Year Ended September 30, 2011

| Account Title | Unadjusted Trial Balance Debit | Unadjusted Trial Balance Credit | Adjustments Debit | Adjustments Credit | Adjusted Trial Balance Debit | Adjusted Trial Balance Credit | Income Statement Debit | Income Statement Credit | Balance Sheet and Statement of Owner's Equity Debit | Balance Sheet and Statement of Owner's Equity Credit |
|---|---|---|---|---|---|---|---|---|---|---|
| Cash | 36,000 | | | | | | | | | |
| Supplies | 18,800 | | | | | | | | | |
| Prepaid insurance | 12,400 | | | | | | | | | |
| Land not currently used | 50,000 | | | | | | | | | |
| Equipment | 106,000 | | | | | | | | | |
| Accum. amort., equipment | | 40,500 | | | | | | | | |
| Copyright | 6,000 | | | | | | | | | |
| Accounts payable | | 9,600 | | | | | | | | |
| Interest payable | | | | | | | | | | |
| Wages payable | | | | | | | | | | |
| Long-term notes payable | | 50,000 | | | | | | | | |
| Chris Challenger, capital | | 55,320 | | | | | | | | |
| Chris Challenger, withdrawals | 72,000 | | | | | | | | | |
| Construction fees earned | | 280,000 | | | | | | | | |
| Amort. Expense, equipment | | | | | | | | | | |
| Wages expense | 82,000 | | | | | | | | | |
| Interest expense | 3,000 | | | | | | | | | |
| Insurance expense | | | | | | | | | | |
| Rent expense | 26,400 | | | | | | | | | |
| Supplies expense | | | | | | | | | | |
| Business taxes expense | 10,000 | | | | | | | | | |
| Repairs expense | 5,020 | | | | | | | | | |
| Utilities expense | 7,800 | | | | | | | | | |
| Totals | 435,420 | 435,420 | | | | | | | | |

**Part 2**

**Adjusting entries:**

## GENERAL JOURNAL    Page____

| Date | Account Titles and Explanation | PR | Debit | Credit |
|------|-------------------------------|----|----|----|
| a. | | | | |
| | | | | |
| | | | | |
| | | | | |
| b. | | | | |
| | | | | |
| | | | | |
| | | | | |
| c. | | | | |
| | | | | |
| | | | | |
| | | | | |
| d. | | | | |
| | | | | |
| | | | | |
| | | | | |
| e. | | | | |
| | | | | |
| | | | | |
| | | | | |
| f. | | | | |
| | | | | |
| | | | | |
| | | | | |

**Part 2**
**Closing entries:**

### GENERAL JOURNAL　　　　　　　　　　　　　Page____

| Date | Account Titles and Explanation | PR | Debit | Credit |
|------|-------------------------------|----|-------|--------|
|      |                               |    |       |        |
|      |                               |    |       |        |
|      |                               |    |       |        |
|      |                               |    |       |        |
|      |                               |    |       |        |
|      |                               |    |       |        |
|      |                               |    |       |        |
|      |                               |    |       |        |
|      |                               |    |       |        |
|      |                               |    |       |        |
|      |                               |    |       |        |
|      |                               |    |       |        |
|      |                               |    |       |        |
|      |                               |    |       |        |
|      |                               |    |       |        |
|      |                               |    |       |        |
|      |                               |    |       |        |
|      |                               |    |       |        |
|      |                               |    |       |        |
|      |                               |    |       |        |
|      |                               |    |       |        |
|      |                               |    |       |        |
|      |                               |    |       |        |
|      |                               |    |       |        |
|      |                               |    |       |        |
|      |                               |    |       |        |
|      |                               |    |       |        |
|      |                               |    |       |        |
|      |                               |    |       |        |
|      |                               |    |       |        |
|      |                               |    |       |        |
|      |                               |    |       |        |
|      |                               |    |       |        |
|      |                               |    |       |        |
|      |                               |    |       |        |
|      |                               |    |       |        |

## Income Statement

| | | |
|---|---|---|
| | | |
| | | |
| | | |
| | | |
| | | |
| | | |
| | | |
| | | |
| | | |
| | | |
| | | |
| | | |
| | | |
| | | |
| | | |
| | | |
| | | |
| | | |
| | | |
| | | |

## Statement of Owner's Equity

| | | |
|---|---|---|
| | | |
| | | |
| | | |
| | | |
| | | |
| | | |
| | | |
| | | |

## Balance Sheet

| | | | |
|---|---|---|---|
| | | | |
| | | | |
| | | | |
| | | | |
| | | | |
| | | | |
| | | | |
| | | | |
| | | | |
| | | | |
| | | | |
| | | | |
| | | | |
| | | | |
| | | | |
| | | | |
| | | | |
| | | | |
| | | | |
| | | | |
| | | | |
| | | | |
| | | | |
| | | | |
| | | | |
| | | | |
| | | | |
| | | | |
| | | | |
| | | | |
| | | | |
| | | | |
| | | | |
| | | | |
| | | | |

*Analysis component:*

a. _____

_____

_____

b. _____

_____

_____

_____

Part 1                    **GENERAL JOURNAL**                    Page____

| Date | Account Titles and Explanation | PR | Debit | Credit |
|------|-------------------------------|----|-------|--------|
|      |                               |    |       |        |
|      |                               |    |       |        |
|      |                               |    |       |        |
|      |                               |    |       |        |
|      |                               |    |       |        |
|      |                               |    |       |        |
|      |                               |    |       |        |
|      |                               |    |       |        |
|      |                               |    |       |        |
|      |                               |    |       |        |
|      |                               |    |       |        |
|      |                               |    |       |        |
|      |                               |    |       |        |
|      |                               |    |       |        |
|      |                               |    |       |        |
|      |                               |    |       |        |
|      |                               |    |       |        |
|      |                               |    |       |        |
|      |                               |    |       |        |
|      |                               |    |       |        |
|      |                               |    |       |        |
|      |                               |    |       |        |
|      |                               |    |       |        |
|      |                               |    |       |        |
|      |                               |    |       |        |

Part 2

**Post-Closing Trial Balance**

|  |  |  |
|--|--|--|
|  |  |  |
|  |  |  |
|  |  |  |
|  |  |  |
|  |  |  |
|  |  |  |
|  |  |  |
|  |  |  |
|  |  |  |
|  |  |  |
|  |  |  |
|  |  |  |

## Income Statement

| | | |
|---|---|---|
| | | |
| | | |
| | | |
| | | |
| | | |
| | | |
| | | |
| | | |
| | | |
| | | |
| | | |
| | | |
| | | |
| | | |
| | | |
| | | |
| | | |
| | | |
| | | |
| | | |
| | | |

## Statement of Owner's Equity

| | | |
|---|---|---|
| | | |
| | | |
| | | |
| | | |

## Balance Sheet

| | | | |
|---|---|---|---|
| | | | |
| | | | |
| | | | |
| | | | |
| | | | |
| | | | |
| | | | |
| | | | |
| | | | |
| | | | |
| | | | |
| | | | |
| | | | |
| | | | |
| | | | |
| | | | |
| | | | |
| | | | |
| | | | |
| | | | |
| | | | |
| | | | |
| | | | |
| | | | |
| | | | |
| | | | |
| | | | |
| | | | |
| | | | |
| | | | |
| | | | |
| | | | |
| | | | |
| | | | |
| | | | |
| | | | |
| | | | |
| | | | |
| | | | |

*Analysis component:*

Name: _____

# GENERAL JOURNAL

Page____

| Date | Account Titles and Explanation | PR | Debit | Credit |
|------|-------------------------------|----|-------|--------|
| | | | | |
| | | | | |
| | | | | |
| | | | | |
| | | | | |
| | | | | |
| | | | | |
| | | | | |
| | | | | |
| | | | | |
| | | | | |
| | | | | |
| | | | | |
| | | | | |
| | | | | |
| | | | | |
| | | | | |
| | | | | |
| | | | | |
| | | | | |
| | | | | |
| | | | | |
| | | | | |
| | | | | |
| | | | | |
| | | | | |
| | | | | |
| | | | | |
| | | | | |
| | | | | |
| | | | | |
| | | | | |
| | | | | |
| | | | | |
| | | | | |
| | | | | |
| | | | | |
| | | | | |
| | | | | |
| | | | | |
| | | | | |
| | | | | |
| | | | | |
| | | | | |

## Income Statement

| | | |
|---|---|---|
| | | |
| | | |
| | | |
| | | |
| | | |
| | | |
| | | |
| | | |
| | | |
| | | |
| | | |
| | | |
| | | |
| | | |
| | | |
| | | |
| | | |
| | | |
| | | |
| | | |
| | | |
| | | |
| | | |
| | | |
| | | |
| | | |
| | | |
| | | |
| | | |

## Statement of Owner's Equity

| | | |
|---|---|---|
| | | |
| | | |
| | | |
| | | |
| | | |
| | | |
| | | |
| | | |

## Balance Sheet

| | | | |
|---|---|---|---|
| | | | |
| | | | |
| | | | |
| | | | |
| | | | |
| | | | |
| | | | |
| | | | |
| | | | |
| | | | |
| | | | |
| | | | |
| | | | |
| | | | |
| | | | |
| | | | |
| | | | |
| | | | |
| | | | |
| | | | |
| | | | |
| | | | |
| | | | |
| | | | |
| | | | |
| | | | |
| | | | |
| | | | |
| | | | |
| | | | |
| | | | |
| | | | |
| | | | |
| | | | |
| | | | |
| | | | |
| | | | |

**Analysis component:** _____

_____

_____

_____

_____

## GENERAL JOURNAL

Page____

| Date | Account Titles and Explanation | PR | Debit | Credit |
|------|-------------------------------|-----|-------|--------|
|  |  |  |  |  |
|  |  |  |  |  |
|  |  |  |  |  |
|  |  |  |  |  |
|  |  |  |  |  |
|  |  |  |  |  |
|  |  |  |  |  |
|  |  |  |  |  |
|  |  |  |  |  |
|  |  |  |  |  |
|  |  |  |  |  |
|  |  |  |  |  |
|  |  |  |  |  |
|  |  |  |  |  |
|  |  |  |  |  |
|  |  |  |  |  |
|  |  |  |  |  |
|  |  |  |  |  |
|  |  |  |  |  |
|  |  |  |  |  |
|  |  |  |  |  |
|  |  |  |  |  |
|  |  |  |  |  |
|  |  |  |  |  |
|  |  |  |  |  |
|  |  |  |  |  |
|  |  |  |  |  |
|  |  |  |  |  |
|  |  |  |  |  |
|  |  |  |  |  |
|  |  |  |  |  |
|  |  |  |  |  |
|  |  |  |  |  |
|  |  |  |  |  |
|  |  |  |  |  |
|  |  |  |  |  |

## Income Statement

| | | |
|---|---|---|
| | | |
| | | |
| | | |
| | | |
| | | |
| | | |
| | | |
| | | |
| | | |
| | | |
| | | |
| | | |
| | | |
| | | |
| | | |
| | | |
| | | |
| | | |
| | | |
| | | |
| | | |
| | | |
| | | |
| | | |
| | | |
| | | |

## Statement of Owner's Equity

| | | |
|---|---|---|
| | | |
| | | |
| | | |
| | | |
| | | |
| | | |
| | | |
| | | |

## Balance Sheet

|  |  |  |  |
|---|---|---|---|
|  |  |  |  |
|  |  |  |  |
|  |  |  |  |
|  |  |  |  |
|  |  |  |  |
|  |  |  |  |
|  |  |  |  |
|  |  |  |  |
|  |  |  |  |
|  |  |  |  |
|  |  |  |  |
|  |  |  |  |
|  |  |  |  |
|  |  |  |  |
|  |  |  |  |
|  |  |  |  |
|  |  |  |  |
|  |  |  |  |
|  |  |  |  |
|  |  |  |  |
|  |  |  |  |
|  |  |  |  |
|  |  |  |  |
|  |  |  |  |
|  |  |  |  |
|  |  |  |  |
|  |  |  |  |
|  |  |  |  |
|  |  |  |  |
|  |  |  |  |
|  |  |  |  |
|  |  |  |  |
|  |  |  |  |
|  |  |  |  |

*Analysis component:* _____

_____

_____

_____

_____

_____

_____

**Part 1**

## Income Statement

| | | |
|---|---|---|
| | | |
| | | |
| | | |
| | | |
| | | |
| | | |
| | | |
| | | |
| | | |
| | | |
| | | |
| | | |
| | | |
| | | |
| | | |
| | | |
| | | |
| | | |
| | | |
| | | |
| | | |
| | | |
| | | |
| | | |

**Part 2**

_____

_____

_____

_____

### Noel Apex, Capital

## Income Statement

| | | |
|---|---|---|
| | | |
| | | |
| | | |
| | | |
| | | |
| | | |
| | | |
| | | |
| | | |
| | | |
| | | |
| | | |
| | | |
| | | |
| | | |
| | | |
| | | |
| | | |
| | | |
| | | |
| | | |
| | | |
| | | |
| | | |
| | | |
| | | |
| | | |

## Statement of Owner's Equity

| | | |
|---|---|---|
| | | |
| | | |
| | | |
| | | |
| | | |
| | | |
| | | |
| | | |
| | | |
| | | |

## Balance Sheet

| | | | |
|---|---|---|---|
| | | | |
| | | | |
| | | | |
| | | | |
| | | | |
| | | | |
| | | | |
| | | | |
| | | | |
| | | | |
| | | | |
| | | | |
| | | | |
| | | | |
| | | | |
| | | | |
| | | | |
| | | | |
| | | | |
| | | | |
| | | | |
| | | | |
| | | | |
| | | | |
| | | | |
| | | | |
| | | | |
| | | | |
| | | | |
| | | | |
| | | | |
| | | | |
| | | | |
| | | | |
| | | | |
| | | | |
| | | | |
| | | | |
| | | | |

*Analysis component:*

_____

_____

_____

_____

_____

_____

**Part 1**

_____

_____

_____

_____

**Wyett North, Capital**

**Part 2**

## Balance Sheet

| | | | |
|---|---|---|---|
| | | | |
| | | | |
| | | | |
| | | | |
| | | | |
| | | | |
| | | | |
| | | | |
| | | | |
| | | | |
| | | | |
| | | | |
| | | | |
| | | | |
| | | | |
| | | | |
| | | | |
| | | | |
| | | | |
| | | | |
| | | | |
| | | | |
| | | | |
| | | | |
| | | | |
| | | | |
| | | | |
| | | | |
| | | | |
| | | | |
| | | | |
| | | | |
| | | | |
| | | | |
| | | | |
| | | | |

## *Analysis component:*

_____
_____
_____
_____
_____
_____
_____

Part 1.  Use either the balance column format or T-accounts; both are provided.

## GENERAL LEDGER

### Cash                                                          ACCOUNT NO. 101

| DATE | EXPLANATION | PR | DEBIT | CREDIT | BALANCE |
|------|-------------|----|-------|--------|---------|
|      |             |    |       |        |         |
|      |             |    |       |        |         |
|      |             |    |       |        |         |
|      |             |    |       |        |         |
|      |             |    |       |        |         |
|      |             |    |       |        |         |
|      |             |    |       |        |         |
|      |             |    |       |        |         |
|      |             |    |       |        |         |
|      |             |    |       |        |         |
|      |             |    |       |        |         |
|      |             |    |       |        |         |
|      |             |    |       |        |         |
|      |             |    |       |        |         |

### Accounts Receivable                                ACCOUNT NO. 106

| DATE | EXPLANATION | PR | DEBIT | CREDIT | BALANCE |
|------|-------------|----|-------|--------|---------|
|      |             |    |       |        |         |
|      |             |    |       |        |         |

### Office Supplies                                       ACCOUNT NO. 124

| DATE | EXPLANATION | PR | DEBIT | CREDIT | BALANCE |
|------|-------------|----|-------|--------|---------|
|      |             |    |       |        |         |
|      |             |    |       |        |         |
|      |             |    |       |        |         |

### Prepaid Insurance                                   ACCOUNT NO. 128

| DATE | EXPLANATION | PR | DEBIT | CREDIT | BALANCE |
|------|-------------|----|-------|--------|---------|
|      |             |    |       |        |         |
|      |             |    |       |        |         |
|      |             |    |       |        |         |

### Computer Equipment                               ACCOUNT NO. 167

| DATE | EXPLANATION | PR | DEBIT | CREDIT | BALANCE |
|------|-------------|----|-------|--------|---------|
|      |             |    |       |        |         |
|      |             |    |       |        |         |

### Accumulated Amortization, Computer Equipment          ACCOUNT NO. 168

| DATE | EXPLANATION | PR | DEBIT | CREDIT | BALANCE |
|------|-------------|----|-------|--------|---------|
|      |             |    |       |        |         |
|      |             |    |       |        |         |

## Salaries Payable                    ACCOUNT NO. 209

| DATE | EXPLANATION | PR | DEBIT | CREDIT | BALANCE |
|------|-------------|----|----|----|----|
|      |             |    |    |    |    |
|      |             |    |    |    |    |

## Sam Near, Capital                    ACCOUNT NO. 301

| DATE | EXPLANATION | PR | DEBIT | CREDIT | BALANCE |
|------|-------------|----|----|----|----|
|      |             |    |    |    |    |
|      |             |    |    |    |    |
|      |             |    |    |    |    |

## Sam Near, Withdrawals                    ACCOUNT NO. 302

| DATE | EXPLANATION | PR | DEBIT | CREDIT | BALANCE |
|------|-------------|----|----|----|----|
|      |             |    |    |    |    |
|      |             |    |    |    |    |
|      |             |    |    |    |    |

## Commissions Earned                    ACCOUNT NO. 405

| DATE | EXPLANATION | PR | DEBIT | CREDIT | BALANCE |
|------|-------------|----|----|----|----|
|      |             |    |    |    |    |
|      |             |    |    |    |    |
|      |             |    |    |    |    |
|      |             |    |    |    |    |

## Amortization Expense, Computer Equipment                    ACCOUNT NO. 612

| DATE | EXPLANATION | PR | DEBIT | CREDIT | BALANCE |
|------|-------------|----|----|----|----|
|      |             |    |    |    |    |
|      |             |    |    |    |    |
|      |             |    |    |    |    |

## Salaries Expense                    ACCOUNT NO. 622

| DATE | EXPLANATION | PR | DEBIT | CREDIT | BALANCE |
|------|-------------|----|----|----|----|
|      |             |    |    |    |    |
|      |             |    |    |    |    |
|      |             |    |    |    |    |
|      |             |    |    |    |    |
|      |             |    |    |    |    |

## Insurance Expense                    ACCOUNT NO. 637

| DATE | EXPLANATION | PR | DEBIT | CREDIT | BALANCE |
|------|-------------|----|----|----|----|
|      |             |    |    |    |    |
|      |             |    |    |    |    |
|      |             |    |    |    |    |

## Rent Expense                                    ACCOUNT NO. 640

| DATE | EXPLANATION | PR | DEBIT | CREDIT | BALANCE |
|------|-------------|----|----|----|----|
|      |             |    |    |    |    |
|      |             |    |    |    |    |
|      |             |    |    |    |    |

## Office Supplies Expense                          ACCOUNT NO. 650

| DATE | EXPLANATION | PR | DEBIT | CREDIT | BALANCE |
|------|-------------|----|----|----|----|
|      |             |    |    |    |    |
|      |             |    |    |    |    |
|      |             |    |    |    |    |

## Repairs Expense                                 ACCOUNT NO. 684

| DATE | EXPLANATION | PR | DEBIT | CREDIT | BALANCE |
|------|-------------|----|----|----|----|
|      |             |    |    |    |    |
|      |             |    |    |    |    |
|      |             |    |    |    |    |

## Telephone Expense                               ACCOUNT NO. 688

| DATE | EXPLANATION | PR | DEBIT | CREDIT | BALANCE |
|------|-------------|----|----|----|----|
|      |             |    |    |    |    |
|      |             |    |    |    |    |
|      |             |    |    |    |    |

## Income Summary                                  ACCOUNT NO. 901

| DATE | EXPLANATION | PR | DEBIT | CREDIT | BALANCE |
|------|-------------|----|----|----|----|
|      |             |    |    |    |    |
|      |             |    |    |    |    |
|      |             |    |    |    |    |
|      |             |    |    |    |    |

Part 1.  Use either T-accounts or the balance column format; both are provided.

| Cash | 101 | | Sam Near, Capital | 301 |

| Accounts Receivable | 106 | | Amort. Exp., Computer Equip. | 612 |

| Office Supplies | 124 | | Sam Near, Withdrawals | 302 |

| | | | Commissions Earned | 405 |

| Prepaid Insurance | 128 | | Salaries Expense | 622 |

| Computer Equipment | 167 | | Insurance Expense | 637 |

| Accum. Amort., Computer Equip. | 168 | | Rent Expense | 640 |

| Salaries Payable | 209 | | Office Supplies Expense | 650 |

| Repairs Expense    684 | Telephone Expense    688 |
|---|---|
|  |  |

| Income Summary    901 |
|---|
|  |

## Part 2.  Transactions for June:

### GENERAL JOURNAL                                Page____

| Date | Account Titles and Explanation | PR | Debit | Credit |
|---|---|---|---|---|
|  |  |  |  |  |
|  |  |  |  |  |
|  |  |  |  |  |
|  |  |  |  |  |
|  |  |  |  |  |
|  |  |  |  |  |
|  |  |  |  |  |
|  |  |  |  |  |
|  |  |  |  |  |
|  |  |  |  |  |
|  |  |  |  |  |
|  |  |  |  |  |
|  |  |  |  |  |
|  |  |  |  |  |
|  |  |  |  |  |
|  |  |  |  |  |
|  |  |  |  |  |
|  |  |  |  |  |
|  |  |  |  |  |
|  |  |  |  |  |
|  |  |  |  |  |
|  |  |  |  |  |
|  |  |  |  |  |
|  |  |  |  |  |
|  |  |  |  |  |
|  |  |  |  |  |
|  |  |  |  |  |
|  |  |  |  |  |
|  |  |  |  |  |

Part 2.  Transactions for June (cont'd.)

GENERAL JOURNAL                    Page____

| Date | Account Titles and Explanation | PR | Debit | Credit |
|------|-------------------------------|----|-------|--------|
|      |                               |    |       |        |
|      |                               |    |       |        |
|      |                               |    |       |        |
|      |                               |    |       |        |
|      |                               |    |       |        |
|      |                               |    |       |        |
|      |                               |    |       |        |
|      |                               |    |       |        |
|      |                               |    |       |        |
|      |                               |    |       |        |
|      |                               |    |       |        |
|      |                               |    |       |        |
|      |                               |    |       |        |
|      |                               |    |       |        |
|      |                               |    |       |        |
|      |                               |    |       |        |
|      |                               |    |       |        |
|      |                               |    |       |        |
|      |                               |    |       |        |
|      |                               |    |       |        |
|      |                               |    |       |        |
|      |                               |    |       |        |
|      |                               |    |       |        |
|      |                               |    |       |        |
|      |                               |    |       |        |
|      |                               |    |       |        |
|      |                               |    |       |        |
|      |                               |    |       |        |
|      |                               |    |       |        |
|      |                               |    |       |        |
|      |                               |    |       |        |
|      |                               |    |       |        |
|      |                               |    |       |        |
|      |                               |    |       |        |
|      |                               |    |       |        |
|      |                               |    |       |        |
|      |                               |    |       |        |
|      |                               |    |       |        |
|      |                               |    |       |        |
|      |                               |    |       |        |

**Part 3. Adjusting entries:**

**GENERAL JOURNAL**                                                    Page____

| Date | Account Titles and Explanation | PR | Debit | Credit |
|------|-------------------------------|----|-------|--------|
|      |                               |    |       |        |
|      |                               |    |       |        |
|      |                               |    |       |        |
|      |                               |    |       |        |
|      |                               |    |       |        |
|      |                               |    |       |        |
|      |                               |    |       |        |
|      |                               |    |       |        |
|      |                               |    |       |        |
|      |                               |    |       |        |
|      |                               |    |       |        |
|      |                               |    |       |        |
|      |                               |    |       |        |
|      |                               |    |       |        |
|      |                               |    |       |        |
|      |                               |    |       |        |
|      |                               |    |       |        |
|      |                               |    |       |        |
|      |                               |    |       |        |
|      |                               |    |       |        |
|      |                               |    |       |        |
|      |                               |    |       |        |
|      |                               |    |       |        |
|      |                               |    |       |        |
|      |                               |    |       |        |
|      |                               |    |       |        |

**Part 4**

**Income Statement**

| | | |
|---|---|---|
|   |   |   |
|   |   |   |
|   |   |   |
|   |   |   |
|   |   |   |
|   |   |   |
|   |   |   |
|   |   |   |
|   |   |   |
|   |   |   |
|   |   |   |
|   |   |   |
|   |   |   |
|   |   |   |
|   |   |   |
|   |   |   |

## Statement of Owner's Equity

| | | | |
|---|---|---|---|
| | | | |
| | | | |
| | | | |
| | | | |
| | | | |
| | | | |
| | | | |
| | | | |
| | | | |
| | | | |

## Balance Sheet

| | | | |
|---|---|---|---|
| | | | |
| | | | |
| | | | |
| | | | |
| | | | |
| | | | |
| | | | |
| | | | |
| | | | |
| | | | |
| | | | |
| | | | |
| | | | |
| | | | |
| | | | |
| | | | |
| | | | |
| | | | |
| | | | |
| | | | |
| | | | |
| | | | |
| | | | |
| | | | |
| | | | |
| | | | |
| | | | |

**Part 5. Closing entries:**

### GENERAL JOURNAL        Page____

| Date | Account Titles and Explanation | PR | Debit | Credit |
|------|-------------------------------|----|----|----|
|  |  |  |  |  |
|  |  |  |  |  |
|  |  |  |  |  |
|  |  |  |  |  |
|  |  |  |  |  |
|  |  |  |  |  |
|  |  |  |  |  |
|  |  |  |  |  |
|  |  |  |  |  |
|  |  |  |  |  |
|  |  |  |  |  |
|  |  |  |  |  |
|  |  |  |  |  |
|  |  |  |  |  |
|  |  |  |  |  |
|  |  |  |  |  |
|  |  |  |  |  |
|  |  |  |  |  |
|  |  |  |  |  |
|  |  |  |  |  |
|  |  |  |  |  |
|  |  |  |  |  |
|  |  |  |  |  |
|  |  |  |  |  |
|  |  |  |  |  |
|  |  |  |  |  |

## Part 6

### Post-Closing Trial Balance

|  | Debit | Credit |
|------|----|----|
|  |  |  |
|  |  |  |
|  |  |  |
|  |  |  |
|  |  |  |
|  |  |  |
|  |  |  |
|  |  |  |
|  |  |  |
|  |  |  |
|  |  |  |
|  |  |  |

## GENERAL JOURNAL      Page____

| Date | Account Titles and Explanation | PR | Debit | Credit |
|------|-------------------------------|----|-------|--------|
| a. | | | | |
| | | | | |
| | | | | |
| | | | | |
| b. | | | | |
| | | | | |
| | | | | |
| | | | | |
| c. | | | | |
| | | | | |
| | | | | |
| | | | | |
| d. | | | | |
| | | | | |
| | | | | |
| | | | | |
| e. | | | | |
| | | | | |
| | | | | |
| | | | | |
| f. | | | | |
| | | | | |
| | | | | |
| | | | | |

## GENERAL JOURNAL                                    Page____

| Date | Account Titles and Explanation | PR | Debit | Credit |
|------|-------------------------------|----|----|-----|
|  |  |  |  |  |
|  |  |  |  |  |
|  |  |  |  |  |
|  |  |  |  |  |
|  |  |  |  |  |
|  |  |  |  |  |
|  |  |  |  |  |
|  |  |  |  |  |
|  |  |  |  |  |
|  |  |  |  |  |
|  |  |  |  |  |
|  |  |  |  |  |
|  |  |  |  |  |
|  |  |  |  |  |
|  |  |  |  |  |
|  |  |  |  |  |
|  |  |  |  |  |
|  |  |  |  |  |
|  |  |  |  |  |
|  |  |  |  |  |
|  |  |  |  |  |
|  |  |  |  |  |

**Part 3**

## GENERAL JOURNAL                                    Page____

| Date | Account Titles and Explanation | PR | Debit | Credit |
|------|-------------------------------|----|----|-----|
|  |  |  |  |  |
|  |  |  |  |  |
|  |  |  |  |  |
|  |  |  |  |  |
|  |  |  |  |  |
|  |  |  |  |  |
|  |  |  |  |  |
|  |  |  |  |  |
|  |  |  |  |  |
|  |  |  |  |  |
|  |  |  |  |  |
|  |  |  |  |  |
|  |  |  |  |  |
|  |  |  |  |  |
|  |  |  |  |  |
|  |  |  |  |  |
|  |  |  |  |  |
|  |  |  |  |  |
|  |  |  |  |  |
|  |  |  |  |  |
|  |  |  |  |  |

**Name** _____

**Landmark Tours**

**Work Sheet**

**For Year Ended June 30, 2011**

| Account Title | Unadjusted Trial Balance | | Adjustments | | Adjusted Trial Balance | | Income Statement | | Balance Sheet and Statement of Owner's Equity | |
|---|---|---|---|---|---|---|---|---|---|---|
| | Debit | Credit | Debit | Credit | Debit | Credit | Debit | Credit | Debit | Credit |
| Cash | 17,800 | | | | | | | | | |
| Accounts receivable | 42,500 | | | | | | | | | |
| Notes receivable, due | 28,000 | | | | | | | | | |
| Prepaid insurance | 21,000 | | | | | | | | | |
| Furniture | 13,500 | | | | | | | | | |
| Accounts payable | | 13,850 | | | | | | | | |
| Unearned tour revenue | | 28,000 | | | | | | | | |
| Jan Rider, capital | | 121,950 | | | | | | | | |
| Jan Rider, withdrawals | -0- | | | | | | | | | |
| Tour revenue | | 31,000 | | | | | | | | |
| Wages expense | 72,000 | | | | | | | | | |
| Totals | 194,800 | 194,800 | | | | | | | | |

Family Photographers

Work Sheet

For Year Ended March 31, 2011

| Account Title | Unadjusted Trial Balance Debit | Unadjusted Trial Balance Credit | Adjustments Debit | Adjustments Credit | Adjusted Trial Balance Debit | Adjusted Trial Balance Credit | Income Statement Debit | Income Statement Credit | Balance Sheet and Statement of Owner's Equity Debit | Balance Sheet and Statement of Owner's Equity Credit |
|---|---|---|---|---|---|---|---|---|---|---|
| Cash | 14,000 | | | | | | | | | |
| Accounts receivable | 3,100 | | | | | | | | | |
| Prepaid equipment rental | 1,930 | | | | | | | | | |
| Automobile | 26,000 | | | | | | | | | |
| Accum. amort., automobile | | -0- | | | | | | | | |
| Accounts payable | | 960 | | | | | | | | |
| Unearned fees | | 2,870 | | | | | | | | |
| Jim Tucker, capital | | 39,400 | | | | | | | | |
| Jim Tucker, withdrawals | 700 | | | | | | | | | |
| Fees earned | | 4,200 | | | | | | | | |
| Amort. Expense, automobile | -0- | | | | | | | | | |
| Equipment rental expense | 1,700 | | | | | | | | | |
| Totals | 47,430 | 47,430 | | | | | | | | |

_____

_____

_____

_____

### Jim Tucker, Capital

*Analysis component:*

_____

_____

_____

_____

_____

_____

_____

**Chapter 5    Problem 5-3B**                    *Name* _____

**Part 1**

Boomer Demolition Company

Work Sheet

For Year Ended September 30, 2011

| Account Title | Unadjusted Trial Balance Debit | Unadjusted Trial Balance Credit | Adjustments Debit | Adjustments Credit | Adjusted Trial Balance Debit | Adjusted Trial Balance Credit | Income Statement Debit | Income Statement Credit | Balance Sheet and Statement of Owner's Equity Debit | Balance Sheet and Statement of Owner's Equity Credit |
|---|---|---|---|---|---|---|---|---|---|---|
| Cash | 9,000 | | | | | | | | | |
| Supplies | 18,000 | | | | | | | | | |
| Prepaid insurance | 14,600 | | | | | | | | | |
| Equipment | 140,000 | | | | | | | | | |
| Accum. amort., equipment | | 10,000 | | | | | | | | |
| Accounts payable | | 16,000 | | | | | | | | |
| Interest payable | | | | | | | | | | |
| Wages payable | | | | | | | | | | |
| Long-term notes payable | | 90,000 | | | | | | | | |
| Rusty Boomer, capital | | 66,900 | | | | | | | | |
| Rusty Boomer, withdrawals | 4,000 | | | | | | | | | |
| Demolition fees earned | | 137,000 | | | | | | | | |
| Amort. expense, equipment | | | | | | | | | | |
| Wages expense | 51,400 | | | | | | | | | |
| Interest expense | 2,200 | | | | | | | | | |
| Insurance expense | | | | | | | | | | |
| Rent expense | 48,800 | | | | | | | | | |
| Supplies expense | | | | | | | | | | |
| Business tax expense | 8,400 | | | | | | | | | |
| Repairs expense | 6,700 | | | | | | | | | |
| Utilities expense | 16,800 | | | | | | | | | |
| Totals | 319,900 | 319,900 | | | | | | | | |

**Part 2**
**Adjusting entries:**

### GENERAL JOURNAL                                   Page____

| Date | Account Titles and Explanation | PR | Debit | Credit |
|------|-------------------------------|----|-------|--------|
| a.   |                               |    |       |        |
|      |                               |    |       |        |
|      |                               |    |       |        |
|      |                               |    |       |        |
| b.   |                               |    |       |        |
|      |                               |    |       |        |
|      |                               |    |       |        |
|      |                               |    |       |        |
| c.   |                               |    |       |        |
|      |                               |    |       |        |
|      |                               |    |       |        |
|      |                               |    |       |        |
| d.   |                               |    |       |        |
|      |                               |    |       |        |
|      |                               |    |       |        |
|      |                               |    |       |        |
| e.   |                               |    |       |        |
|      |                               |    |       |        |
|      |                               |    |       |        |
|      |                               |    |       |        |
| f.   |                               |    |       |        |
|      |                               |    |       |        |
|      |                               |    |       |        |
|      |                               |    |       |        |
|      |                               |    |       |        |

**Part 2**
**Closing entries:**

### GENERAL JOURNAL        Page____

| Date | Account Titles and Explanation | PR | Debit | Credit |
|------|-------------------------------|----|-------|--------|
|      |                               |    |       |        |
|      |                               |    |       |        |
|      |                               |    |       |        |
|      |                               |    |       |        |
|      |                               |    |       |        |
|      |                               |    |       |        |
|      |                               |    |       |        |
|      |                               |    |       |        |
|      |                               |    |       |        |
|      |                               |    |       |        |
|      |                               |    |       |        |
|      |                               |    |       |        |
|      |                               |    |       |        |
|      |                               |    |       |        |
|      |                               |    |       |        |
|      |                               |    |       |        |
|      |                               |    |       |        |
|      |                               |    |       |        |
|      |                               |    |       |        |
|      |                               |    |       |        |
|      |                               |    |       |        |
|      |                               |    |       |        |
|      |                               |    |       |        |
|      |                               |    |       |        |
|      |                               |    |       |        |
|      |                               |    |       |        |
|      |                               |    |       |        |
|      |                               |    |       |        |
|      |                               |    |       |        |
|      |                               |    |       |        |
|      |                               |    |       |        |
|      |                               |    |       |        |
|      |                               |    |       |        |
|      |                               |    |       |        |
|      |                               |    |       |        |
|      |                               |    |       |        |

## Income Statement

| | | |
|---|---|---|
| | | |
| | | |
| | | |
| | | |
| | | |
| | | |
| | | |
| | | |
| | | |
| | | |
| | | |
| | | |
| | | |
| | | |
| | | |
| | | |
| | | |
| | | |
| | | |
| | | |
| | | |
| | | |
| | | |
| | | |
| | | |
| | | |

## Statement of Owner's Equity

| | | |
|---|---|---|
| | | |
| | | |
| | | |
| | | |
| | | |
| | | |
| | | |
| | | |
| | | |
| | | |
| | | |
| | | |

## Balance Sheet

| | | | |
|---|---|---|---|
| | | | |
| | | | |
| | | | |
| | | | |
| | | | |
| | | | |
| | | | |
| | | | |
| | | | |
| | | | |
| | | | |
| | | | |
| | | | |
| | | | |
| | | | |
| | | | |
| | | | |
| | | | |
| | | | |
| | | | |
| | | | |
| | | | |
| | | | |
| | | | |
| | | | |
| | | | |
| | | | |
| | | | |
| | | | |
| | | | |
| | | | |
| | | | |
| | | | |
| | | | |
| | | | |

*Analysis component:*

a. _____

_____

_____

b. _____

_____

_____

_____

Part 1    GENERAL JOURNAL    Page____

| Date | Account Titles and Explanation | PR | Debit | Credit |
|---|---|---|---|---|
|  |  |  |  |  |
|  |  |  |  |  |
|  |  |  |  |  |
|  |  |  |  |  |
|  |  |  |  |  |
|  |  |  |  |  |
|  |  |  |  |  |
|  |  |  |  |  |
|  |  |  |  |  |
|  |  |  |  |  |
|  |  |  |  |  |
|  |  |  |  |  |
|  |  |  |  |  |
|  |  |  |  |  |
|  |  |  |  |  |
|  |  |  |  |  |
|  |  |  |  |  |
|  |  |  |  |  |
|  |  |  |  |  |
|  |  |  |  |  |
|  |  |  |  |  |
|  |  |  |  |  |
|  |  |  |  |  |
|  |  |  |  |  |
|  |  |  |  |  |
|  |  |  |  |  |
|  |  |  |  |  |
|  |  |  |  |  |
|  |  |  |  |  |

Part 2

## Post-Closing Trial Balance

|  | Debit | Credit |
|---|---|---|
|  |  |  |
|  |  |  |
|  |  |  |
|  |  |  |
|  |  |  |
|  |  |  |
|  |  |  |
|  |  |  |
|  |  |  |
|  |  |  |
|  |  |  |
|  |  |  |
|  |  |  |

## Income Statement

|  |  |  |
|---|---|---|
|  |  |  |
|  |  |  |
|  |  |  |
|  |  |  |
|  |  |  |
|  |  |  |
|  |  |  |
|  |  |  |
|  |  |  |
|  |  |  |
|  |  |  |
|  |  |  |
|  |  |  |
|  |  |  |
|  |  |  |
|  |  |  |
|  |  |  |
|  |  |  |
|  |  |  |
|  |  |  |
|  |  |  |
|  |  |  |
|  |  |  |
|  |  |  |
|  |  |  |
|  |  |  |
|  |  |  |
|  |  |  |
|  |  |  |
|  |  |  |

## Statement of Owner's Equity

|  |  |  |
|---|---|---|
|  |  |  |
|  |  |  |
|  |  |  |
|  |  |  |
|  |  |  |
|  |  |  |
|  |  |  |
|  |  |  |
|  |  |  |

## Balance Sheet

| | | | |
|---|---|---|---|
| | | | |
| | | | |
| | | | |
| | | | |
| | | | |
| | | | |
| | | | |
| | | | |
| | | | |
| | | | |
| | | | |
| | | | |
| | | | |
| | | | |
| | | | |
| | | | |
| | | | |
| | | | |
| | | | |
| | | | |
| | | | |
| | | | |
| | | | |
| | | | |
| | | | |
| | | | |
| | | | |
| | | | |
| | | | |
| | | | |
| | | | |
| | | | |
| | | | |
| | | | |
| | | | |
| | | | |

*Analysis component:* _____

_____
_____
_____
_____
_____

## GENERAL JOURNAL                          Page____

| Date | Account Titles and Explanation | PR | Debit | Credit |
|------|-------------------------------|-----|-------|--------|
|      |                               |     |       |        |
|      |                               |     |       |        |
|      |                               |     |       |        |
|      |                               |     |       |        |
|      |                               |     |       |        |
|      |                               |     |       |        |
|      |                               |     |       |        |
|      |                               |     |       |        |
|      |                               |     |       |        |
|      |                               |     |       |        |
|      |                               |     |       |        |
|      |                               |     |       |        |
|      |                               |     |       |        |
|      |                               |     |       |        |
|      |                               |     |       |        |
|      |                               |     |       |        |
|      |                               |     |       |        |
|      |                               |     |       |        |
|      |                               |     |       |        |
|      |                               |     |       |        |
|      |                               |     |       |        |
|      |                               |     |       |        |
|      |                               |     |       |        |
|      |                               |     |       |        |
|      |                               |     |       |        |
|      |                               |     |       |        |
|      |                               |     |       |        |
|      |                               |     |       |        |
|      |                               |     |       |        |
|      |                               |     |       |        |
|      |                               |     |       |        |
|      |                               |     |       |        |
|      |                               |     |       |        |
|      |                               |     |       |        |
|      |                               |     |       |        |
|      |                               |     |       |        |
|      |                               |     |       |        |
|      |                               |     |       |        |

## Income Statement

| | | |
|---|---|---|
| | | |
| | | |
| | | |
| | | |
| | | |
| | | |
| | | |
| | | |
| | | |
| | | |
| | | |
| | | |
| | | |
| | | |
| | | |
| | | |
| | | |
| | | |
| | | |
| | | |
| | | |
| | | |
| | | |
| | | |

## Statement of Owner's Equity

| | | |
|---|---|---|
| | | |
| | | |
| | | |
| | | |
| | | |
| | | |
| | | |
| | | |
| | | |
| | | |
| | | |

## Balance Sheet

| | | | |
|---|---|---|---|
| | | | |
| | | | |
| | | | |
| | | | |
| | | | |
| | | | |
| | | | |
| | | | |
| | | | |
| | | | |
| | | | |
| | | | |
| | | | |
| | | | |
| | | | |
| | | | |
| | | | |
| | | | |
| | | | |
| | | | |
| | | | |
| | | | |
| | | | |
| | | | |
| | | | |
| | | | |
| | | | |
| | | | |
| | | | |
| | | | |
| | | | |
| | | | |
| | | | |
| | | | |
| | | | |
| | | | |
| | | | |
| | | | |

*Analysis component:* _____

_____

_____

_____

_____

_____

_____

_____

## GENERAL JOURNAL                                    Page____

| Date | Account Titles and Explanation | PR | Debit | Credit |
|------|-------------------------------|----|-------|--------|
|      |                               |    |       |        |
|      |                               |    |       |        |
|      |                               |    |       |        |
|      |                               |    |       |        |
|      |                               |    |       |        |
|      |                               |    |       |        |
|      |                               |    |       |        |
|      |                               |    |       |        |
|      |                               |    |       |        |
|      |                               |    |       |        |
|      |                               |    |       |        |
|      |                               |    |       |        |
|      |                               |    |       |        |
|      |                               |    |       |        |
|      |                               |    |       |        |
|      |                               |    |       |        |
|      |                               |    |       |        |
|      |                               |    |       |        |
|      |                               |    |       |        |
|      |                               |    |       |        |
|      |                               |    |       |        |
|      |                               |    |       |        |
|      |                               |    |       |        |
|      |                               |    |       |        |
|      |                               |    |       |        |
|      |                               |    |       |        |
|      |                               |    |       |        |
|      |                               |    |       |        |
|      |                               |    |       |        |
|      |                               |    |       |        |
|      |                               |    |       |        |
|      |                               |    |       |        |
|      |                               |    |       |        |
|      |                               |    |       |        |
|      |                               |    |       |        |
|      |                               |    |       |        |
|      |                               |    |       |        |
|      |                               |    |       |        |
|      |                               |    |       |        |
|      |                               |    |       |        |
|      |                               |    |       |        |
|      |                               |    |       |        |
|      |                               |    |       |        |
|      |                               |    |       |        |
|      |                               |    |       |        |
|      |                               |    |       |        |

## Income Statement

| | | |
|---|---|---|
| | | |
| | | |
| | | |
| | | |
| | | |
| | | |
| | | |
| | | |
| | | |
| | | |
| | | |
| | | |
| | | |
| | | |
| | | |
| | | |
| | | |
| | | |
| | | |
| | | |
| | | |
| | | |
| | | |
| | | |
| | | |
| | | |

## Statement of Owner's Equity

| | | |
|---|---|---|
| | | |
| | | |
| | | |
| | | |
| | | |
| | | |
| | | |
| | | |
| | | |
| | | |
| | | |

## Balance Sheet

| | | | |
|---|---|---|---|
| | | | |
| | | | |
| | | | |
| | | | |
| | | | |
| | | | |
| | | | |
| | | | |
| | | | |
| | | | |
| | | | |
| | | | |
| | | | |
| | | | |
| | | | |
| | | | |
| | | | |
| | | | |
| | | | |
| | | | |
| | | | |
| | | | |
| | | | |
| | | | |
| | | | |
| | | | |
| | | | |
| | | | |
| | | | |
| | | | |
| | | | |
| | | | |
| | | | |
| | | | |

*Analysis component:* _____

_____
_____
_____
_____
_____
_____

**Part 1**

## Income Statement

| | | |
|---|---|---|
| | | |
| | | |
| | | |
| | | |
| | | |
| | | |
| | | |
| | | |
| | | |
| | | |
| | | |
| | | |
| | | |
| | | |
| | | |
| | | |
| | | |
| | | |
| | | |
| | | |
| | | |
| | | |
| | | |
| | | |

**Part 2**

**Grant Craig, Capital**

## Income Statement

| | | |
|---|---|---|
| | | |
| | | |
| | | |
| | | |
| | | |
| | | |
| | | |
| | | |
| | | |
| | | |
| | | |
| | | |
| | | |
| | | |
| | | |
| | | |
| | | |
| | | |
| | | |
| | | |
| | | |
| | | |
| | | |
| | | |
| | | |
| | | |

## Statement of Owner's Equity

| | | |
|---|---|---|
| | | |
| | | |
| | | |
| | | |
| | | |
| | | |
| | | |
| | | |
| | | |
| | | |
| | | |

## Balance Sheet

| | | | |
|---|---|---|---|
| | | | |
| | | | |
| | | | |
| | | | |
| | | | |
| | | | |
| | | | |
| | | | |
| | | | |
| | | | |
| | | | |
| | | | |
| | | | |
| | | | |
| | | | |
| | | | |
| | | | |
| | | | |
| | | | |
| | | | |
| | | | |
| | | | |
| | | | |
| | | | |
| | | | |
| | | | |
| | | | |
| | | | |
| | | | |
| | | | |
| | | | |
| | | | |
| | | | |
| | | | |
| | | | |
| | | | |

*Analysis component:*
_____
_____
_____
_____
_____
_____
_____

**Part 1**

_____

_____                    **Jan Rider, Capital**
_____
_____

_____

**Part 2**

## Balance Sheet

| | | | |
|---|---|---|---|
| | | | |
| | | | |
| | | | |
| | | | |
| | | | |
| | | | |
| | | | |
| | | | |
| | | | |
| | | | |
| | | | |
| | | | |
| | | | |
| | | | |
| | | | |
| | | | |
| | | | |
| | | | |
| | | | |
| | | | |
| | | | |
| | | | |
| | | | |
| | | | |
| | | | |
| | | | |
| | | | |
| | | | |
| | | | |
| | | | |
| | | | |
| | | | |
| | | | |
| | | | |

Part 1.  Use either the balance column format or T-accounts; both are provided.

## GENERAL LEDGER

### Cash                                                                   ACCOUNT NO. 101

| DATE | EXPLANATION | PR | DEBIT | CREDIT | BALANCE |
|------|-------------|----|-------|--------|---------|
|      |             |    |       |        |         |
|      |             |    |       |        |         |
|      |             |    |       |        |         |
|      |             |    |       |        |         |
|      |             |    |       |        |         |
|      |             |    |       |        |         |

### Accounts Receivable                                          ACCOUNT NO. 106

| DATE | EXPLANATION | PR | DEBIT | CREDIT | BALANCE |
|------|-------------|----|-------|--------|---------|
|      |             |    |       |        |         |
|      |             |    |       |        |         |

### Office Supplies                                                  ACCOUNT NO. 124

| DATE | EXPLANATION | PR | DEBIT | CREDIT | BALANCE |
|------|-------------|----|-------|--------|---------|
|      |             |    |       |        |         |
|      |             |    |       |        |         |
|      |             |    |       |        |         |

### Prepaid Insurance                                             ACCOUNT NO. 128

| DATE | EXPLANATION | PR | DEBIT | CREDIT | BALANCE |
|------|-------------|----|-------|--------|---------|
|      |             |    |       |        |         |
|      |             |    |       |        |         |
|      |             |    |       |        |         |

### Buildings                                                           ACCOUNT NO. 173

| DATE | EXPLANATION | PR | DEBIT | CREDIT | BALANCE |
|------|-------------|----|-------|--------|---------|
|      |             |    |       |        |         |
|      |             |    |       |        |         |

### Accumulated Amortization, Buildings                 ACCOUNT NO. 174

| DATE | EXPLANATION | PR | DEBIT | CREDIT | BALANCE |
|------|-------------|----|-------|--------|---------|
|      |             |    |       |        |         |
|      |             |    |       |        |         |

## Salaries Payable                                         ACCOUNT NO. 209

| DATE | EXPLANATION | PR | DEBIT | CREDIT | BALANCE |
|------|-------------|----|-------|--------|---------|
|      |             |    |       |        |         |
|      |             |    |       |        |         |

## Cindy Tucker, Capital                                    ACCOUNT NO. 301

| DATE | EXPLANATION | PR | DEBIT | CREDIT | BALANCE |
|------|-------------|----|-------|--------|---------|
|      |             |    |       |        |         |
|      |             |    |       |        |         |
|      |             |    |       |        |         |
|      |             |    |       |        |         |

## Cindy Tucker, Withdrawals                                ACCOUNT NO. 302

| DATE | EXPLANATION | PR | DEBIT | CREDIT | BALANCE |
|------|-------------|----|-------|--------|---------|
|      |             |    |       |        |         |
|      |             |    |       |        |         |
|      |             |    |       |        |         |

## Storage Fees Earned                                      ACCOUNT NO. 401

| DATE | EXPLANATION | PR | DEBIT | CREDIT | BALANCE |
|------|-------------|----|-------|--------|---------|
|      |             |    |       |        |         |
|      |             |    |       |        |         |
|      |             |    |       |        |         |
|      |             |    |       |        |         |

## Amortization Expense, Buildings                          ACCOUNT NO. 606

| DATE | EXPLANATION | PR | DEBIT | CREDIT | BALANCE |
|------|-------------|----|-------|--------|---------|
|      |             |    |       |        |         |
|      |             |    |       |        |         |

## Salaries Expense                                         ACCOUNT NO. 622

| DATE | EXPLANATION | PR | DEBIT | CREDIT | BALANCE |
|------|-------------|----|-------|--------|---------|
|      |             |    |       |        |         |
|      |             |    |       |        |         |
|      |             |    |       |        |         |
|      |             |    |       |        |         |
|      |             |    |       |        |         |

## Insurance Expense                                        ACCOUNT NO. 637

| DATE | EXPLANATION | PR | DEBIT | CREDIT | BALANCE |
|------|-------------|----|-------|--------|---------|
|      |             |    |       |        |         |
|      |             |    |       |        |         |
|      |             |    |       |        |         |

### Equipment Rental Expense — ACCOUNT NO. 640

| DATE | EXPLANATION | PR | DEBIT | CREDIT | BALANCE |
|------|-------------|----|-------|--------|---------|
|      |             |    |       |        |         |
|      |             |    |       |        |         |
|      |             |    |       |        |         |

### Office Supplies Expense — ACCOUNT NO. 650

| DATE | EXPLANATION | PR | DEBIT | CREDIT | BALANCE |
|------|-------------|----|-------|--------|---------|
|      |             |    |       |        |         |
|      |             |    |       |        |         |
|      |             |    |       |        |         |

### Repairs Expense — ACCOUNT NO. 684

| DATE | EXPLANATION | PR | DEBIT | CREDIT | BALANCE |
|------|-------------|----|-------|--------|---------|
|      |             |    |       |        |         |
|      |             |    |       |        |         |
|      |             |    |       |        |         |

### Telephone Expense — ACCOUNT NO. 688

| DATE | EXPLANATION | PR | DEBIT | CREDIT | BALANCE |
|------|-------------|----|-------|--------|---------|
|      |             |    |       |        |         |
|      |             |    |       |        |         |
|      |             |    |       |        |         |

### Income Summary — ACCOUNT NO. 901

| DATE | EXPLANATION | PR | DEBIT | CREDIT | BALANCE |
|------|-------------|----|-------|--------|---------|
|      |             |    |       |        |         |
|      |             |    |       |        |         |
|      |             |    |       |        |         |
|      |             |    |       |        |         |

Part 1.  Use either T-accounts or the balance column format; both are provided.

| Cash | 101 | | Cindy Tucker, Capital | 301 |
|---|---|---|---|---|

| Accounts Receivable | 106 | | Amort. Exp., Buildings | 606 |
|---|---|---|---|---|

| Office Supplies | 124 | | Salaries Expense | 622 |
|---|---|---|---|---|

| Prepaid Insurance | 128 | | Insurance Expense | 637 |
|---|---|---|---|---|

| Buildings | 173 | | Equipment Rental Expense | 640 |
|---|---|---|---|---|

| Accum. Amort., Buildings | 174 | | Office Supplies Expense | 650 |
|---|---|---|---|---|

| Salaries Payable | 209 |
|---|---|

Cindy Tucker, Withdrawals     302

Storage Fees Earned     405

| Repairs Expense | 684 | | Telephone Expense | 688 |
|---|---|---|---|---|

| Income Summary | 901 |
|---|---|

## Part 2. Transactions for July:

### GENERAL JOURNAL                                Page____

| Date | Account Titles and Explanation | PR | Debit | Credit |
|---|---|---|---|---|
| | | | | |
| | | | | |
| | | | | |
| | | | | |
| | | | | |
| | | | | |
| | | | | |
| | | | | |
| | | | | |
| | | | | |
| | | | | |
| | | | | |
| | | | | |
| | | | | |
| | | | | |
| | | | | |
| | | | | |
| | | | | |
| | | | | |
| | | | | |
| | | | | |
| | | | | |
| | | | | |
| | | | | |
| | | | | |
| | | | | |
| | | | | |
| | | | | |
| | | | | |
| | | | | |
| | | | | |

Part 2.  Transactions for July (cont'd.)

**GENERAL JOURNAL**                                           Page____

| Date | Account Titles and Explanation | PR | Debit | Credit |
|------|-------------------------------|-----|-------|--------|
|      |                               |     |       |        |
|      |                               |     |       |        |
|      |                               |     |       |        |
|      |                               |     |       |        |
|      |                               |     |       |        |
|      |                               |     |       |        |
|      |                               |     |       |        |
|      |                               |     |       |        |
|      |                               |     |       |        |
|      |                               |     |       |        |
|      |                               |     |       |        |
|      |                               |     |       |        |
|      |                               |     |       |        |
|      |                               |     |       |        |
|      |                               |     |       |        |
|      |                               |     |       |        |
|      |                               |     |       |        |
|      |                               |     |       |        |
|      |                               |     |       |        |
|      |                               |     |       |        |
|      |                               |     |       |        |
|      |                               |     |       |        |
|      |                               |     |       |        |
|      |                               |     |       |        |
|      |                               |     |       |        |
|      |                               |     |       |        |
|      |                               |     |       |        |
|      |                               |     |       |        |
|      |                               |     |       |        |
|      |                               |     |       |        |
|      |                               |     |       |        |
|      |                               |     |       |        |
|      |                               |     |       |        |
|      |                               |     |       |        |
|      |                               |     |       |        |
|      |                               |     |       |        |
|      |                               |     |       |        |
|      |                               |     |       |        |

**Part 3.  Adjusting entries:**

### GENERAL JOURNAL    Page____

| Date | Account Titles and Explanation | PR | Debit | Credit |
|---|---|---|---|---|
| | | | | |
| | | | | |
| | | | | |
| | | | | |
| | | | | |
| | | | | |
| | | | | |
| | | | | |
| | | | | |
| | | | | |
| | | | | |
| | | | | |
| | | | | |
| | | | | |
| | | | | |
| | | | | |
| | | | | |
| | | | | |
| | | | | |
| | | | | |
| | | | | |
| | | | | |
| | | | | |
| | | | | |
| | | | | |
| | | | | |
| | | | | |

**Part 4**

### Income Statement

| | | |
|---|---|---|
| | | |
| | | |
| | | |
| | | |
| | | |
| | | |
| | | |
| | | |
| | | |
| | | |
| | | |
| | | |
| | | |
| | | |
| | | |
| | | |
| | | |

## Statement of Owner's Equity

| | | |
|---|---|---|
| | | |
| | | |
| | | |
| | | |
| | | |
| | | |
| | | |
| | | |
| | | |

## Balance Sheet

| | | | |
|---|---|---|---|
| | | | |
| | | | |
| | | | |
| | | | |
| | | | |
| | | | |
| | | | |
| | | | |
| | | | |
| | | | |
| | | | |
| | | | |
| | | | |
| | | | |
| | | | |
| | | | |
| | | | |
| | | | |
| | | | |
| | | | |
| | | | |
| | | | |
| | | | |
| | | | |
| | | | |
| | | | |
| | | | |
| | | | |
| | | | |

**Part 5.  Closing entries:**

## GENERAL JOURNAL

Page____

| Date | Account Titles and Explanation | PR | Debit | Credit |
|------|-------------------------------|-----|-------|--------|
|  |  |  |  |  |
|  |  |  |  |  |
|  |  |  |  |  |
|  |  |  |  |  |
|  |  |  |  |  |
|  |  |  |  |  |
|  |  |  |  |  |
|  |  |  |  |  |
|  |  |  |  |  |
|  |  |  |  |  |
|  |  |  |  |  |
|  |  |  |  |  |
|  |  |  |  |  |
|  |  |  |  |  |
|  |  |  |  |  |
|  |  |  |  |  |
|  |  |  |  |  |
|  |  |  |  |  |
|  |  |  |  |  |
|  |  |  |  |  |
|  |  |  |  |  |
|  |  |  |  |  |
|  |  |  |  |  |
|  |  |  |  |  |
|  |  |  |  |  |
|  |  |  |  |  |
|  |  |  |  |  |

**Part 6**

## Post-Closing Trial Balance

|  | Debit | Credit |
|--|-------|--------|
|  |  |  |
|  |  |  |
|  |  |  |
|  |  |  |
|  |  |  |
|  |  |  |
|  |  |  |
|  |  |  |
|  |  |  |
|  |  |  |
|  |  |  |

## GENERAL JOURNAL                                    Page____

| Date | Account Titles and Explanation | PR | Debit | Credit |
|------|-------------------------------|----|----|----|
|  |  |  |  |  |
|  |  |  |  |  |
|  |  |  |  |  |
|  |  |  |  |  |
|  |  |  |  |  |
|  |  |  |  |  |
|  |  |  |  |  |
|  |  |  |  |  |
|  |  |  |  |  |
|  |  |  |  |  |
|  |  |  |  |  |
|  |  |  |  |  |
|  |  |  |  |  |
|  |  |  |  |  |
|  |  |  |  |  |
|  |  |  |  |  |
|  |  |  |  |  |
|  |  |  |  |  |
|  |  |  |  |  |
|  |  |  |  |  |
|  |  |  |  |  |
|  |  |  |  |  |
|  |  |  |  |  |
|  |  |  |  |  |
|  |  |  |  |  |
|  |  |  |  |  |
|  |  |  |  |  |
|  |  |  |  |  |
|  |  |  |  |  |
|  |  |  |  |  |
|  |  |  |  |  |
|  |  |  |  |  |
|  |  |  |  |  |
|  |  |  |  |  |
|  |  |  |  |  |
|  |  |  |  |  |
|  |  |  |  |  |
|  |  |  |  |  |
|  |  |  |  |  |

## GENERAL JOURNAL     Page____

| Date | Account Titles and Explanation | PR | Debit | Credit |
|------|-------------------------------|----|-------|--------|
|  |  |  |  |  |
|  |  |  |  |  |
|  |  |  |  |  |
|  |  |  |  |  |
|  |  |  |  |  |
|  |  |  |  |  |
|  |  |  |  |  |
|  |  |  |  |  |
|  |  |  |  |  |
|  |  |  |  |  |
|  |  |  |  |  |
|  |  |  |  |  |
|  |  |  |  |  |
|  |  |  |  |  |
|  |  |  |  |  |
|  |  |  |  |  |
|  |  |  |  |  |
|  |  |  |  |  |
|  |  |  |  |  |
|  |  |  |  |  |
|  |  |  |  |  |
|  |  |  |  |  |
|  |  |  |  |  |
|  |  |  |  |  |

**Part 3**

## GENERAL JOURNAL     Page____

| Date | Account Titles and Explanation | PR | Debit | Credit |
|------|-------------------------------|----|-------|--------|
|  |  |  |  |  |
|  |  |  |  |  |
|  |  |  |  |  |
|  |  |  |  |  |
|  |  |  |  |  |
|  |  |  |  |  |
|  |  |  |  |  |
|  |  |  |  |  |
|  |  |  |  |  |
|  |  |  |  |  |
|  |  |  |  |  |
|  |  |  |  |  |
|  |  |  |  |  |
|  |  |  |  |  |
|  |  |  |  |  |
|  |  |  |  |  |
|  |  |  |  |  |

## GENERAL LEDGER

### Cash                                                    ACCOUNT NO. 101

| DATE | EXPLANATION | PR | DEBIT | CREDIT | BALANCE |
|------|-------------|----|-------|--------|---------|
| 2011 Dec. 31 | Balance | | | | 89,090 |
| | | | | | |
| | | | | | |

### Accounts Receivable                                    ACCOUNT NO. 106

| DATE | EXPLANATION | PR | DEBIT | CREDIT | BALANCE |
|------|-------------|----|-------|--------|---------|
| 2011 Dec. 31 | Balance | | | | 5,700 |
| | | | | | |
| | | | | | |

### Computer Supplies                                      ACCOUNT NO. 126

| DATE | EXPLANATION | PR | DEBIT | CREDIT | BALANCE |
|------|-------------|----|-------|--------|---------|
| 2011 Dec. 31 | Balance | | | | 1,440 |
| | | | | | |
| | | | | | |

### Prepaid Insurance                                      ACCOUNT NO. 128

| DATE | EXPLANATION | PR | DEBIT | CREDIT | BALANCE |
|------|-------------|----|-------|--------|---------|
| 2011 Dec. 31 | Balance | | | | 3,240 |
| | | | | | |
| | | | | | |

### Prepaid Rent                                           ACCOUNT NO. 131

| DATE | EXPLANATION | PR | DEBIT | CREDIT | BALANCE |
|------|-------------|----|-------|--------|---------|
| 2011 Dec. 31 | Balance | | | | 2,250 |
| | | | | | |
| | | | | | |

### Office Equipment                                       ACCOUNT NO. 163

| DATE | EXPLANATION | PR | DEBIT | CREDIT | BALANCE |
|------|-------------|----|-------|--------|---------|
| 2011 Dec. 31 | Balance | | | | 18,000 |
| | | | | | |
| | | | | | |

### Accumulated Amortization, Office Equipment             ACCOUNT NO. 164

| DATE | EXPLANATION | PR | DEBIT | CREDIT | BALANCE |
|------|-------------|----|-------|--------|---------|
| 2011 Dec. 31 | Balance | | | | 1,500 |
| | | | | | |

### Computer Equipment

ACCOUNT NO. 167

| DATE | EXPLANATION | PR | DEBIT | CREDIT | BALANCE |
|------|-------------|----|-------|--------|---------|
| 2011<br>Dec. 31 | Balance | | | | 36,000 |
| | | | | | |
| | | | | | |

### Accumulated Amortization, Computer Equipment

ACCOUNT NO. 168

| DATE | EXPLANATION | PR | DEBIT | CREDIT | BALANCE |
|------|-------------|----|-------|--------|---------|
| 2011<br>Dec. 31 | Balance | | | | 2,250 |
| | | | | | |
| | | | | | |

### Accounts Payable

ACCOUNT NO. 201

| DATE | EXPLANATION | PR | DEBIT | CREDIT | BALANCE |
|------|-------------|----|-------|--------|---------|
| 2011<br>Dec. 31 | Balance | | | | 2,310 |
| | | | | | |
| | | | | | |

### Wages Payable

ACCOUNT NO. 210

| DATE | EXPLANATION | PR | DEBIT | CREDIT | BALANCE |
|------|-------------|----|-------|--------|---------|
| 2011<br>Dec. 31 | Balance | | | | 800 |
| | | | | | |
| | | | | | |

### Unearned Computer Services Revenue

ACCOUNT NO. 236

| DATE | EXPLANATION | PR | DEBIT | CREDIT | BALANCE |
|------|-------------|----|-------|--------|---------|
| 2011<br>Dec. 31 | Balance | | | | 3,000 |
| | | | | | |
| | | | | | |

### Mary Graham, Capital

ACCOUNT NO. 301

| DATE | EXPLANATION | PR | DEBIT | CREDIT | BALANCE |
|------|-------------|----|-------|--------|---------|
| 2011<br>Dec. 31 | Balance | | | | 144,000 |
| | | | | | |
| | | | | | |
| | | | | | |

### Mary Graham, Withdrawals

ACCOUNT NO. 302

| DATE | EXPLANATION | PR | DEBIT | CREDIT | BALANCE |
|------|-------------|----|-------|--------|---------|
| 2011<br>Dec. 31 | Balance | | | | 14,400 |
| | | | | | |
| | | | | | |

## Computer Services Revenue                 ACCOUNT NO. 403

| DATE | EXPLANATION | PR | DEBIT | CREDIT | BALANCE |
|------|-------------|----|-------|--------|---------|
| 2011<br>Dec. 31 | Balance | | | | 52,200 |
| | | | | | |
| | | | | | |
| | | | | | |

## Amortization Expense, Office Equipment          ACCOUNT NO. 612

| DATE | EXPLANATION | PR | DEBIT | CREDIT | BALANCE |
|------|-------------|----|-------|--------|---------|
| 2011<br>Dec. 31 | Balance | | | | 1,500 |
| | | | | | |
| | | | | | |

## Amortization Expense, Computer Equipment        ACCOUNT NO. 613

| DATE | EXPLANATION | PR | DEBIT | CREDIT | BALANCE |
|------|-------------|----|-------|--------|---------|
| 2011<br>Dec. 31 | Balance | | | | 2,250 |
| | | | | | |
| | | | | | |

## Wages Expense                            ACCOUNT NO. 623

| DATE | EXPLANATION | PR | DEBIT | CREDIT | BALANCE |
|------|-------------|----|-------|--------|---------|
| 2011<br>Dec. 31 | Balance | | | | 6,200 |
| | | | | | |
| | | | | | |

## Insurance Expense                        ACCOUNT NO. 637

| DATE | EXPLANATION | PR | DEBIT | CREDIT | BALANCE |
|------|-------------|----|-------|--------|---------|
| 2011<br>Dec. 31 | Balance | | | | 1,080 |
| | | | | | |
| | | | | | |
| | | | | | |

## Rent Expense                             ACCOUNT NO. 640

| DATE | EXPLANATION | PR | DEBIT | CREDIT | BALANCE |
|------|-------------|----|-------|--------|---------|
| 2011<br>Dec. 31 | Balance | | | | 6,750 |
| | | | | | |
| | | | | | |

## Computer Supplies Expense                ACCOUNT NO. 652

| DATE | EXPLANATION | PR | DEBIT | CREDIT | BALANCE |
|------|-------------|----|-------|--------|---------|
| 2011<br>Dec. 31 | Balance | | | | 5,430 |
| | | | | | |
| | | | | | |

## Advertising Expense                              ACCOUNT NO. 655

| DATE | EXPLANATION | PR | DEBIT | CREDIT | BALANCE |
|------|-------------|----|-------|--------|---------|
| 2011 Dec. 31 | Balance | | | | 5,820 |
| | | | | | |
| | | | | | |

## Mileage Expense                                 ACCOUNT NO. 676

| DATE | EXPLANATION | PR | DEBIT | CREDIT | BALANCE |
|------|-------------|----|-------|--------|---------|
| 2011 Dec. 31 | Balance | | | | 2,800 |
| | | | | | |
| | | | | | |

## Repairs Expense, Computer                       ACCOUNT NO. 684

| DATE | EXPLANATION | PR | DEBIT | CREDIT | BALANCE |
|------|-------------|----|-------|--------|---------|
| 2011 Dec. 31 | Balance | | | | 2,610 |
| | | | | | |
| | | | | | |

## Charitable Donations Expense                    ACCOUNT NO. 699

| DATE | EXPLANATION | PR | DEBIT | CREDIT | BALANCE |
|------|-------------|----|-------|--------|---------|
| 2011 Dec. 31 | Balance | | | | 1,500 |
| | | | | | |
| | | | | | |

## Income Summary                                  ACCOUNT NO. 901

| DATE | EXPLANATION | PR | DEBIT | CREDIT | BALANCE |
|------|-------------|----|-------|--------|---------|
| 2011 Dec. 31 | Balance | | | | |
| | | | | | |
| | | | | | |
| | | | | | |

## ECHO SYSTEMS
### Post-Closing Trial Balance
### December 31, 2011

| | Debit | Credit |
|---|---|---|
| | | |
| | | |
| | | |
| | | |
| | | |
| | | |
| | | |
| | | |
| | | |
| | | |
| | | |
| | | |
| | | |
| | | |
| | | |
| | | |
| | | |
| | | |
| | | |
| | | |
| | | |
| | | |
| | | |
| | | |
| | | |
| | | |
| | | |
| | | |
| | | |
| | | |
| | | |
| | | |
| | | |
| | | |
| | | |
| | | |

|  | a. | b. | c. | d. | e. |
|---|---|---|---|---|---|
| Net sales | | | | | |
| Cost of goods sold | | | | | |
| Gross profit from sales | | | | | |
| Operating expenses | | | | | |
| Net income (loss) | | | | | |

## Quick Study 6-2

a. _____

b. _____

c. _____

d. _____

e. _____

## Quick Study 6-3

a. _____

_____

b. _____

_____

_____

## Quick Study 6-4

a. _____

_____

b. _____

_____

_____

## Quick Study 6-5

### GENERAL JOURNAL                                    Page____

| Date | Account Titles and Explanation | PR | Debit | Credit |
|---|---|---|---|---|
| | | | | |
| | | | | |
| | | | | |
| | | | | |
| | | | | |
| | | | | |
| | | | | |
| | | | | |
| | | | | |
| | | | | |

## GENERAL JOURNAL                              Page____

| Date | Account Titles and Explanation | PR | Debit | Credit |
|------|-------------------------------|----|-------|--------|
|      |                               |    |       |        |
|      |                               |    |       |        |
|      |                               |    |       |        |
|      |                               |    |       |        |
|      |                               |    |       |        |
|      |                               |    |       |        |
|      |                               |    |       |        |
|      |                               |    |       |        |
|      |                               |    |       |        |
|      |                               |    |       |        |

## Quick Study 6-6

### GENERAL JOURNAL                             Page____

| Date | Account Titles and Explanation | PR | Debit | Credit |
|------|-------------------------------|----|-------|--------|
|      |                               |    |       |        |
|      |                               |    |       |        |
|      |                               |    |       |        |
|      |                               |    |       |        |
|      |                               |    |       |        |
|      |                               |    |       |        |
|      |                               |    |       |        |
|      |                               |    |       |        |
|      |                               |    |       |        |
|      |                               |    |       |        |
|      |                               |    |       |        |
|      |                               |    |       |        |
|      |                               |    |       |        |
|      |                               |    |       |        |
|      |                               |    |       |        |

## Quick Study 6-7

### GENERAL JOURNAL                             Page____

| Date | Account Titles and Explanation | PR | Debit | Credit |
|------|-------------------------------|----|-------|--------|
|      |                               |    |       |        |
|      |                               |    |       |        |
|      |                               |    |       |        |
|      |                               |    |       |        |
|      |                               |    |       |        |
|      |                               |    |       |        |
|      |                               |    |       |        |

## GENERAL JOURNAL                              Page____

| Date | Account Titles and Explanation | PR | Debit | Credit |
|------|-------------------------------|----|-------|--------|
|  |  |  |  |  |
|  |  |  |  |  |
|  |  |  |  |  |
|  |  |  |  |  |
|  |  |  |  |  |
|  |  |  |  |  |
|  |  |  |  |  |
|  |  |  |  |  |

## Quick Study 6-8

## GENERAL JOURNAL                              Page____

| Date | Account Titles and Explanation | PR | Debit | Credit |
|------|-------------------------------|----|-------|--------|
|  |  |  |  |  |
|  |  |  |  |  |
|  |  |  |  |  |
|  |  |  |  |  |
|  |  |  |  |  |
|  |  |  |  |  |
|  |  |  |  |  |
|  |  |  |  |  |
|  |  |  |  |  |
|  |  |  |  |  |
|  |  |  |  |  |
|  |  |  |  |  |
|  |  |  |  |  |
|  |  |  |  |  |
|  |  |  |  |  |
|  |  |  |  |  |
|  |  |  |  |  |
|  |  |  |  |  |
|  |  |  |  |  |
|  |  |  |  |  |
|  |  |  |  |  |
|  |  |  |  |  |
|  |  |  |  |  |
|  |  |  |  |  |
|  |  |  |  |  |
|  |  |  |  |  |
|  |  |  |  |  |
|  |  |  |  |  |

Name _____

## GENERAL JOURNAL                                                          Page____

| Date | Account Titles and Explanation | PR | Debit | Credit |
|------|-------------------------------|----|----|----|
|  |  |  |  |  |
|  |  |  |  |  |
|  |  |  |  |  |
|  |  |  |  |  |
|  |  |  |  |  |
|  |  |  |  |  |
|  |  |  |  |  |
|  |  |  |  |  |
|  |  |  |  |  |
|  |  |  |  |  |
|  |  |  |  |  |
|  |  |  |  |  |
|  |  |  |  |  |
|  |  |  |  |  |
|  |  |  |  |  |
|  |  |  |  |  |

## Quick Study 6-10

## GENERAL JOURNAL                                                          Page____

| Date | Account Titles and Explanation | PR | Debit | Credit |
|------|-------------------------------|----|----|----|
|  |  |  |  |  |
|  |  |  |  |  |
|  |  |  |  |  |
|  |  |  |  |  |
|  |  |  |  |  |
|  |  |  |  |  |
|  |  |  |  |  |
|  |  |  |  |  |
|  |  |  |  |  |
|  |  |  |  |  |
|  |  |  |  |  |
|  |  |  |  |  |
|  |  |  |  |  |
|  |  |  |  |  |
|  |  |  |  |  |
|  |  |  |  |  |
|  |  |  |  |  |
|  |  |  |  |  |
|  |  |  |  |  |
|  |  |  |  |  |

### GENERAL JOURNAL                    Page____

| Date | Account Titles and Explanation | PR | Debit | Credit |
|------|-------------------------------|----|-------|--------|
|      |                               |    |       |        |
|      |                               |    |       |        |
|      |                               |    |       |        |
|      |                               |    |       |        |
|      |                               |    |       |        |

## Quick Study 6-11

|  | a. | b. | c. | d. |
|--|----|----|----|----|
|  |    |    |    |    |
|  |    |    |    |    |
|  |    |    |    |    |
|  |    |    |    |    |
|  |    |    |    |    |
|  |    |    |    |    |
|  |    |    |    |    |

### Calculations:

_____

_____

_____

_____

_____

_____

_____

_____

_____

## Quick Study 6-12

### GENERAL JOURNAL                    Page____

| Date | Account Titles and Explanation | PR | Debit | Credit |
|------|-------------------------------|----|-------|--------|
|      |                               |    |       |        |
|      |                               |    |       |        |
|      |                               |    |       |        |
|      |                               |    |       |        |
|      |                               |    |       |        |
|      |                               |    |       |        |

### Calculations:

_____

_____

_____

_____

a. **Classified Multi-Step:**

| Income Statement | | | |
|---|---|---|---|
| | | | |
| | | | |
| | | | |
| | | | |
| | | | |
| | | | |
| | | | |
| | | | |
| | | | |
| | | | |
| | | | |
| | | | |
| | | | |
| | | | |
| | | | |
| | | | |
| | | | |
| | | | |
| | | | |
| | | | |
| | | | |
| | | | |
| | | | |

b. **Single-Step:**

| Income Statement | | | |
|---|---|---|---|
| | | | |
| | | | |
| | | | |
| | | | |
| | | | |
| | | | |
| | | | |
| | | | |
| | | | |
| | | | |
| | | | |
| | | | |
| | | | |

_____
_____
_____
_____
_____
_____
_____
_____
_____

## Quick Study 6-15

### GENERAL JOURNAL                              Page____

| Date | Account Titles and Explanation | PR | Debit | Credit |
|------|-------------------------------|----|-------|--------|
|      |                               |    |       |        |
|      |                               |    |       |        |
|      |                               |    |       |        |
|      |                               |    |       |        |
|      |                               |    |       |        |
|      |                               |    |       |        |
|      |                               |    |       |        |
|      |                               |    |       |        |
|      |                               |    |       |        |
|      |                               |    |       |        |
|      |                               |    |       |        |
|      |                               |    |       |        |
|      |                               |    |       |        |
|      |                               |    |       |        |
|      |                               |    |       |        |
|      |                               |    |       |        |
|      |                               |    |       |        |
|      |                               |    |       |        |
|      |                               |    |       |        |
|      |                               |    |       |        |
|      |                               |    |       |        |
|      |                               |    |       |        |

a.                  GENERAL JOURNAL           Page____

| Date | Account Titles and Explanation | PR | Debit | Credit |
|------|-------------------------------|----|-------|--------|
|      |                               |    |       |        |
|      |                               |    |       |        |
|      |                               |    |       |        |
|      |                               |    |       |        |
|      |                               |    |       |        |
|      |                               |    |       |        |
|      |                               |    |       |        |
|      |                               |    |       |        |
|      |                               |    |       |        |
|      |                               |    |       |        |
|      |                               |    |       |        |
|      |                               |    |       |        |
|      |                               |    |       |        |
|      |                               |    |       |        |
|      |                               |    |       |        |
|      |                               |    |       |        |
|      |                               |    |       |        |
|      |                               |    |       |        |
|      |                               |    |       |        |
|      |                               |    |       |        |

b.                  GENERAL JOURNAL           Page____

| Date | Account Titles and Explanation | PR | Debit | Credit |
|------|-------------------------------|----|-------|--------|
|      |                               |    |       |        |
|      |                               |    |       |        |
|      |                               |    |       |        |
|      |                               |    |       |        |
|      |                               |    |       |        |
|      |                               |    |       |        |
|      |                               |    |       |        |
|      |                               |    |       |        |
|      |                               |    |       |        |
|      |                               |    |       |        |
|      |                               |    |       |        |
|      |                               |    |       |        |
|      |                               |    |       |        |
|      |                               |    |       |        |
|      |                               |    |       |        |

c.                         **GENERAL JOURNAL**                    Page____

| Date | Account Titles and Explanation | PR | Debit | Credit |
|------|-------------------------------|----|-------|--------|
|      |                               |    |       |        |
|      |                               |    |       |        |
|      |                               |    |       |        |
|      |                               |    |       |        |
|      |                               |    |       |        |
|      |                               |    |       |        |
|      |                               |    |       |        |
|      |                               |    |       |        |
|      |                               |    |       |        |
|      |                               |    |       |        |
|      |                               |    |       |        |
|      |                               |    |       |        |
|      |                               |    |       |        |
|      |                               |    |       |        |

**\*Quick Study 6-17**

a.                         **GENERAL JOURNAL**                    Page____

| Date | Account Titles and Explanation | PR | Debit | Credit |
|------|-------------------------------|----|-------|--------|
|      |                               |    |       |        |
|      |                               |    |       |        |
|      |                               |    |       |        |
|      |                               |    |       |        |
|      |                               |    |       |        |
|      |                               |    |       |        |
|      |                               |    |       |        |
|      |                               |    |       |        |
|      |                               |    |       |        |
|      |                               |    |       |        |
|      |                               |    |       |        |
|      |                               |    |       |        |
|      |                               |    |       |        |
|      |                               |    |       |        |
|      |                               |    |       |        |
|      |                               |    |       |        |
|      |                               |    |       |        |
|      |                               |    |       |        |

b. GENERAL JOURNAL Page____

| Date | Account Titles and Explanation | PR | Debit | Credit |
|---|---|---|---|---|
| | | | | |
| | | | | |
| | | | | |
| | | | | |
| | | | | |
| | | | | |
| | | | | |
| | | | | |
| | | | | |
| | | | | |
| | | | | |
| | | | | |
| | | | | |
| | | | | |
| | | | | |
| | | | | |
| | | | | |

c. GENERAL JOURNAL Page____

| Date | Account Titles and Explanation | PR | Debit | Credit |
|---|---|---|---|---|
| | | | | |
| | | | | |
| | | | | |
| | | | | |
| | | | | |
| | | | | |
| | | | | |
| | | | | |
| | | | | |
| | | | | |
| | | | | |
| | | | | |
| | | | | |
| | | | | |
| | | | | |
| | | | | |

|  |  |  |
|---|---|---|
|  |  |  |
|  |  |  |
|  |  |  |
|  |  |  |
|  |  |  |
|  |  |  |
|  |  |  |
|  |  |  |
|  |  |  |

## *Quick Study 6-19

**GENERAL JOURNAL**                                        Page____

| Date | Account Titles and Explanation | PR | Debit | Credit |
|---|---|---|---|---|
|  |  |  |  |  |
|  |  |  |  |  |
|  |  |  |  |  |
|  |  |  |  |  |
|  |  |  |  |  |
|  |  |  |  |  |
|  |  |  |  |  |
|  |  |  |  |  |
|  |  |  |  |  |
|  |  |  |  |  |
|  |  |  |  |  |
|  |  |  |  |  |
|  |  |  |  |  |
|  |  |  |  |  |
|  |  |  |  |  |
|  |  |  |  |  |
|  |  |  |  |  |
|  |  |  |  |  |
|  |  |  |  |  |
|  |  |  |  |  |
|  |  |  |  |  |
|  |  |  |  |  |
|  |  |  |  |  |
|  |  |  |  |  |
|  |  |  |  |  |
|  |  |  |  |  |
|  |  |  |  |  |

|  | a. | b. | c. | d. |
|---|---|---|---|---|
|  |  |  |  |  |
|  |  |  |  |  |
|  |  |  |  |  |
|  |  |  |  |  |
|  |  |  |  |  |
|  |  |  |  |  |
|  |  |  |  |  |
|  |  |  |  |  |
|  |  |  |  |  |
|  |  |  |  |  |
|  |  |  |  |  |
|  |  |  |  |  |
|  |  |  |  |  |
|  |  |  |  |  |
|  |  |  |  |  |

**Calculations:**

_____

_____

_____

_____

_____

**\*Quick Study 6-21**

### GENERAL JOURNAL                                                     Page____

| Date | Account Titles and Explanation | PR | Debit | Credit |
|---|---|---|---|---|
|  |  |  |  |  |
|  |  |  |  |  |
|  |  |  |  |  |
|  |  |  |  |  |
|  |  |  |  |  |

**\*Quick Study 6-22**

### GENERAL JOURNAL                                                     Page____

| Date | Account Titles and Explanation | PR | Debit | Credit |
|---|---|---|---|---|
|  |  |  |  |  |
|  |  |  |  |  |
|  |  |  |  |  |
|  |  |  |  |  |
|  |  |  |  |  |
|  |  |  |  |  |
|  |  |  |  |  |
|  |  |  |  |  |
|  |  |  |  |  |
|  |  |  |  |  |
|  |  |  |  |  |

*Name* _____

### GENERAL JOURNAL                                     Page____

| Date | Account Titles and Explanation | PR | Debit | Credit |
|------|-------------------------------|----|-------|--------|
|      |                               |    |       |        |
|      |                               |    |       |        |
|      |                               |    |       |        |
|      |                               |    |       |        |
|      |                               |    |       |        |

### *Quick Study 6-24

### GENERAL JOURNAL                                     Page____

| Date | Account Titles and Explanation | PR | Debit | Credit |
|------|-------------------------------|----|-------|--------|
|      |                               |    |       |        |
|      |                               |    |       |        |
|      |                               |    |       |        |
|      |                               |    |       |        |
|      |                               |    |       |        |
|      |                               |    |       |        |

### Exercise 6-1

|                        | a.      | b.       | c.      | d.      | e.       |
|------------------------|---------|----------|---------|---------|----------|
| Sales                  | 240,000 | 140,000  | 75,000  |         |          |
| Cost of goods sold     |         |          | 42,000  | 268,000 | 46,000   |
| Gross profit from sales| 114,000 |          |         |         | 39,000   |
| Operating expenses     | 95,000  | 82,000   |         | 146,000 |          |
| Net income (loss)      |         | (28,000) | (8,000) | 48,000  | (14,000) |

### Exercise 6-2

### GENERAL JOURNAL                                     Page____

| Date | Account Titles and Explanation | PR | Debit | Credit |
|------|-------------------------------|----|-------|--------|
|      |                               |    |       |        |
|      |                               |    |       |        |
|      |                               |    |       |        |
|      |                               |    |       |        |
|      |                               |    |       |        |
|      |                               |    |       |        |
|      |                               |    |       |        |
|      |                               |    |       |        |
|      |                               |    |       |        |
|      |                               |    |       |        |
|      |                               |    |       |        |
|      |                               |    |       |        |
|      |                               |    |       |        |

## GENERAL JOURNAL                              Page____

| Date | Account Titles and Explanation | PR | Debit | Credit |
|------|-------------------------------|----|----|----|
|  |  |  |  |  |
|  |  |  |  |  |
|  |  |  |  |  |
|  |  |  |  |  |
|  |  |  |  |  |
|  |  |  |  |  |
|  |  |  |  |  |
|  |  |  |  |  |
|  |  |  |  |  |
|  |  |  |  |  |
|  |  |  |  |  |
|  |  |  |  |  |
|  |  |  |  |  |
|  |  |  |  |  |
|  |  |  |  |  |
|  |  |  |  |  |
|  |  |  |  |  |
|  |  |  |  |  |
|  |  |  |  |  |
|  |  |  |  |  |
|  |  |  |  |  |
|  |  |  |  |  |
|  |  |  |  |  |

## Exercise 6-3

## GENERAL JOURNAL                              Page____

| Date | Account Titles and Explanation | PR | Debit | Credit |
|------|-------------------------------|----|----|----|
|  |  |  |  |  |
|  |  |  |  |  |
|  |  |  |  |  |
|  |  |  |  |  |
|  |  |  |  |  |
|  |  |  |  |  |
|  |  |  |  |  |
|  |  |  |  |  |
|  |  |  |  |  |
|  |  |  |  |  |
|  |  |  |  |  |
|  |  |  |  |  |
|  |  |  |  |  |
|  |  |  |  |  |

## GENERAL JOURNAL                                    Page____

| Date | Account Titles and Explanation | PR | Debit | Credit |
|------|-------------------------------|----|-------|--------|
|      |                               |    |       |        |
|      |                               |    |       |        |
|      |                               |    |       |        |
|      |                               |    |       |        |
|      |                               |    |       |        |
|      |                               |    |       |        |
|      |                               |    |       |        |
|      |                               |    |       |        |
|      |                               |    |       |        |
|      |                               |    |       |        |
|      |                               |    |       |        |
|      |                               |    |       |        |
|      |                               |    |       |        |
|      |                               |    |       |        |
|      |                               |    |       |        |
|      |                               |    |       |        |
|      |                               |    |       |        |
|      |                               |    |       |        |
|      |                               |    |       |        |
|      |                               |    |       |        |
|      |                               |    |       |        |
|      |                               |    |       |        |
|      |                               |    |       |        |
|      |                               |    |       |        |

## Exercise 6-4

## GENERAL JOURNAL                                    Page____

| Date | Account Titles and Explanation | PR | Debit | Credit |
|------|-------------------------------|----|-------|--------|
|      |                               |    |       |        |
|      |                               |    |       |        |
|      |                               |    |       |        |
|      |                               |    |       |        |
|      |                               |    |       |        |
|      |                               |    |       |        |
|      |                               |    |       |        |
|      |                               |    |       |        |
|      |                               |    |       |        |
|      |                               |    |       |        |
|      |                               |    |       |        |
|      |                               |    |       |        |
|      |                               |    |       |        |
|      |                               |    |       |        |
|      |                               |    |       |        |
|      |                               |    |       |        |
|      |                               |    |       |        |

## GENERAL JOURNAL     Page____

| Date | Account Titles and Explanation | PR | Debit | Credit |
|------|-------------------------------|----|----|----|
|  |  |  |  |  |
|  |  |  |  |  |
|  |  |  |  |  |
|  |  |  |  |  |
|  |  |  |  |  |
|  |  |  |  |  |
|  |  |  |  |  |
|  |  |  |  |  |
|  |  |  |  |  |
|  |  |  |  |  |
|  |  |  |  |  |
|  |  |  |  |  |
|  |  |  |  |  |
|  |  |  |  |  |
|  |  |  |  |  |
|  |  |  |  |  |
|  |  |  |  |  |
|  |  |  |  |  |

### Exercise 6-5

## GENERAL JOURNAL     Page____

| Date | Account Titles and Explanation | PR | Debit | Credit |
|------|-------------------------------|----|----|----|
|  |  |  |  |  |
|  |  |  |  |  |
|  |  |  |  |  |
|  |  |  |  |  |
|  |  |  |  |  |
|  |  |  |  |  |
|  |  |  |  |  |
|  |  |  |  |  |
|  |  |  |  |  |
|  |  |  |  |  |
|  |  |  |  |  |
|  |  |  |  |  |
|  |  |  |  |  |
|  |  |  |  |  |
|  |  |  |  |  |
|  |  |  |  |  |

## GENERAL JOURNAL                                    Page____

| Date | Account Titles and Explanation | PR | Debit | Credit |
|------|-------------------------------|----|-------|--------|
|  |  |  |  |  |
|  |  |  |  |  |
|  |  |  |  |  |
|  |  |  |  |  |
|  |  |  |  |  |

## Exercise 6-6

## GENERAL JOURNAL                                    Page____

| Date | Account Titles and Explanation | PR | Debit | Credit |
|------|-------------------------------|----|-------|--------|
|  |  |  |  |  |
|  |  |  |  |  |
|  |  |  |  |  |
|  |  |  |  |  |
|  |  |  |  |  |
|  |  |  |  |  |
|  |  |  |  |  |
|  |  |  |  |  |
|  |  |  |  |  |
|  |  |  |  |  |
|  |  |  |  |  |
|  |  |  |  |  |
|  |  |  |  |  |
|  |  |  |  |  |
|  |  |  |  |  |
|  |  |  |  |  |
|  |  |  |  |  |
|  |  |  |  |  |
|  |  |  |  |  |
|  |  |  |  |  |
|  |  |  |  |  |
|  |  |  |  |  |
|  |  |  |  |  |
|  |  |  |  |  |
|  |  |  |  |  |
|  |  |  |  |  |
|  |  |  |  |  |
|  |  |  |  |  |
|  |  |  |  |  |
|  |  |  |  |  |
|  |  |  |  |  |

## GENERAL JOURNAL                                         Page____

| Date | Account Titles and Explanation | PR | Debit | Credit |
|------|-------------------------------|----|-------|--------|
|      |                               |    |       |        |
|      |                               |    |       |        |
|      |                               |    |       |        |
|      |                               |    |       |        |
|      |                               |    |       |        |
|      |                               |    |       |        |
|      |                               |    |       |        |
|      |                               |    |       |        |
|      |                               |    |       |        |
|      |                               |    |       |        |
|      |                               |    |       |        |
|      |                               |    |       |        |
|      |                               |    |       |        |
|      |                               |    |       |        |

**Calculations:**

_____
_____
_____
_____
_____
_____
_____
_____

**Exercise 6-7**

## GENERAL JOURNAL                                         Page____

| Date | Account Titles and Explanation | PR | Debit | Credit |
|------|-------------------------------|----|-------|--------|
|      |                               |    |       |        |
|      |                               |    |       |        |
|      |                               |    |       |        |
|      |                               |    |       |        |
|      |                               |    |       |        |
|      |                               |    |       |        |
|      |                               |    |       |        |
|      |                               |    |       |        |
|      |                               |    |       |        |
|      |                               |    |       |        |
|      |                               |    |       |        |
|      |                               |    |       |        |
|      |                               |    |       |        |

## GENERAL JOURNAL     Page____

| Date | Account Titles and Explanation | PR | Debit | Credit |
|------|-------------------------------|----|-------|--------|
|      |                               |    |       |        |
|      |                               |    |       |        |
|      |                               |    |       |        |
|      |                               |    |       |        |
|      |                               |    |       |        |
|      |                               |    |       |        |
|      |                               |    |       |        |
|      |                               |    |       |        |
|      |                               |    |       |        |
|      |                               |    |       |        |
|      |                               |    |       |        |
|      |                               |    |       |        |
|      |                               |    |       |        |
|      |                               |    |       |        |
|      |                               |    |       |        |
|      |                               |    |       |        |
|      |                               |    |       |        |
|      |                               |    |       |        |
|      |                               |    |       |        |
|      |                               |    |       |        |
|      |                               |    |       |        |
|      |                               |    |       |        |
|      |                               |    |       |        |
|      |                               |    |       |        |
|      |                               |    |       |        |
|      |                               |    |       |        |
|      |                               |    |       |        |
|      |                               |    |       |        |
|      |                               |    |       |        |
|      |                               |    |       |        |
|      |                               |    |       |        |
|      |                               |    |       |        |

*Analysis component:*

_____

_____

_____

_____

_____

_____

_____

_____

_____

| 1. | 6. |
|---|---|
| 2. | 7. |
| 3. | 8. |
| 4. | 9. |
| 5. | 10. |

## Exercise 6-9

| Merchandise Inventory | Cost of Goods Sold |
|---|---|
| | |

*Analysis component:* _____

_____

_____

_____

_____

_____

_____

## Exercise 6-10

a. _____

b. _____

c. _____

d. _____

*Analysis component:* _____

_____

_____

_____

_____

| | Company A | | Company B | |
|---|---|---|---|---|
| | 2011 | 2010 | 2011 | 2010 |
| Sales | 256,000 | 160,000 | | 50,000 |
| Sales discounts | 2,560 | | 1,100 | 500 |
| Sales returns and allowances | | 16,000 | 5,500 | |
| Net sales | | 142,400 | | 47,000 |
| | | | | |
| Cost of goods sold | 153,600 | | 55,000 | |
| | | | | |
| Gross profit from sales | 48,640 | | 48,400 | 22,000 |
| | | | | |
| Selling expenses | 17,920 | 16,000 | 24,200 | |
| Administrative expenses | 25,600 | | 29,700 | 11,000 |
| Total operating expenses | | 40,000 | | |
| | | | | |
| Net income (loss) | | 14,400 | | 2,000 |
| Gross profit ratio | | | | |

Calculations:

_____
_____
_____
_____
_____
_____
_____
_____

*Analysis component:* _____

_____
_____
_____
_____
_____

| Exercise 6-12 | a. | b. | c. |
|---|---|---|---|
| Purchases | 90,000 | 160,000 | 122,000 |
| Purchases discounts | (4,000) | | (2,600) |
| Purchase returns and allowances | (3,000) | (6,000) | (4,400) |
| Transportation-in | | 14,000 | 16,000 |
| Cost of goods purchased | 89,400 | 158,000 | |
| | | | |
| Beginning inventory | 7,000 | | 36,000 |
| Cost of goods purchased | 89,400 | 158,000 | |
| Ending inventory | (4,400) | (30,000) | |
| Cost of goods sold | | 166,400 | 136,520 |

| | Company A | | Company B | |
|---|---|---|---|---|
| | 2011 | 2010 | 2011 | 2010 |
| Sales | 120,000 | 180,000 | 90,000 | |
| Cost of goods sold: | | | | |
|   Merch. inventory (beginning) | 18,700 | 22,300 | 9,875 | 9,000 |
|   Total cost of merchandise purchases | 72,000 | | | 26,100 |
|   Merch. Inventory (ending) | | (18,700) | (8,920) | (9,875) |
|   Cost of goods sold | 74,300 | 108,000 | | |
| Gross profit from sales | | | 39,545 | 19,775 |
| Operating expenses | 36,000 | 54,000 | 27,000 | |
| Net income (loss) | 9,700 | 18,000 | | 6,275 |
| | | | | |
| Gross profit ratio | | | | |

*Analysis component:* _____
_____
_____
_____

| Exercise 6-14 | a. | b. | c. |
|---|---|---|---|
| Invoice cost of merch. purchases | 45,000 | 20,000 | 15,250 |
| Purchase discounts | 2,000 | | 325 |
| Purchase returns and allowances | 1,500 | 750 | 550 |
| Cost of transportation-in | | 1,750 | 2,000 |
| | | | |
| Merchandise inventory (beginning) | 3,500 | | 4,500 |
| Net cost of merchandise purchases | 44,700 | 19,750 | |
| Merchandise inventory (ending) | 2,200 | 3,750 | |
| Cost of goods sold | | 20,800 | 17,065 |

Exercise 6-15

a. _____

## Income Statement

| | | |
|---|---|---|
| | | |
| | | |
| | | |
| | | |
| | | |
| | | |
| | | |
| | | |
| | | |
| | | |
| | | |
| | | |
| | | |
| | | |

b.                              **GENERAL JOURNAL**                    Page____

| Date | Account Titles and Explanation | PR | Debit | Credit |
|------|-------------------------------|----|-------|--------|
|      |                               |    |       |        |
|      |                               |    |       |        |
|      |                               |    |       |        |
|      |                               |    |       |        |
|      |                               |    |       |        |
|      |                               |    |       |        |
|      |                               |    |       |        |
|      |                               |    |       |        |
|      |                               |    |       |        |
|      |                               |    |       |        |
|      |                               |    |       |        |
|      |                               |    |       |        |
|      |                               |    |       |        |
|      |                               |    |       |        |
|      |                               |    |       |        |
|      |                               |    |       |        |
|      |                               |    |       |        |
|      |                               |    |       |        |
|      |                               |    |       |        |
|      |                               |    |       |        |
|      |                               |    |       |        |
|      |                               |    |       |        |
|      |                               |    |       |        |
|      |                               |    |       |        |
|      |                               |    |       |        |
|      |                               |    |       |        |
|      |                               |    |       |        |
|      |                               |    |       |        |

c:    _____          _____ **Peter Delta, Capital** _____

_____

_____

_____

*Analysis component:* _____

_____

_____

_____

_____

_____

_____

_____

Part a

Perdu Sales

Work Sheet

For Year Ended December 31, 2011

| Account Title | Unadjusted Trial Balance Debit | Unadjusted Trial Balance Credit | Adjustments Debit | Adjustments Credit | Adjusted Trial Balance Debit | Adjusted Trial Balance Credit | Income Statement Debit | Income Statement Credit | Balance Sheet and Statement of Owner's Equity Debit | Balance Sheet and Statement of Owner's Equity Credit |
|---|---|---|---|---|---|---|---|---|---|---|
| Cash | 26,000 | | | | | | | | | |
| Merchandise inventory | 2,000 | | | | | | | | | |
| Prepaid selling expenses | 8,000 | | | | | | | | | |
| Store equipment | 40,000 | | | | | | | | | |
| Accum. amort., store equip. | | 9,000 | | | | | | | | |
| Accounts payable | | 14,840 | | | | | | | | |
| Salaries payable | | 0 | | | | | | | | |
| Eldon Perdu, capital | | 45,600 | | | | | | | | |
| Eldon Perdu, withdrawals | 3,600 | | | | | | | | | |
| Sales | | 858,000 | | | | | | | | |
| Sales returns and allowances | 33,000 | | | | | | | | | |
| Sales discounts | 8,000 | | | | | | | | | |
| Cost of goods sold | 424,840 | | | | | | | | | |
| Sales salaries expense | 94,000 | | | | | | | | | |
| Utilities expense, store | 28,000 | | | | | | | | | |
| Other selling expenses | 70,000 | | | | | | | | | |
| Other administrative expenses | 190,000 | | | | | | | | | |
| Totals | 927,440 | 927,440 | | | | | | | | |

## Income Statement

| | | | |
|---|---|---|---|
| | | | |
| | | | |
| | | | |
| | | | |
| | | | |
| | | | |
| | | | |
| | | | |
| | | | |
| | | | |
| | | | |
| | | | |
| | | | |
| | | | |
| | | | |
| | | | |
| | | | |
| | | | |
| | | | |
| | | | |
| | | | |

**Part c**　　　　　　　　　　**GENERAL JOURNAL**　　　　　　　　　Page____

| Date | | Account Titles and Explanation | PR | Debit | Credit |
|---|---|---|---|---|---|
| | | | | | |
| | | | | | |
| | | | | | |
| | | | | | |
| | | | | | |
| | | | | | |
| | | | | | |
| | | | | | |
| | | | | | |
| | | | | | |
| | | | | | |
| | | | | | |
| | | | | | |
| | | | | | |
| | | | | | |
| | | | | | |
| | | | | | |
| | | | | | |
| | | | | | |
| | | | | | |
| | | | | | |

## GENERAL JOURNAL                                      Page____

| Date | Account Titles and Explanation | PR | Debit | Credit |
|------|-------------------------------|----|-------|--------|
|      |                               |    |       |        |
|      |                               |    |       |        |
|      |                               |    |       |        |
|      |                               |    |       |        |
|      |                               |    |       |        |
|      |                               |    |       |        |
|      |                               |    |       |        |
|      |                               |    |       |        |
|      |                               |    |       |        |

*Analysis component:*

_____
_____
_____
_____
_____
_____
_____

### Exercise 6-17

a. _____

b. _____

### Income Statement

|  |  |  |
|--|--|--|
|  |  |  |
|  |  |  |
|  |  |  |
|  |  |  |
|  |  |  |
|  |  |  |
|  |  |  |
|  |  |  |
|  |  |  |
|  |  |  |
|  |  |  |
|  |  |  |
|  |  |  |
|  |  |  |
|  |  |  |
|  |  |  |
|  |  |  |

## GENERAL JOURNAL                    Page____

| Date | Account Titles and Explanation | PR | Debit | Credit |
|------|-------------------------------|----|----|----|
|  |  |  |  |  |
|  |  |  |  |  |
|  |  |  |  |  |
|  |  |  |  |  |
|  |  |  |  |  |
|  |  |  |  |  |
|  |  |  |  |  |
|  |  |  |  |  |
|  |  |  |  |  |
|  |  |  |  |  |
|  |  |  |  |  |
|  |  |  |  |  |
|  |  |  |  |  |
|  |  |  |  |  |
|  |  |  |  |  |

## GENERAL JOURNAL                                      Page____

| Date | | Account Titles and Explanation | PR | Debit | Credit |
|------|---|--------------------------------|----|----|----|
| | | | | | |
| | | | | | |
| | | | | | |
| | | | | | |
| | | | | | |
| | | | | | |
| | | | | | |
| | | | | | |
| | | | | | |
| | | | | | |
| | | | | | |
| | | | | | |
| | | | | | |
| | | | | | |
| | | | | | |
| | | | | | |
| | | | | | |
| | | | | | |
| | | | | | |
| | | | | | |
| | | | | | |
| | | | | | |
| | | | | | |
| | | | | | |
| | | | | | |
| | | | | | |
| | | | | | |
| | | | | | |
| | | | | | |
| | | | | | |
| | | | | | |
| | | | | | |
| | | | | | |
| | | | | | |
| | | | | | |
| | | | | | |
| | | | | | |
| | | | | | |
| | | | | | |
| | | | | | |
| | | | | | |
| | | | | | |
| | | | | | |
| | | | | | |

## GENERAL JOURNAL

| Date | Account Titles and Explanation | PR | Debit | Credit |
|------|-------------------------------|----|-------|--------|
|  |  |  |  |  |
|  |  |  |  |  |
|  |  |  |  |  |
|  |  |  |  |  |
|  |  |  |  |  |
|  |  |  |  |  |
|  |  |  |  |  |
|  |  |  |  |  |
|  |  |  |  |  |
|  |  |  |  |  |
|  |  |  |  |  |
|  |  |  |  |  |
|  |  |  |  |  |
|  |  |  |  |  |
|  |  |  |  |  |
|  |  |  |  |  |
|  |  |  |  |  |
|  |  |  |  |  |
|  |  |  |  |  |
|  |  |  |  |  |
|  |  |  |  |  |
|  |  |  |  |  |
|  |  |  |  |  |
|  |  |  |  |  |
|  |  |  |  |  |
|  |  |  |  |  |
|  |  |  |  |  |
|  |  |  |  |  |
|  |  |  |  |  |
|  |  |  |  |  |
|  |  |  |  |  |
|  |  |  |  |  |
|  |  |  |  |  |
|  |  |  |  |  |
|  |  |  |  |  |
|  |  |  |  |  |
|  |  |  |  |  |
|  |  |  |  |  |
|  |  |  |  |  |
|  |  |  |  |  |
|  |  |  |  |  |
|  |  |  |  |  |
|  |  |  |  |  |
|  |  |  |  |  |

## GENERAL JOURNAL

| Date | Account Titles and Explanation | PR | Debit | Credit |
|------|-------------------------------|----|----|----|
| | | | | |
| | | | | |
| | | | | |
| | | | | |
| | | | | |
| | | | | |
| | | | | |
| | | | | |
| | | | | |
| | | | | |
| | | | | |
| | | | | |
| | | | | |
| | | | | |
| | | | | |
| | | | | |
| | | | | |
| | | | | |
| | | | | |
| | | | | |
| | | | | |
| | | | | |
| | | | | |
| | | | | |
| | | | | |
| | | | | |
| | | | | |
| | | | | |
| | | | | |
| | | | | |
| | | | | |
| | | | | |
| | | | | |
| | | | | |
| | | | | |
| | | | | |
| | | | | |
| | | | | |
| | | | | |
| | | | | |
| | | | | |
| | | | | |

## GENERAL JOURNAL                                        Page____

| Date | Account Titles and Explanation | PR | Debit | Credit |
|------|-------------------------------|----|-------|--------|
|      |                               |    |       |        |
|      |                               |    |       |        |
|      |                               |    |       |        |
|      |                               |    |       |        |
|      |                               |    |       |        |
|      |                               |    |       |        |
|      |                               |    |       |        |
|      |                               |    |       |        |
|      |                               |    |       |        |
|      |                               |    |       |        |
|      |                               |    |       |        |
|      |                               |    |       |        |
|      |                               |    |       |        |
|      |                               |    |       |        |
|      |                               |    |       |        |
|      |                               |    |       |        |
|      |                               |    |       |        |
|      |                               |    |       |        |
|      |                               |    |       |        |
|      |                               |    |       |        |
|      |                               |    |       |        |
|      |                               |    |       |        |
|      |                               |    |       |        |
|      |                               |    |       |        |
|      |                               |    |       |        |
|      |                               |    |       |        |
|      |                               |    |       |        |
|      |                               |    |       |        |
|      |                               |    |       |        |
|      |                               |    |       |        |

*Exercise 6-22

## GENERAL JOURNAL                                        Page____

| Date | Account Titles and Explanation | PR | Debit | Credit |
|------|-------------------------------|----|-------|--------|
|      |                               |    |       |        |
|      |                               |    |       |        |
|      |                               |    |       |        |
|      |                               |    |       |        |
|      |                               |    |       |        |
|      |                               |    |       |        |
|      |                               |    |       |        |
|      |                               |    |       |        |
|      |                               |    |       |        |
|      |                               |    |       |        |
|      |                               |    |       |        |
|      |                               |    |       |        |
|      |                               |    |       |        |

## GENERAL JOURNAL

Page____

| Date | Account Titles and Explanation | PR | Debit | Credit |
|------|-------------------------------|----|----|----|
|  |  |  |  |  |
|  |  |  |  |  |
|  |  |  |  |  |
|  |  |  |  |  |
|  |  |  |  |  |
|  |  |  |  |  |
|  |  |  |  |  |
|  |  |  |  |  |
|  |  |  |  |  |
|  |  |  |  |  |
|  |  |  |  |  |
|  |  |  |  |  |
|  |  |  |  |  |
|  |  |  |  |  |
|  |  |  |  |  |
|  |  |  |  |  |
|  |  |  |  |  |
|  |  |  |  |  |
|  |  |  |  |  |
|  |  |  |  |  |
|  |  |  |  |  |
|  |  |  |  |  |
|  |  |  |  |  |

**\*Exercise 6-23**

## GENERAL JOURNAL

Page____

| Date | Account Titles and Explanation | PR | Debit | Credit |
|------|-------------------------------|----|----|----|
|  |  |  |  |  |
|  |  |  |  |  |
|  |  |  |  |  |
|  |  |  |  |  |
|  |  |  |  |  |
|  |  |  |  |  |
|  |  |  |  |  |
|  |  |  |  |  |
|  |  |  |  |  |
|  |  |  |  |  |
|  |  |  |  |  |
|  |  |  |  |  |
|  |  |  |  |  |
|  |  |  |  |  |
|  |  |  |  |  |
|  |  |  |  |  |
|  |  |  |  |  |
|  |  |  |  |  |
|  |  |  |  |  |
|  |  |  |  |  |
|  |  |  |  |  |
|  |  |  |  |  |

## GENERAL JOURNAL

| Date | Account Titles and Explanation | PR | Debit | Credit |
|------|-------------------------------|----|-------|--------|
| | | | | |
| | | | | |
| | | | | |
| | | | | |
| | | | | |
| | | | | |
| | | | | |
| | | | | |
| | | | | |
| | | | | |
| | | | | |
| | | | | |
| | | | | |
| | | | | |
| | | | | |
| | | | | |
| | | | | |
| | | | | |
| | | | | |
| | | | | |
| | | | | |
| | | | | |
| | | | | |
| | | | | |
| | | | | |
| | | | | |
| | | | | |
| | | | | |
| | | | | |
| | | | | |
| | | | | |
| | | | | |
| | | | | |
| | | | | |
| | | | | |
| | | | | |

## *Exercise 6-25

| a. | | |
|----|---|---|
| | | |
| | | |
| | | |
| | | |
| | | |
| | | |

**b.**

| | | |
|---|---|---|
| | | |
| | | |
| | | |
| | | |
| | | |
| | | |
| | | |
| | | |
| | | |

**c.**

| | | |
|---|---|---|
| | | |
| | | |
| | | |
| | | |
| | | |
| | | |
| | | |
| | | |
| | | |
| | | |
| | | |
| | | |
| | | |
| | | |
| | | |
| | | |

**d.** _____

_____

_____

**Analysis component:** _____

_____

_____

_____

_____

_____

Dewer's Stop'n Shop

Work Sheet

For Year Ended December 31, 2011

| Account Title | Unadjusted Trial Balance | | Adjustments | | Income Statement | | Balance Sheet and Statement of Owner's Equity | |
|---|---|---|---|---|---|---|---|---|
| | Debit | Credit | Debit | Credit | Debit | Credit | Debit | Credit |
| Cash | 7,400 | | | | | | | |
| Accounts receivable | 3,600 | | | | | | | |
| Merchandise inventory | 2,400 | | | | | | | |
| Store supplies | 1,200 | | | | | | | |
| Accounts payable | | 280 | | | | | | |
| Salaries payable | | | | | | | | |
| Mi Dewer, capital | | 11,570 | | | | | | |
| Mi Dewer, withdrawals | 750 | | | | | | | |
| Sales | | 12,000 | | | | | | |
| Sales returns and allowances | 290 | | | | | | | |
| Purchases | 6,400 | | | | | | | |
| Purchase discounts | | 250 | | | | | | |
| Transportation-in | 160 | | | | | | | |
| Salaries expense | 1,400 | | | | | | | |
| Rent expense | 500 | | | | | | | |
| Store supplies expense | | | | | | | | |
| Totals | 24,100 | 24,100 | | | | | | |

**a.** _____

_____

_____

_____

_____

_____

_____

**b.** _____

_____

_____

_____

_____

_____

_____

**c.** _____

_____

_____

_____

_____

_____

_____

**d.** _____

**Income Statement**

| | | |
|---|---|---|
| | | |
| | | |
| | | |
| | | |
| | | |
| | | |
| | | |
| | | |
| | | |
| | | |
| | | |
| | | |
| | | |
| | | |
| | | |
| | | |
| | | |
| | | |
| | | |
| | | |

a. _____

b. _____

c. _____

## Income Statement

| | | |
|---|---|---|
| | | |
| | | |
| | | |
| | | |
| | | |
| | | |
| | | |
| | | |
| | | |
| | | |
| | | |
| | | |
| | | |
| | | |
| | | |
| | | |
| | | |
| | | |
| | | |
| | | |
| | | |
| | | |
| | | |
| | | |
| | | |
| | | |
| | | |
| | | |
| | | |
| | | |
| | | |
| | | |
| | | |
| | | |
| | | |
| | | |
| | | |

d.               **GENERAL JOURNAL**           Page____

| Date | Account Titles and Explanation | PR | Debit | Credit |
|------|-------------------------------|----|-------|--------|
|      |                               |    |       |        |
|      |                               |    |       |        |
|      |                               |    |       |        |
|      |                               |    |       |        |
|      |                               |    |       |        |
|      |                               |    |       |        |
|      |                               |    |       |        |
|      |                               |    |       |        |
|      |                               |    |       |        |
|      |                               |    |       |        |
|      |                               |    |       |        |
|      |                               |    |       |        |
|      |                               |    |       |        |
|      |                               |    |       |        |
|      |                               |    |       |        |
|      |                               |    |       |        |
|      |                               |    |       |        |
|      |                               |    |       |        |
|      |                               |    |       |        |
|      |                               |    |       |        |
|      |                               |    |       |        |
|      |                               |    |       |        |
|      |                               |    |       |        |
|      |                               |    |       |        |
|      |                               |    |       |        |
|      |                               |    |       |        |
|      |                               |    |       |        |
|      |                               |    |       |        |
|      |                               |    |       |        |
|      |                               |    |       |        |
|      |                               |    |       |        |
|      |                               |    |       |        |
|      |                               |    |       |        |

e.

_____

_____        _____ **John Yu, Capital**

_____

_____

_____

_____

*Name* _____

## GENERAL JOURNAL                    Page____

| Date | | Account Titles and Explanation | PR | Debit | Credit |
|---|---|---|---|---|---|
| | | | | | |
| | | | | | |
| | | | | | |
| | | | | | |
| | | | | | |
| | | | | | |
| | | | | | |
| | | | | | |
| | | | | | |
| | | | | | |
| | | | | | |
| | | | | | |
| | | | | | |
| | | | | | |
| | | | | | |
| | | | | | |
| | | | | | |
| | | | | | |
| | | | | | |
| | | | | | |
| | | | | | |
| | | | | | |
| | | | | | |
| | | | | | |
| | | | | | |

*Exercise 6-30

## GENERAL JOURNAL                    Page____

| Date | | Account Titles and Explanation | PR | Debit | Credit |
|---|---|---|---|---|---|
| | | | | | |
| | | | | | |
| | | | | | |
| | | | | | |
| | | | | | |
| | | | | | |
| | | | | | |
| | | | | | |
| | | | | | |
| | | | | | |
| | | | | | |
| | | | | | |
| | | | | | |
| | | | | | |
| | | | | | |

| Date | Account Titles and Explanation | PR | Debit | Credit |
|------|-------------------------------|----|-------|--------|
|  |  |  |  |  |
|  |  |  |  |  |
|  |  |  |  |  |
|  |  |  |  |  |
|  |  |  |  |  |
|  |  |  |  |  |
|  |  |  |  |  |
|  |  |  |  |  |
|  |  |  |  |  |
|  |  |  |  |  |
|  |  |  |  |  |
|  |  |  |  |  |
|  |  |  |  |  |
|  |  |  |  |  |
|  |  |  |  |  |
|  |  |  |  |  |
|  |  |  |  |  |
|  |  |  |  |  |
|  |  |  |  |  |
|  |  |  |  |  |
|  |  |  |  |  |
|  |  |  |  |  |
|  |  |  |  |  |
|  |  |  |  |  |
|  |  |  |  |  |
|  |  |  |  |  |
|  |  |  |  |  |
|  |  |  |  |  |
|  |  |  |  |  |
|  |  |  |  |  |
|  |  |  |  |  |
|  |  |  |  |  |
|  |  |  |  |  |
|  |  |  |  |  |
|  |  |  |  |  |
|  |  |  |  |  |
|  |  |  |  |  |
|  |  |  |  |  |
|  |  |  |  |  |
|  |  |  |  |  |
|  |  |  |  |  |

## GENERAL JOURNAL    Page____

| Date | | Account Titles and Explanation | PR | Debit | Credit |
|---|---|---|---|---|---|
| | | | | | |
| | | | | | |
| | | | | | |
| | | | | | |
| | | | | | |
| | | | | | |
| | | | | | |
| | | | | | |
| | | | | | |
| | | | | | |
| | | | | | |
| | | | | | |
| | | | | | |
| | | | | | |
| | | | | | |
| | | | | | |
| | | | | | |
| | | | | | |
| | | | | | |
| | | | | | |
| | | | | | |
| | | | | | |
| | | | | | |
| | | | | | |

**Part 2**  _____
_____
_____
_____
_____

## Problem 6-2A

## GENERAL JOURNAL    Page____

| Date | | Account Titles and Explanation | PR | Debit | Credit |
|---|---|---|---|---|---|
| | | | | | |
| | | | | | |
| | | | | | |
| | | | | | |
| | | | | | |
| | | | | | |
| | | | | | |
| | | | | | |
| | | | | | |
| | | | | | |
| | | | | | |

## GENERAL JOURNAL                                    Page____

| Date | | Account Titles and Explanation | PR | Debit | Credit |
|---|---|---|---|---|---|
| | | | | | |
| | | | | | |
| | | | | | |
| | | | | | |
| | | | | | |
| | | | | | |
| | | | | | |
| | | | | | |
| | | | | | |
| | | | | | |
| | | | | | |
| | | | | | |
| | | | | | |
| | | | | | |
| | | | | | |
| | | | | | |
| | | | | | |
| | | | | | |
| | | | | | |
| | | | | | |
| | | | | | |
| | | | | | |
| | | | | | |
| | | | | | |
| | | | | | |
| | | | | | |
| | | | | | |
| | | | | | |
| | | | | | |
| | | | | | |
| | | | | | |
| | | | | | |
| | | | | | |
| | | | | | |
| | | | | | |
| | | | | | |
| | | | | | |
| | | | | | |
| | | | | | |
| | | | | | |
| | | | | | |
| | | | | | |

## GENERAL JOURNAL
Page____

| Date | Account Titles and Explanation | PR | Debit | Credit |
|---|---|---|---|---|
| | | | | |
| | | | | |
| | | | | |
| | | | | |
| | | | | |
| | | | | |
| | | | | |
| | | | | |
| | | | | |
| | | | | |
| | | | | |
| | | | | |
| | | | | |
| | | | | |
| | | | | |
| | | | | |
| | | | | |
| | | | | |
| | | | | |
| | | | | |
| | | | | |
| | | | | |
| | | | | |
| | | | | |
| | | | | |
| | | | | |

*Analysis component:*

_____

_____

_____

_____

_____

_____

_____

_____

_____

_____

_____

_____

_____

Name _____

## GENERAL JOURNAL

Page____

| Date | Account Titles and Explanation | PR | Debit | Credit |
|------|-------------------------------|----|-------|--------|
|      |                               |    |       |        |
|      |                               |    |       |        |
|      |                               |    |       |        |
|      |                               |    |       |        |
|      |                               |    |       |        |
|      |                               |    |       |        |
|      |                               |    |       |        |
|      |                               |    |       |        |
|      |                               |    |       |        |
|      |                               |    |       |        |
|      |                               |    |       |        |
|      |                               |    |       |        |
|      |                               |    |       |        |
|      |                               |    |       |        |
|      |                               |    |       |        |
|      |                               |    |       |        |
|      |                               |    |       |        |
|      |                               |    |       |        |
|      |                               |    |       |        |
|      |                               |    |       |        |
|      |                               |    |       |        |
|      |                               |    |       |        |
|      |                               |    |       |        |
|      |                               |    |       |        |
|      |                               |    |       |        |
|      |                               |    |       |        |
|      |                               |    |       |        |
|      |                               |    |       |        |
|      |                               |    |       |        |
|      |                               |    |       |        |
|      |                               |    |       |        |
|      |                               |    |       |        |
|      |                               |    |       |        |
|      |                               |    |       |        |
|      |                               |    |       |        |
|      |                               |    |       |        |
|      |                               |    |       |        |
|      |                               |    |       |        |
|      |                               |    |       |        |
|      |                               |    |       |        |

## GENERAL JOURNAL                                    Page____

| Date | Account Titles and Explanation | PR | Debit | Credit |
|------|-------------------------------|----|----|----|
|  |  |  |  |  |
|  |  |  |  |  |
|  |  |  |  |  |
|  |  |  |  |  |
|  |  |  |  |  |
|  |  |  |  |  |
|  |  |  |  |  |
|  |  |  |  |  |
|  |  |  |  |  |
|  |  |  |  |  |
|  |  |  |  |  |
|  |  |  |  |  |
|  |  |  |  |  |
|  |  |  |  |  |
|  |  |  |  |  |
|  |  |  |  |  |
|  |  |  |  |  |
|  |  |  |  |  |
|  |  |  |  |  |
|  |  |  |  |  |
|  |  |  |  |  |
|  |  |  |  |  |
|  |  |  |  |  |
|  |  |  |  |  |
|  |  |  |  |  |
|  |  |  |  |  |
|  |  |  |  |  |
|  |  |  |  |  |
|  |  |  |  |  |
|  |  |  |  |  |
|  |  |  |  |  |
|  |  |  |  |  |
|  |  |  |  |  |
|  |  |  |  |  |
|  |  |  |  |  |
|  |  |  |  |  |
|  |  |  |  |  |
|  |  |  |  |  |
|  |  |  |  |  |
|  |  |  |  |  |

Jumbo's
Work Sheet
For Year Ended December 31, 2011

| Account Title | Unadjusted Trial Balance | | Adjustments | | Adjusted Trial Balance | | Income Statement | | Balance Sheet and Statement of Owner's Equity | |
|---|---|---|---|---|---|---|---|---|---|---|
| | Debit | Credit | Debit | Credit | Debit | Credit | Debit | Credit | Debit | Credit |
| Cash | 10,275 | | | | | | | | | |
| Accounts receivable | 22,665 | | | | | | | | | |
| Merchandise inventory | 54,365 | | | | | | | | | |
| Store supplies | 3,190 | | | | | | | | | |
| Prepaid insurance | 3,255 | | | | | | | | | |
| Equipment | 74,490 | | | | | | | | | |
| Accum. amortization, equip. | | 13,655 | | | | | | | | |
| Accounts payable | | 8,000 | | | | | | | | |
| Salaries payable | | | | | | | | | | |
| Sally Fowler, capital | | 166,015 | | | | | | | | |
| Sally Fowler, withdrawals | 15,000 | | | | | | | | | |
| Interest revenue | | 310 | | | | | | | | |
| Sales | | 502,140 | | | | | | | | |
| Sales returns and allowances | 5,070 | | | | | | | | | |
| Cost of goods sold | 381,160 | | | | | | | | | |
| Salaries expenses | 91,550 | | | | | | | | | |
| Rent expense | 29,100 | | | | | | | | | |
| Supplies expense | | | | | | | | | | |
| Amortization exp., equipment | | | | | | | | | | |
| Insurance expense | | | | | | | | | | |
| Totals | 690,120 | 690,120 | | | | | | | | |

## Income Statement

| | | |
|---|---|---|
| | | |
| | | |
| | | |
| | | |
| | | |
| | | |
| | | |
| | | |
| | | |
| | | |
| | | |
| | | |
| | | |
| | | |
| | | |
| | | |
| | | |
| | | |
| | | |
| | | |
| | | |

*Analysis component:* _____

_____
_____
_____
_____
_____
_____

**1. Classified, multiple-step:**

### Income Statement

| | | | |
|---|---|---|---|
| | | | |

**2. Single-step:**

### Income Statement

| | | |
|---|---|---|
| | | |

## GENERAL JOURNAL Page____

| Date | | Account Titles and Explanation | PR | Debit | Credit |
|------|--|-------------------------------|----|-------|--------|
| | | | | | |
| | | | | | |
| | | | | | |
| | | | | | |
| | | | | | |
| | | | | | |
| | | | | | |
| | | | | | |
| | | | | | |
| | | | | | |
| | | | | | |
| | | | | | |
| | | | | | |
| | | | | | |
| | | | | | |
| | | | | | |
| | | | | | |
| | | | | | |
| | | | | | |
| | | | | | |
| | | | | | |
| | | | | | |
| | | | | | |
| | | | | | |
| | | | | | |
| | | | | | |
| | | | | | |
| | | | | | |
| | | | | | |
| | | | | | |
| | | | | | |
| | | | | | |
| | | | | | |
| | | | | | |

**Part 1 – Classified, multiple-step**

## Income Statement

| | | | |
|---|---|---|---|
| | | | |
| | | | |
| | | | |
| | | | |
| | | | |
| | | | |
| | | | |
| | | | |
| | | | |
| | | | |
| | | | |
| | | | |
| | | | |
| | | | |
| | | | |
| | | | |
| | | | |
| | | | |
| | | | |
| | | | |
| | | | |
| | | | |
| | | | |
| | | | |
| | | | |
| | | | |
| | | | |
| | | | |
| | | | |
| | | | |
| | | | |
| | | | |
| | | | |
| | | | |
| | | | |
| | | | |
| | | | |

Part 2 – Single-step

## Income Statement

| | | |
|---|---|---|
| | | |
| | | |
| | | |
| | | |
| | | |
| | | |
| | | |
| | | |
| | | |
| | | |
| | | |
| | | |
| | | |
| | | |
| | | |
| | | |

*Analysis component:* _____

_____

_____

_____

_____

_____

_____

_____

## GENERAL JOURNAL

| Date | Account Titles and Explanation | PR | Debit | Credit |
|------|-------------------------------|----|-------|--------|
|      |                               |    |       |        |
|      |                               |    |       |        |
|      |                               |    |       |        |
|      |                               |    |       |        |
|      |                               |    |       |        |
|      |                               |    |       |        |
|      |                               |    |       |        |
|      |                               |    |       |        |
|      |                               |    |       |        |
|      |                               |    |       |        |
|      |                               |    |       |        |
|      |                               |    |       |        |
|      |                               |    |       |        |
|      |                               |    |       |        |
|      |                               |    |       |        |
|      |                               |    |       |        |
|      |                               |    |       |        |
|      |                               |    |       |        |
|      |                               |    |       |        |
|      |                               |    |       |        |
|      |                               |    |       |        |
|      |                               |    |       |        |
|      |                               |    |       |        |
|      |                               |    |       |        |
|      |                               |    |       |        |
|      |                               |    |       |        |
|      |                               |    |       |        |
|      |                               |    |       |        |
|      |                               |    |       |        |
|      |                               |    |       |        |
|      |                               |    |       |        |
|      |                               |    |       |        |
|      |                               |    |       |        |
|      |                               |    |       |        |
|      |                               |    |       |        |
|      |                               |    |       |        |
|      |                               |    |       |        |
|      |                               |    |       |        |
|      |                               |    |       |        |
|      |                               |    |       |        |
|      |                               |    |       |        |

*Name* _____

**Part 1 – Classified, multiple-step**

Income Statement

| | | | |
|---|---|---|---|
| | | | |
| | | | |
| | | | |
| | | | |
| | | | |
| | | | |
| | | | |
| | | | |
| | | | |
| | | | |
| | | | |
| | | | |
| | | | |
| | | | |
| | | | |
| | | | |
| | | | |
| | | | |
| | | | |
| | | | |
| | | | |
| | | | |
| | | | |
| | | | |
| | | | |

**Part 2 – Multiple-step**

Income Statement

| | | |
|---|---|---|
| | | |
| | | |
| | | |
| | | |
| | | |
| | | |
| | | |
| | | |
| | | |
| | | |
| | | |

**Part 3 – Single-step**

| Income Statement | | |
|---|---|---|
| | | |
| | | |
| | | |
| | | |
| | | |
| | | |
| | | |
| | | |
| | | |
| | | |
| | | |

*Analysis component:*

_____

_____

_____

_____

_____

_____

_____

_____

## GENERAL JOURNAL

| Date | Account Titles and Explanation | PR | Debit | Credit |
|------|-------------------------------|----|-------|--------|
|  |  |  |  |  |
|  |  |  |  |  |
|  |  |  |  |  |
|  |  |  |  |  |
|  |  |  |  |  |
|  |  |  |  |  |
|  |  |  |  |  |
|  |  |  |  |  |
|  |  |  |  |  |
|  |  |  |  |  |
|  |  |  |  |  |
|  |  |  |  |  |
|  |  |  |  |  |
|  |  |  |  |  |
|  |  |  |  |  |
|  |  |  |  |  |
|  |  |  |  |  |
|  |  |  |  |  |
|  |  |  |  |  |
|  |  |  |  |  |
|  |  |  |  |  |
|  |  |  |  |  |
|  |  |  |  |  |
|  |  |  |  |  |
|  |  |  |  |  |
|  |  |  |  |  |
|  |  |  |  |  |
|  |  |  |  |  |
|  |  |  |  |  |
|  |  |  |  |  |
|  |  |  |  |  |
|  |  |  |  |  |
|  |  |  |  |  |
|  |  |  |  |  |
|  |  |  |  |  |
|  |  |  |  |  |
|  |  |  |  |  |
|  |  |  |  |  |
|  |  |  |  |  |
|  |  |  |  |  |
|  |  |  |  |  |
|  |  |  |  |  |
|  |  |  |  |  |
|  |  |  |  |  |
|  |  |  |  |  |

## GENERAL JOURNAL

| Date | Account Titles and Explanation | PR | Debit | Credit |
|---|---|---|---|---|
| | | | | |
| | | | | |
| | | | | |
| | | | | |
| | | | | |
| | | | | |
| | | | | |
| | | | | |
| | | | | |
| | | | | |
| | | | | |
| | | | | |
| | | | | |
| | | | | |
| | | | | |
| | | | | |
| | | | | |
| | | | | |
| | | | | |
| | | | | |
| | | | | |
| | | | | |
| | | | | |
| | | | | |
| | | | | |
| | | | | |
| | | | | |
| | | | | |
| | | | | |
| | | | | |
| | | | | |
| | | | | |
| | | | | |
| | | | | |
| | | | | |
| | | | | |
| | | | | |
| | | | | |
| | | | | |
| | | | | |
| | | | | |
| | | | | |
| | | | | |
| | | | | |
| | | | | |

## GENERAL JOURNAL

Page____

| Date | Account Titles and Explanation | PR | Debit | Credit |
|------|-------------------------------|----|----|----|
|  |  |  |  |  |
|  |  |  |  |  |
|  |  |  |  |  |
|  |  |  |  |  |
|  |  |  |  |  |
|  |  |  |  |  |
|  |  |  |  |  |
|  |  |  |  |  |
|  |  |  |  |  |
|  |  |  |  |  |
|  |  |  |  |  |
|  |  |  |  |  |
|  |  |  |  |  |
|  |  |  |  |  |
|  |  |  |  |  |
|  |  |  |  |  |
|  |  |  |  |  |
|  |  |  |  |  |
|  |  |  |  |  |
|  |  |  |  |  |
|  |  |  |  |  |
|  |  |  |  |  |
|  |  |  |  |  |
|  |  |  |  |  |
|  |  |  |  |  |
|  |  |  |  |  |
|  |  |  |  |  |
|  |  |  |  |  |
|  |  |  |  |  |
|  |  |  |  |  |
|  |  |  |  |  |
|  |  |  |  |  |
|  |  |  |  |  |
|  |  |  |  |  |
|  |  |  |  |  |
|  |  |  |  |  |
|  |  |  |  |  |

**1.** _____

**2.** _____

**3.** _____

**4.**

## Income Statement

| | | |
|---|---|---|
| | | |
| | | |
| | | |
| | | |
| | | |
| | | |
| | | |
| | | |
| | | |
| | | |
| | | |
| | | |
| | | |
| | | |
| | | |
| | | |
| | | |
| | | |
| | | |

**5.**

## Income Statement

| | | |
|---|---|---|
| | | |
| | | |
| | | |
| | | |
| | | |
| | | |
| | | |
| | | |
| | | |
| | | |
| | | |

## GENERAL JOURNAL

| Date | Account Titles and Explanation | PR | Debit | Credit |
|------|-------------------------------|----|-------|--------|
|      |                               |    |       |        |
|      |                               |    |       |        |
|      |                               |    |       |        |
|      |                               |    |       |        |
|      |                               |    |       |        |
|      |                               |    |       |        |
|      |                               |    |       |        |
|      |                               |    |       |        |
|      |                               |    |       |        |
|      |                               |    |       |        |
|      |                               |    |       |        |
|      |                               |    |       |        |
|      |                               |    |       |        |
|      |                               |    |       |        |
|      |                               |    |       |        |
|      |                               |    |       |        |
|      |                               |    |       |        |
|      |                               |    |       |        |
|      |                               |    |       |        |
|      |                               |    |       |        |
|      |                               |    |       |        |
|      |                               |    |       |        |
|      |                               |    |       |        |
|      |                               |    |       |        |
|      |                               |    |       |        |
|      |                               |    |       |        |
|      |                               |    |       |        |
|      |                               |    |       |        |
|      |                               |    |       |        |
|      |                               |    |       |        |
|      |                               |    |       |        |
|      |                               |    |       |        |
|      |                               |    |       |        |
|      |                               |    |       |        |
|      |                               |    |       |        |

Woodstock Store
Work Sheet
For Year Ended December 31, 2011

| Account Title | Unadjusted Trial Balance | | Adjustments | | Income Statement | | Balance Sheet and Statement of Owner's Equity | |
|---|---|---|---|---|---|---|---|---|
| | Debit | Credit | Debit | Credit | Debit | Credit | Debit | Credit |
| Cash | 7,305 | | | | | | | |
| Merchandise inventory | 47,000 | | | | | | | |
| Store supplies | 1,715 | | | | | | | |
| Office supplies | 645 | | | | | | | |
| Prepaid insurance | 3,840 | | | | | | | |
| Store equipment | 57,735 | | | | | | | |
| Accum. amort., store equip. | | 9,575 | | | | | | |
| Office equipment | 14,130 | | | | | | | |
| Accum. amort., office equip. | | 3,670 | | | | | | |
| Accounts payable | | 4,000 | | | | | | |
| Zen Woodstock, capital | | 93,585 | | | | | | |
| Zen Woodstock, withdrawals | 31,500 | | | | | | | |
| Rental revenue | | 680 | | | | | | |
| Sales | | 478,850 | | | | | | |
| Sales returns and allowances | 3,185 | | | | | | | |
| Sales discounts | 5,190 | | | | | | | |
| Purchases | 331,315 | | | | | | | |
| Purchase returns and allowances | | 1,845 | | | | | | |
| Purchase discounts | | 4,725 | | | | | | |
| Transportation-in | 2,810 | | | | | | | |
| Sales salaries expenses | 34,710 | | | | | | | |
| Rent expense, selling space | 24,000 | | | | | | | |
| Advertising expense | 1,220 | | | | | | | |
| Store supplies expense | | | | | | | | |
| Amort. exp., store equipment | | | | | | | | |
| Office salaries expense | 27,630 | | | | | | | |
| Rent expense, office space | 3,000 | | | | | | | |
| Office supplies expense | | | | | | | | |
| Insurance expense | | | | | | | | |
| Amort. exp., office equipment | | | | | | | | |
| Totals | 596,930 | 596,930 | | | | | | |

Part 2                          GENERAL JOURNAL                          Page____

| Date | Account Titles and Explanation | PR | Debit | Credit |
|------|-------------------------------|----|----|----|
|  |  |  |  |  |
|  |  |  |  |  |
|  |  |  |  |  |
|  |  |  |  |  |
|  |  |  |  |  |
|  |  |  |  |  |
|  |  |  |  |  |
|  |  |  |  |  |
|  |  |  |  |  |
|  |  |  |  |  |
|  |  |  |  |  |
|  |  |  |  |  |
|  |  |  |  |  |
|  |  |  |  |  |
|  |  |  |  |  |
|  |  |  |  |  |
|  |  |  |  |  |
|  |  |  |  |  |
|  |  |  |  |  |
|  |  |  |  |  |
|  |  |  |  |  |
|  |  |  |  |  |
|  |  |  |  |  |
|  |  |  |  |  |
|  |  |  |  |  |
|  |  |  |  |  |
|  |  |  |  |  |
|  |  |  |  |  |
|  |  |  |  |  |
|  |  |  |  |  |
|  |  |  |  |  |
|  |  |  |  |  |
|  |  |  |  |  |
|  |  |  |  |  |
|  |  |  |  |  |
|  |  |  |  |  |
|  |  |  |  |  |
|  |  |  |  |  |
|  |  |  |  |  |
|  |  |  |  |  |

## GENERAL LEDGER

Merchandise Inventory                                     ACCOUNT NO. 119

| DATE | EXPLANATION | PR | DEBIT | CREDIT | BALANCE |
|------|-------------|----|-------|--------|---------|
|      |             |    |       |        |         |
|      |             |    |       |        |         |
|      |             |    |       |        |         |
|      |             |    |       |        |         |

## *Problem 6-15A

### Income Statement

|  |  |  |  |
|--|--|--|--|
|  |  |  |  |
|  |  |  |  |
|  |  |  |  |
|  |  |  |  |
|  |  |  |  |
|  |  |  |  |
|  |  |  |  |
|  |  |  |  |
|  |  |  |  |
|  |  |  |  |
|  |  |  |  |
|  |  |  |  |
|  |  |  |  |
|  |  |  |  |
|  |  |  |  |
|  |  |  |  |
|  |  |  |  |
|  |  |  |  |
|  |  |  |  |
|  |  |  |  |
|  |  |  |  |
|  |  |  |  |
|  |  |  |  |
|  |  |  |  |
|  |  |  |  |
|  |  |  |  |
|  |  |  |  |
|  |  |  |  |
|  |  |  |  |
|  |  |  |  |
|  |  |  |  |
|  |  |  |  |

| | | | |
|---|---|---|---|
| | | | |
| | | | |
| | | | |
| | | | |
| | | | |
| | | | |
| | | | |
| | | | |
| | | | |
| | | | |
| | | | |
| | | | |
| | | | |
| | | | |
| | | | |
| | | | |
| | | | |

*Problem 6-16A

## GENERAL JOURNAL                                          Page____

| Date | Account Titles and Explanation | PR | Debit | Credit |
|---|---|---|---|---|
| | | | | |
| | | | | |
| | | | | |
| | | | | |
| | | | | |
| | | | | |
| | | | | |
| | | | | |
| | | | | |
| | | | | |
| | | | | |
| | | | | |
| | | | | |
| | | | | |
| | | | | |
| | | | | |
| | | | | |
| | | | | |
| | | | | |
| | | | | |
| | | | | |
| | | | | |

## GENERAL JOURNAL                                           Page____

| Date | | Account Titles and Explanation | PR | Debit | Credit |
|---|---|---|---|---|---|
| | | | | | |
| | | | | | |
| | | | | | |
| | | | | | |
| | | | | | |
| | | | | | |
| | | | | | |
| | | | | | |
| | | | | | |
| | | | | | |
| | | | | | |
| | | | | | |
| | | | | | |
| | | | | | |
| | | | | | |
| | | | | | |
| | | | | | |
| | | | | | |
| | | | | | |
| | | | | | |
| | | | | | |
| | | | | | |
| | | | | | |
| | | | | | |
| | | | | | |
| | | | | | |
| | | | | | |
| | | | | | |
| | | | | | |

## *Problem 6-17A

## GENERAL JOURNAL                                           Page____

| Date | | Account Titles and Explanation | PR | Debit | Credit |
|---|---|---|---|---|---|
| | | | | | |
| | | | | | |
| | | | | | |
| | | | | | |
| | | | | | |
| | | | | | |
| | | | | | |
| | | | | | |
| | | | | | |
| | | | | | |
| | | | | | |
| | | | | | |
| | | | | | |
| | | | | | |

## GENERAL JOURNAL

| Date | Account Titles and Explanation | PR | Debit | Credit |
|------|-------------------------------|----|----|----|
|      |                               |    |    |    |
|      |                               |    |    |    |
|      |                               |    |    |    |
|      |                               |    |    |    |
|      |                               |    |    |    |
|      |                               |    |    |    |
|      |                               |    |    |    |
|      |                               |    |    |    |
|      |                               |    |    |    |
|      |                               |    |    |    |
|      |                               |    |    |    |
|      |                               |    |    |    |
|      |                               |    |    |    |
|      |                               |    |    |    |
|      |                               |    |    |    |
|      |                               |    |    |    |
|      |                               |    |    |    |
|      |                               |    |    |    |
|      |                               |    |    |    |
|      |                               |    |    |    |
|      |                               |    |    |    |
|      |                               |    |    |    |
|      |                               |    |    |    |
|      |                               |    |    |    |
|      |                               |    |    |    |
|      |                               |    |    |    |
|      |                               |    |    |    |
|      |                               |    |    |    |
|      |                               |    |    |    |
|      |                               |    |    |    |
|      |                               |    |    |    |
|      |                               |    |    |    |
|      |                               |    |    |    |
|      |                               |    |    |    |
|      |                               |    |    |    |
|      |                               |    |    |    |
|      |                               |    |    |    |
|      |                               |    |    |    |
|      |                               |    |    |    |
|      |                               |    |    |    |
|      |                               |    |    |    |
|      |                               |    |    |    |

| Date | Account Titles and Explanation | PR | Debit | Credit |
|------|-------------------------------|----|-------|--------|
|      |                               |    |       |        |
|      |                               |    |       |        |
|      |                               |    |       |        |
|      |                               |    |       |        |
|      |                               |    |       |        |
|      |                               |    |       |        |
|      |                               |    |       |        |
|      |                               |    |       |        |
|      |                               |    |       |        |
|      |                               |    |       |        |
|      |                               |    |       |        |
|      |                               |    |       |        |
|      |                               |    |       |        |
|      |                               |    |       |        |
|      |                               |    |       |        |
|      |                               |    |       |        |
|      |                               |    |       |        |
|      |                               |    |       |        |
|      |                               |    |       |        |
|      |                               |    |       |        |
|      |                               |    |       |        |
|      |                               |    |       |        |
|      |                               |    |       |        |
|      |                               |    |       |        |
|      |                               |    |       |        |
|      |                               |    |       |        |
|      |                               |    |       |        |
|      |                               |    |       |        |
|      |                               |    |       |        |
|      |                               |    |       |        |
|      |                               |    |       |        |
|      |                               |    |       |        |
|      |                               |    |       |        |
|      |                               |    |       |        |
|      |                               |    |       |        |
|      |                               |    |       |        |
|      |                               |    |       |        |
|      |                               |    |       |        |
|      |                               |    |       |        |

## GENERAL JOURNAL                                    Page____

| Date | Account Titles and Explanation | PR | Debit | Credit |
|------|-------------------------------|----|----|----|
|  |  |  |  |  |
|  |  |  |  |  |
|  |  |  |  |  |
|  |  |  |  |  |
|  |  |  |  |  |
|  |  |  |  |  |
|  |  |  |  |  |
|  |  |  |  |  |
|  |  |  |  |  |
|  |  |  |  |  |
|  |  |  |  |  |
|  |  |  |  |  |
|  |  |  |  |  |
|  |  |  |  |  |
|  |  |  |  |  |
|  |  |  |  |  |

**Part 2**  _____

_____

_____

_____

_____

## Problem 6-2B

## GENERAL JOURNAL                                    Page____

| Date | Account Titles and Explanation | PR | Debit | Credit |
|------|-------------------------------|----|----|----|
|  |  |  |  |  |
|  |  |  |  |  |
|  |  |  |  |  |
|  |  |  |  |  |
|  |  |  |  |  |
|  |  |  |  |  |
|  |  |  |  |  |
|  |  |  |  |  |
|  |  |  |  |  |
|  |  |  |  |  |
|  |  |  |  |  |
|  |  |  |  |  |
|  |  |  |  |  |
|  |  |  |  |  |
|  |  |  |  |  |
|  |  |  |  |  |
|  |  |  |  |  |
|  |  |  |  |  |

## GENERAL JOURNAL

Page____

| Date | Account Titles and Explanation | PR | Debit | Credit |
|------|-------------------------------|----|-------|--------|
|      |                               |    |       |        |
|      |                               |    |       |        |
|      |                               |    |       |        |
|      |                               |    |       |        |
|      |                               |    |       |        |
|      |                               |    |       |        |
|      |                               |    |       |        |
|      |                               |    |       |        |
|      |                               |    |       |        |
|      |                               |    |       |        |
|      |                               |    |       |        |
|      |                               |    |       |        |
|      |                               |    |       |        |
|      |                               |    |       |        |
|      |                               |    |       |        |
|      |                               |    |       |        |
|      |                               |    |       |        |
|      |                               |    |       |        |
|      |                               |    |       |        |
|      |                               |    |       |        |
|      |                               |    |       |        |
|      |                               |    |       |        |
|      |                               |    |       |        |
|      |                               |    |       |        |
|      |                               |    |       |        |
|      |                               |    |       |        |
|      |                               |    |       |        |
|      |                               |    |       |        |
|      |                               |    |       |        |
|      |                               |    |       |        |
|      |                               |    |       |        |
|      |                               |    |       |        |
|      |                               |    |       |        |
|      |                               |    |       |        |
|      |                               |    |       |        |
|      |                               |    |       |        |
|      |                               |    |       |        |
|      |                               |    |       |        |
|      |                               |    |       |        |

## GENERAL JOURNAL

| Date | Account Titles and Explanation | PR | Debit | Credit |
|------|-------------------------------|-----|-------|--------|
|      |                               |     |       |        |
|      |                               |     |       |        |
|      |                               |     |       |        |
|      |                               |     |       |        |
|      |                               |     |       |        |
|      |                               |     |       |        |
|      |                               |     |       |        |
|      |                               |     |       |        |
|      |                               |     |       |        |
|      |                               |     |       |        |
|      |                               |     |       |        |
|      |                               |     |       |        |
|      |                               |     |       |        |
|      |                               |     |       |        |
|      |                               |     |       |        |
|      |                               |     |       |        |
|      |                               |     |       |        |
|      |                               |     |       |        |
|      |                               |     |       |        |
|      |                               |     |       |        |
|      |                               |     |       |        |
|      |                               |     |       |        |
|      |                               |     |       |        |
|      |                               |     |       |        |
|      |                               |     |       |        |
|      |                               |     |       |        |
|      |                               |     |       |        |
|      |                               |     |       |        |
|      |                               |     |       |        |

*Analysis component:*

_____

_____

_____

_____

_____

_____

_____

_____

_____

_____

_____

_____

_____

_____

_____

*Name* _____

## GENERAL JOURNAL                                           Page____

| Date | Account Titles and Explanation | PR | Debit | Credit |
|------|-------------------------------|----|----|----|
|  |  |  |  |  |
|  |  |  |  |  |
|  |  |  |  |  |
|  |  |  |  |  |
|  |  |  |  |  |
|  |  |  |  |  |
|  |  |  |  |  |
|  |  |  |  |  |
|  |  |  |  |  |
|  |  |  |  |  |
|  |  |  |  |  |
|  |  |  |  |  |
|  |  |  |  |  |
|  |  |  |  |  |
|  |  |  |  |  |
|  |  |  |  |  |
|  |  |  |  |  |
|  |  |  |  |  |
|  |  |  |  |  |
|  |  |  |  |  |
|  |  |  |  |  |
|  |  |  |  |  |
|  |  |  |  |  |
|  |  |  |  |  |
|  |  |  |  |  |
|  |  |  |  |  |
|  |  |  |  |  |
|  |  |  |  |  |
|  |  |  |  |  |
|  |  |  |  |  |
|  |  |  |  |  |
|  |  |  |  |  |
|  |  |  |  |  |
|  |  |  |  |  |
|  |  |  |  |  |
|  |  |  |  |  |
|  |  |  |  |  |

## GENERAL JOURNAL                    Page____

| Date | Account Titles and Explanation | PR | Debit | Credit |
|------|-------------------------------|----|----|----|
|  |  |  |  |  |
|  |  |  |  |  |
|  |  |  |  |  |
|  |  |  |  |  |
|  |  |  |  |  |
|  |  |  |  |  |
|  |  |  |  |  |
|  |  |  |  |  |
|  |  |  |  |  |
|  |  |  |  |  |
|  |  |  |  |  |
|  |  |  |  |  |
|  |  |  |  |  |
|  |  |  |  |  |
|  |  |  |  |  |
|  |  |  |  |  |
|  |  |  |  |  |
|  |  |  |  |  |
|  |  |  |  |  |
|  |  |  |  |  |
|  |  |  |  |  |
|  |  |  |  |  |
|  |  |  |  |  |
|  |  |  |  |  |
|  |  |  |  |  |
|  |  |  |  |  |
|  |  |  |  |  |
|  |  |  |  |  |
|  |  |  |  |  |
|  |  |  |  |  |
|  |  |  |  |  |
|  |  |  |  |  |
|  |  |  |  |  |
|  |  |  |  |  |

*Analysis component:* _____

_____

_____

_____

_____

_____

**Part 1**

Resource Products Company
Work Sheet
For Year Ended October 31, 2005

| Account Title | Unadjusted Trial Balance | | Adjustments | | Adjusted Trial Balance | | Income Statement | | Balance Sheet and Statement of Owner's Equity | |
|---|---|---|---|---|---|---|---|---|---|---|
| | Debit | Credit | Debit | Credit | Debit | Credit | Debit | Credit | Debit | Credit |
| Cash | 6,400 | | | | | | | | | |
| Merchandise inventory | 23,000 | | | | | | | | | |
| Store supplies | 9,600 | | | | | | | | | |
| Prepaid insurance | 4,600 | | | | | | | | | |
| Store equipment | 83,800 | | | | | | | | | |
| Accum. amort., store equip. | | 30,000 | | | | | | | | |
| Accounts payable | | 16,000 | | | | | | | | |
| Jan Smithers, capital | | 80,400 | | | | | | | | |
| Jan Smithers, withdrawals | 6,000 | | | | | | | | | |
| Sales | | 198,000 | | | | | | | | |
| Sales discounts | 2,000 | | | | | | | | | |
| Sales returns and allowances | 4,000 | | | | | | | | | |
| Cost of goods sold | 74,800 | | | | | | | | | |
| Amort. expense, store equip. | | | | | | | | | | |
| Salaries expense | 62,000 | | | | | | | | | |
| Interest expense | 400 | | | | | | | | | |
| Insurance expense | | | | | | | | | | |
| Rent expense | 28,000 | | | | | | | | | |
| Store supplies expense | | | | | | | | | | |
| Advertising expense | 19,800 | | | | | | | | | |
| Totals | 324,400 | 324,400 | | | | | | | | |

## Income Statement

|  |  |  |
|---|---|---|
|  |  |  |
|  |  |  |
|  |  |  |
|  |  |  |
|  |  |  |
|  |  |  |
|  |  |  |
|  |  |  |
|  |  |  |
|  |  |  |
|  |  |  |
|  |  |  |
|  |  |  |
|  |  |  |
|  |  |  |
|  |  |  |
|  |  |  |
|  |  |  |
|  |  |  |
|  |  |  |
|  |  |  |
|  |  |  |
|  |  |  |
|  |  |  |

*Analysis component:*

_____

_____

_____

_____

_____

_____

_____

Name _____

**1. Classified, multiple-step**

### Income Statement

| | | | |
|---|---|---|---|
| | | | |
| | | | |
| | | | |
| | | | |
| | | | |
| | | | |
| | | | |
| | | | |
| | | | |
| | | | |
| | | | |
| | | | |
| | | | |
| | | | |
| | | | |
| | | | |
| | | | |
| | | | |
| | | | |
| | | | |
| | | | |
| | | | |
| | | | |
| | | | |
| | | | |
| | | | |
| | | | |
| | | | |
| | | | |
| | | | |

**2. Single-step**

### Income Statement

| | | |
|---|---|---|
| | | |
| | | |
| | | |
| | | |
| | | |
| | | |
| | | |
| | | |
| | | |
| | | |
| | | |

*Name* _____

## GENERAL JOURNAL    Page____

| Date | Account Titles and Explanation | PR | Debit | Credit |
|---|---|---|---|---|
| | | | | |
| | | | | |
| | | | | |
| | | | | |
| | | | | |
| | | | | |
| | | | | |
| | | | | |
| | | | | |
| | | | | |
| | | | | |
| | | | | |
| | | | | |
| | | | | |
| | | | | |
| | | | | |
| | | | | |
| | | | | |
| | | | | |
| | | | | |
| | | | | |
| | | | | |
| | | | | |
| | | | | |
| | | | | |
| | | | | |
| | | | | |
| | | | | |
| | | | | |
| | | | | |
| | | | | |

**Part 1 – Classified, multiple-step**

### Income Statement

| | | | |
|---|---|---|---|
| | | | |
| | | | |
| | | | |
| | | | |
| | | | |
| | | | |
| | | | |
| | | | |
| | | | |
| | | | |
| | | | |
| | | | |
| | | | |
| | | | |
| | | | |
| | | | |
| | | | |
| | | | |
| | | | |
| | | | |
| | | | |
| | | | |
| | | | |
| | | | |
| | | | |

**Part 2 – Single-step**

### Income Statement

| | | |
|---|---|---|
| | | |
| | | |
| | | |
| | | |
| | | |
| | | |
| | | |
| | | |
| | | |

*Analysis component:* _____

_____

_____

_____

## GENERAL JOURNAL

| Date | Account Titles and Explanation | PR | Debit | Credit |
|------|-------------------------------|----|-------|--------|
|      |                               |    |       |        |
|      |                               |    |       |        |
|      |                               |    |       |        |
|      |                               |    |       |        |
|      |                               |    |       |        |
|      |                               |    |       |        |
|      |                               |    |       |        |
|      |                               |    |       |        |
|      |                               |    |       |        |
|      |                               |    |       |        |
|      |                               |    |       |        |
|      |                               |    |       |        |
|      |                               |    |       |        |
|      |                               |    |       |        |
|      |                               |    |       |        |
|      |                               |    |       |        |
|      |                               |    |       |        |
|      |                               |    |       |        |
|      |                               |    |       |        |
|      |                               |    |       |        |
|      |                               |    |       |        |
|      |                               |    |       |        |
|      |                               |    |       |        |
|      |                               |    |       |        |
|      |                               |    |       |        |
|      |                               |    |       |        |
|      |                               |    |       |        |
|      |                               |    |       |        |
|      |                               |    |       |        |
|      |                               |    |       |        |
|      |                               |    |       |        |
|      |                               |    |       |        |
|      |                               |    |       |        |
|      |                               |    |       |        |
|      |                               |    |       |        |

## Income Statement

|  |  |  |  |
|---|---|---|---|
|  |  |  |  |
|  |  |  |  |
|  |  |  |  |
|  |  |  |  |
|  |  |  |  |
|  |  |  |  |
|  |  |  |  |
|  |  |  |  |
|  |  |  |  |
|  |  |  |  |
|  |  |  |  |
|  |  |  |  |
|  |  |  |  |
|  |  |  |  |
|  |  |  |  |
|  |  |  |  |
|  |  |  |  |
|  |  |  |  |
|  |  |  |  |
|  |  |  |  |
|  |  |  |  |
|  |  |  |  |
|  |  |  |  |
|  |  |  |  |
|  |  |  |  |
|  |  |  |  |
|  |  |  |  |
|  |  |  |  |

## Part 2 – Multiple-step

### Income Statement

| | | |
|---|---|---|
| | | |
| | | |
| | | |
| | | |
| | | |
| | | |
| | | |
| | | |
| | | |
| | | |
| | | |
| | | |
| | | |
| | | |
| | | |
| | | |
| | | |
| | | |
| | | |
| | | |
| | | |

## Part 3 – Single-step

### Income Statement

| | | |
|---|---|---|
| | | |
| | | |
| | | |
| | | |
| | | |
| | | |
| | | |
| | | |

## *Problem 6-10B

### GENERAL JOURNAL                                Page____

| Date | Account Titles and Explanation | PR | Debit | Credit |
|---|---|---|---|---|
| | | | | |
| | | | | |
| | | | | |
| | | | | |

## GENERAL JOURNAL

Page____

| Date | Account Titles and Explanation | PR | Debit | Credit |
|------|-------------------------------|----|----|----|
|  |  |  |  |  |
|  |  |  |  |  |
|  |  |  |  |  |
|  |  |  |  |  |
|  |  |  |  |  |
|  |  |  |  |  |
|  |  |  |  |  |
|  |  |  |  |  |
|  |  |  |  |  |
|  |  |  |  |  |
|  |  |  |  |  |
|  |  |  |  |  |
|  |  |  |  |  |
|  |  |  |  |  |
|  |  |  |  |  |
|  |  |  |  |  |
|  |  |  |  |  |
|  |  |  |  |  |
|  |  |  |  |  |
|  |  |  |  |  |
|  |  |  |  |  |
|  |  |  |  |  |
|  |  |  |  |  |
|  |  |  |  |  |
|  |  |  |  |  |
|  |  |  |  |  |
|  |  |  |  |  |
|  |  |  |  |  |
|  |  |  |  |  |
|  |  |  |  |  |
|  |  |  |  |  |
|  |  |  |  |  |
|  |  |  |  |  |
|  |  |  |  |  |
|  |  |  |  |  |
|  |  |  |  |  |
|  |  |  |  |  |
|  |  |  |  |  |
|  |  |  |  |  |
|  |  |  |  |  |
|  |  |  |  |  |
|  |  |  |  |  |

## GENERAL JOURNAL

| Date | Account Titles and Explanation | PR | Debit | Credit |
|------|-------------------------------|----|-------|--------|
|  |  |  |  |  |
|  |  |  |  |  |
|  |  |  |  |  |
|  |  |  |  |  |
|  |  |  |  |  |
|  |  |  |  |  |
|  |  |  |  |  |
|  |  |  |  |  |
|  |  |  |  |  |
|  |  |  |  |  |
|  |  |  |  |  |
|  |  |  |  |  |
|  |  |  |  |  |
|  |  |  |  |  |
|  |  |  |  |  |
|  |  |  |  |  |
|  |  |  |  |  |
|  |  |  |  |  |
|  |  |  |  |  |
|  |  |  |  |  |
|  |  |  |  |  |
|  |  |  |  |  |
|  |  |  |  |  |
|  |  |  |  |  |
|  |  |  |  |  |
|  |  |  |  |  |
|  |  |  |  |  |
|  |  |  |  |  |
|  |  |  |  |  |
|  |  |  |  |  |
|  |  |  |  |  |
|  |  |  |  |  |
|  |  |  |  |  |
|  |  |  |  |  |
|  |  |  |  |  |
|  |  |  |  |  |
|  |  |  |  |  |
|  |  |  |  |  |
|  |  |  |  |  |
|  |  |  |  |  |

## GENERAL JOURNAL                    Page____

| Date | | Account Titles and Explanation | PR | Debit | Credit |
|---|---|---|---|---|---|
| | | | | | |
| | | | | | |
| | | | | | |
| | | | | | |
| | | | | | |
| | | | | | |
| | | | | | |
| | | | | | |
| | | | | | |
| | | | | | |
| | | | | | |
| | | | | | |
| | | | | | |
| | | | | | |
| | | | | | |
| | | | | | |
| | | | | | |
| | | | | | |
| | | | | | |
| | | | | | |
| | | | | | |
| | | | | | |
| | | | | | |
| | | | | | |
| | | | | | |
| | | | | | |
| | | | | | |
| | | | | | |
| | | | | | |
| | | | | | |
| | | | | | |
| | | | | | |
| | | | | | |
| | | | | | |
| | | | | | |
| | | | | | |
| | | | | | |
| | | | | | |
| | | | | | |
| | | | | | |
| | | | | | |

1. _____

2. _____

3. _____

## 4. Multiple-step

### Income Statement

| | | |
|---|---|---|
| | | |
| | | |
| | | |
| | | |
| | | |
| | | |
| | | |
| | | |
| | | |
| | | |
| | | |
| | | |
| | | |
| | | |
| | | |
| | | |
| | | |
| | | |
| | | |
| | | |
| | | |
| | | |
| | | |
| | | |
| | | |
| | | |
| | | |

## 5. Single-step

### Income Statement

| | | |
|---|---|---|
| | | |
| | | |
| | | |
| | | |
| | | |
| | | |
| | | |
| | | |
| | | |

## GENERAL JOURNAL

| Date | Account Titles and Explanation | PR | Debit | Credit |
|------|-------------------------------|-----|-------|--------|
|      |                               |     |       |        |
|      |                               |     |       |        |
|      |                               |     |       |        |
|      |                               |     |       |        |
|      |                               |     |       |        |
|      |                               |     |       |        |
|      |                               |     |       |        |
|      |                               |     |       |        |
|      |                               |     |       |        |
|      |                               |     |       |        |
|      |                               |     |       |        |
|      |                               |     |       |        |
|      |                               |     |       |        |
|      |                               |     |       |        |
|      |                               |     |       |        |
|      |                               |     |       |        |
|      |                               |     |       |        |
|      |                               |     |       |        |
|      |                               |     |       |        |
|      |                               |     |       |        |
|      |                               |     |       |        |
|      |                               |     |       |        |
|      |                               |     |       |        |
|      |                               |     |       |        |
|      |                               |     |       |        |
|      |                               |     |       |        |
|      |                               |     |       |        |
|      |                               |     |       |        |
|      |                               |     |       |        |
|      |                               |     |       |        |
|      |                               |     |       |        |
|      |                               |     |       |        |
|      |                               |     |       |        |
|      |                               |     |       |        |
|      |                               |     |       |        |
|      |                               |     |       |        |
|      |                               |     |       |        |
|      |                               |     |       |        |
|      |                               |     |       |        |
|      |                               |     |       |        |
|      |                               |     |       |        |
|      |                               |     |       |        |
|      |                               |     |       |        |
|      |                               |     |       |        |
|      |                               |     |       |        |

**The Downtown Store**
**Work Sheet**
**For Year Ended March 31, 2011**

| Account Title | Unadjusted Trial Balance Debit | Unadjusted Trial Balance Credit | Adjustments Debit | Adjustments Credit | Income Statement Debit | Income Statement Credit | Balance Sheet and Statement of Owner's Equity Debit | Balance Sheet and Statement of Owner's Equity Credit |
|---|---|---|---|---|---|---|---|---|
| Cash | 14,000 | | | | | | | |
| Merchandise inventory | 96,000 | | | | | | | |
| Supplies | 1,200 | | | | | | | |
| Prepaid rent | 14,000 | | | | | | | |
| Store equipment | 120,000 | | | | | | | |
| Accum. amort., store equip. | | 28,000 | | | | | | |
| Office equipment | 46,000 | | | | | | | |
| Accum. amort., office equip. | | 13,000 | | | | | | |
| Accounts payable | | 32,000 | | | | | | |
| Lucy Baker, capital | | 269,200 | | | | | | |
| Lucy Baker, withdrawals | 68,000 | | | | | | | |
| Sales | | 998,000 | | | | | | |
| Sales returns and allowances | 23,000 | | | | | | | |
| Sales discounts | 12,000 | | | | | | | |
| Purchases | 692,000 | | | | | | | |
| Purchases returns and allowances | | 5,700 | | | | | | |
| Purchase discounts | | 14,300 | | | | | | |
| Transportation-in | 32,000 | | | | | | | |
| Salaries expenses | 120,000 | | | | | | | |
| Rent expense | 91,000 | | | | | | | |
| Advertising expense | 14,000 | | | | | | | |
| Supplies expense | 17,000 | | | | | | | |
| Amort. exp., store equipment | 0 | | | | | | | |
| Amort. exp., office equipment | 0 | | | | | | | |
| Totals | 1,360,200 | 1,360,200 | | | | | | |

Part 2                          GENERAL JOURNAL                          Page____

| Date | Account Titles and Explanation | PR | Debit | Credit |
|------|-------------------------------|----|----|----|
|  |  |  |  |  |
|  |  |  |  |  |
|  |  |  |  |  |
|  |  |  |  |  |
|  |  |  |  |  |
|  |  |  |  |  |
|  |  |  |  |  |
|  |  |  |  |  |
|  |  |  |  |  |
|  |  |  |  |  |
|  |  |  |  |  |
|  |  |  |  |  |
|  |  |  |  |  |
|  |  |  |  |  |
|  |  |  |  |  |
|  |  |  |  |  |
|  |  |  |  |  |
|  |  |  |  |  |
|  |  |  |  |  |
|  |  |  |  |  |
|  |  |  |  |  |
|  |  |  |  |  |
|  |  |  |  |  |
|  |  |  |  |  |
|  |  |  |  |  |
|  |  |  |  |  |
|  |  |  |  |  |

Part 3

## GENERAL LEDGER

Merchandise Inventory                          ACCOUNT NO. 119

| DATE | EXPLANATION | PR | DEBIT | CREDIT | BALANCE |
|------|-------------|----|----|----|----|
|  |  |  |  |  |  |
|  |  |  |  |  |  |
|  |  |  |  |  |  |
|  |  |  |  |  |  |

## Income Statement

| | | | |
|---|---|---|---|
| | | | |
| | | | |
| | | | |
| | | | |
| | | | |
| | | | |
| | | | |
| | | | |
| | | | |
| | | | |
| | | | |
| | | | |
| | | | |
| | | | |
| | | | |
| | | | |
| | | | |
| | | | |
| | | | |
| | | | |
| | | | |
| | | | |
| | | | |
| | | | |
| | | | |
| | | | |
| | | | |
| | | | |
| | | | |
| | | | |
| | | | |
| | | | |
| | | | |
| | | | |
| | | | |
| | | | |
| | | | |
| | | | |

## GENERAL JOURNAL

| Date | Account Titles and Explanation | PR | Debit | Credit |
|------|-------------------------------|----|-------|--------|
|      |                               |    |       |        |
|      |                               |    |       |        |
|      |                               |    |       |        |
|      |                               |    |       |        |
|      |                               |    |       |        |
|      |                               |    |       |        |
|      |                               |    |       |        |
|      |                               |    |       |        |
|      |                               |    |       |        |
|      |                               |    |       |        |
|      |                               |    |       |        |
|      |                               |    |       |        |
|      |                               |    |       |        |
|      |                               |    |       |        |
|      |                               |    |       |        |
|      |                               |    |       |        |
|      |                               |    |       |        |
|      |                               |    |       |        |
|      |                               |    |       |        |
|      |                               |    |       |        |
|      |                               |    |       |        |
|      |                               |    |       |        |
|      |                               |    |       |        |
|      |                               |    |       |        |
|      |                               |    |       |        |
|      |                               |    |       |        |
|      |                               |    |       |        |
|      |                               |    |       |        |
|      |                               |    |       |        |
|      |                               |    |       |        |
|      |                               |    |       |        |
|      |                               |    |       |        |
|      |                               |    |       |        |
|      |                               |    |       |        |
|      |                               |    |       |        |
|      |                               |    |       |        |

## GENERAL JOURNAL                                    Page____

| Date | Account Titles and Explanation | PR | Debit | Credit |
|------|-------------------------------|----|-------|--------|
|      |                               |    |       |        |
|      |                               |    |       |        |
|      |                               |    |       |        |
|      |                               |    |       |        |
|      |                               |    |       |        |
|      |                               |    |       |        |
|      |                               |    |       |        |
|      |                               |    |       |        |
|      |                               |    |       |        |
|      |                               |    |       |        |
|      |                               |    |       |        |
|      |                               |    |       |        |
|      |                               |    |       |        |

**\*Problem 6-17B**

## GENERAL JOURNAL                                    Page____

| Date | Account Titles and Explanation | PR | Debit | Credit |
|------|-------------------------------|----|-------|--------|
|      |                               |    |       |        |
|      |                               |    |       |        |
|      |                               |    |       |        |
|      |                               |    |       |        |
|      |                               |    |       |        |
|      |                               |    |       |        |
|      |                               |    |       |        |
|      |                               |    |       |        |
|      |                               |    |       |        |
|      |                               |    |       |        |
|      |                               |    |       |        |
|      |                               |    |       |        |
|      |                               |    |       |        |
|      |                               |    |       |        |
|      |                               |    |       |        |
|      |                               |    |       |        |
|      |                               |    |       |        |
|      |                               |    |       |        |
|      |                               |    |       |        |
|      |                               |    |       |        |
|      |                               |    |       |        |
|      |                               |    |       |        |
|      |                               |    |       |        |
|      |                               |    |       |        |
|      |                               |    |       |        |
|      |                               |    |       |        |

## GENERAL JOURNAL                                    Page____

| Date | Account Titles and Explanation | PR | Debit | Credit |
|------|-------------------------------|----|-------|--------|
|      |                               |    |       |        |
|      |                               |    |       |        |
|      |                               |    |       |        |
|      |                               |    |       |        |
|      |                               |    |       |        |
|      |                               |    |       |        |
|      |                               |    |       |        |
|      |                               |    |       |        |
|      |                               |    |       |        |
|      |                               |    |       |        |
|      |                               |    |       |        |
|      |                               |    |       |        |
|      |                               |    |       |        |
|      |                               |    |       |        |
|      |                               |    |       |        |
|      |                               |    |       |        |
|      |                               |    |       |        |
|      |                               |    |       |        |
|      |                               |    |       |        |
|      |                               |    |       |        |
|      |                               |    |       |        |
|      |                               |    |       |        |
|      |                               |    |       |        |
|      |                               |    |       |        |
|      |                               |    |       |        |
|      |                               |    |       |        |
|      |                               |    |       |        |
|      |                               |    |       |        |
|      |                               |    |       |        |
|      |                               |    |       |        |
|      |                               |    |       |        |
|      |                               |    |       |        |
|      |                               |    |       |        |
|      |                               |    |       |        |
|      |                               |    |       |        |
|      |                               |    |       |        |
|      |                               |    |       |        |
|      |                               |    |       |        |
|      |                               |    |       |        |
|      |                               |    |       |        |

## GENERAL JOURNAL                                           Page____

| Date | | Account Titles and Explanation | PR | Debit | Credit |
|------|--|-------------------------------|----|-------|--------|
| | | | | | |
| | | | | | |
| | | | | | |
| | | | | | |
| | | | | | |
| | | | | | |
| | | | | | |
| | | | | | |
| | | | | | |
| | | | | | |
| | | | | | |
| | | | | | |
| | | | | | |
| | | | | | |
| | | | | | |
| | | | | | |
| | | | | | |
| | | | | | |
| | | | | | |
| | | | | | |
| | | | | | |
| | | | | | |
| | | | | | |
| | | | | | |
| | | | | | |
| | | | | | |
| | | | | | |
| | | | | | |
| | | | | | |
| | | | | | |
| | | | | | |
| | | | | | |
| | | | | | |
| | | | | | |
| | | | | | |
| | | | | | |
| | | | | | |
| | | | | | |
| | | | | | |
| | | | | | |
| | | | | | |
| | | | | | |
| | | | | | |
| | | | | | |
| | | | | | |

## GENERAL JOURNAL                                         Page____

| Date | Account Titles and Explanation | PR | Debit | Credit |
|------|-------------------------------|----|-------|--------|
|  |  |  |  |  |
|  |  |  |  |  |
|  |  |  |  |  |
|  |  |  |  |  |
|  |  |  |  |  |
|  |  |  |  |  |
|  |  |  |  |  |
|  |  |  |  |  |
|  |  |  |  |  |
|  |  |  |  |  |
|  |  |  |  |  |
|  |  |  |  |  |
|  |  |  |  |  |
|  |  |  |  |  |
|  |  |  |  |  |
|  |  |  |  |  |
|  |  |  |  |  |
|  |  |  |  |  |
|  |  |  |  |  |
|  |  |  |  |  |
|  |  |  |  |  |
|  |  |  |  |  |
|  |  |  |  |  |
|  |  |  |  |  |
|  |  |  |  |  |
|  |  |  |  |  |
|  |  |  |  |  |
|  |  |  |  |  |
|  |  |  |  |  |
|  |  |  |  |  |
|  |  |  |  |  |
|  |  |  |  |  |
|  |  |  |  |  |
|  |  |  |  |  |
|  |  |  |  |  |
|  |  |  |  |  |
|  |  |  |  |  |
|  |  |  |  |  |
|  |  |  |  |  |
|  |  |  |  |  |

## GENERAL JOURNAL                                          Page____

| Date | Account Titles and Explanation | PR | Debit | Credit |
|------|-------------------------------|----|-------|--------|
|      |                               |    |       |        |
|      |                               |    |       |        |
|      |                               |    |       |        |
|      |                               |    |       |        |
|      |                               |    |       |        |
|      |                               |    |       |        |
|      |                               |    |       |        |
|      |                               |    |       |        |
|      |                               |    |       |        |
|      |                               |    |       |        |
|      |                               |    |       |        |
|      |                               |    |       |        |
|      |                               |    |       |        |
|      |                               |    |       |        |
|      |                               |    |       |        |
|      |                               |    |       |        |
|      |                               |    |       |        |
|      |                               |    |       |        |
|      |                               |    |       |        |
|      |                               |    |       |        |
|      |                               |    |       |        |
|      |                               |    |       |        |
|      |                               |    |       |        |
|      |                               |    |       |        |
|      |                               |    |       |        |
|      |                               |    |       |        |
|      |                               |    |       |        |
|      |                               |    |       |        |
|      |                               |    |       |        |
|      |                               |    |       |        |
|      |                               |    |       |        |
|      |                               |    |       |        |
|      |                               |    |       |        |
|      |                               |    |       |        |
|      |                               |    |       |        |
|      |                               |    |       |        |
|      |                               |    |       |        |
|      |                               |    |       |        |
|      |                               |    |       |        |
|      |                               |    |       |        |

## GENERAL JOURNAL

| Date | Account Titles and Explanation | PR | Debit | Credit |
|------|-------------------------------|----|-------|--------|
|  |  |  |  |  |
|  |  |  |  |  |
|  |  |  |  |  |
|  |  |  |  |  |
|  |  |  |  |  |
|  |  |  |  |  |
|  |  |  |  |  |
|  |  |  |  |  |
|  |  |  |  |  |
|  |  |  |  |  |
|  |  |  |  |  |
|  |  |  |  |  |
|  |  |  |  |  |
|  |  |  |  |  |
|  |  |  |  |  |
|  |  |  |  |  |
|  |  |  |  |  |
|  |  |  |  |  |
|  |  |  |  |  |
|  |  |  |  |  |
|  |  |  |  |  |
|  |  |  |  |  |
|  |  |  |  |  |
|  |  |  |  |  |
|  |  |  |  |  |
|  |  |  |  |  |
|  |  |  |  |  |
|  |  |  |  |  |
|  |  |  |  |  |
|  |  |  |  |  |
|  |  |  |  |  |
|  |  |  |  |  |
|  |  |  |  |  |
|  |  |  |  |  |
|  |  |  |  |  |
|  |  |  |  |  |
|  |  |  |  |  |
|  |  |  |  |  |
|  |  |  |  |  |
|  |  |  |  |  |

## GENERAL LEDGER

Cash                                                                    ACCOUNT NO. 101

| DATE | EXPLANATION | PR | DEBIT | CREDIT | BALANCE |
|---|---|---|---|---|---|
| 2011 Dec. 31 | Balance | | | | 89,090 |
| | | | | | |
| | | | | | |
| | | | | | |
| | | | | | |
| | | | | | |
| | | | | | |
| | | | | | |
| | | | | | |
| | | | | | |
| | | | | | |
| | | | | | |
| | | | | | |
| | | | | | |
| | | | | | |
| | | | | | |
| | | | | | |
| | | | | | |
| | | | | | |
| | | | | | |
| | | | | | |
| | | | | | |
| | | | | | |
| | | | | | |
| | | | | | |
| | | | | | |
| | | | | | |
| | | | | | |
| | | | | | |
| | | | | | |
| | | | | | |
| | | | | | |
| | | | | | |
| | | | | | |
| | | | | | |
| | | | | | |
| | | | | | |
| | | | | | |
| | | | | | |

### Accounts Receivable – Alamo Engineering          ACCOUNT NO. 106.1

| DATE | EXPLANATION | PR | DEBIT | CREDIT | BALANCE |
|---|---|---|---|---|---|
| 2011 Dec. 31 | Balance | | | | -0- |
| | | | | | |
| | | | | | |
| | | | | | |
| | | | | | |

### Accounts Receivable – Buckman Services          ACCOUNT NO. 106.2

| DATE | EXPLANATION | PR | DEBIT | CREDIT | BALANCE |
|---|---|---|---|---|---|
| 2011 Dec. 31 | Balance | | | | -0- |
| | | | | | |
| | | | | | |
| | | | | | |

### Accounts Receivable – Capital Leasing          ACCOUNT NO. 106.3

| DATE | EXPLANATION | PR | DEBIT | CREDIT | BALANCE |
|---|---|---|---|---|---|
| 2011 Dec. 31 | Balance | | | | -0- |
| | | | | | |
| | | | | | |
| | | | | | |

### Accounts Receivable – Decker Co.          ACCOUNT NO. 106.4

| DATE | EXPLANATION | PR | DEBIT | CREDIT | BALANCE |
|---|---|---|---|---|---|
| 2011 Dec. 31 | Balance | | | | 2,700 |
| | | | | | |
| | | | | | |
| | | | | | |

### Accounts Receivable – Elite Corporation          ACCOUNT NO. 106.5

| DATE | EXPLANATION | PR | DEBIT | CREDIT | BALANCE |
|---|---|---|---|---|---|
| 2011 Dec. 31 | Balance | | | | -0- |
| | | | | | |
| | | | | | |
| | | | | | |
| | | | | | |

### Accounts Receivable – Fostek Co.        ACCOUNT NO. 106.6

| DATE | EXPLANATION | PR | DEBIT | CREDIT | BALANCE |
|------|-------------|----|-------|--------|---------|
| 2011<br>Dec. 31 | Balance | | | | 3,000 |
| | | | | | |
| | | | | | |

### Accounts Receivable – Grandview Co.      ACCOUNT NO. 106.7

| DATE | EXPLANATION | PR | DEBIT | CREDIT | BALANCE |
|------|-------------|----|-------|--------|---------|
| 2011<br>Dec. 31 | Balance | | | | -0- |
| | | | | | |
| | | | | | |
| | | | | | |

### Accounts Receivable – Hacienda, Inc.      ACCOUNT NO. 106.8

| DATE | EXPLANATION | PR | DEBIT | CREDIT | BALANCE |
|------|-------------|----|-------|--------|---------|
| 2011<br>Dec. 31 | Balance | | | | -0- |
| | | | | | |
| | | | | | |

### Accounts Receivable – Images, Inc.      ACCOUNT NO. 106.9

| DATE | EXPLANATION | PR | DEBIT | CREDIT | BALANCE |
|------|-------------|----|-------|--------|---------|
| 2011<br>Dec. 31 | Balance | | | | -0- |
| | | | | | |

### Merchandise Inventory ACCOUNT NO. 119

| DATE | EXPLANATION | PR | DEBIT | CREDIT | BALANCE |
|------|-------------|----|-------|--------|---------|
|      |             |    |       |        |         |
|      |             |    |       |        |         |
|      |             |    |       |        |         |
|      |             |    |       |        |         |
|      |             |    |       |        |         |
|      |             |    |       |        |         |
|      |             |    |       |        |         |
|      |             |    |       |        |         |
|      |             |    |       |        |         |
|      |             |    |       |        |         |
|      |             |    |       |        |         |
|      |             |    |       |        |         |
|      |             |    |       |        |         |
|      |             |    |       |        |         |
|      |             |    |       |        |         |

### Computer Supplies ACCOUNT NO. 126

| DATE | EXPLANATION | PR | DEBIT | CREDIT | BALANCE |
|------|-------------|----|-------|--------|---------|
| 2011 Dec. 31 | Balance |    |       |        | 1,440 |
|      |             |    |       |        |         |
|      |             |    |       |        |         |

### Prepaid Insurance ACCOUNT NO. 128

| DATE | EXPLANATION | PR | DEBIT | CREDIT | BALANCE |
|------|-------------|----|-------|--------|---------|
| 2011 Dec. 31 | Balance |    |       |        | 3,240 |
|      |             |    |       |        |         |

### Prepaid Rent ACCOUNT NO. 131

| DATE | EXPLANATION | PR | DEBIT | CREDIT | BALANCE |
|------|-------------|----|-------|--------|---------|
| 2011 Dec. 31 | Balance |    |       |        | 2,250 |
|      |             |    |       |        |         |
|      |             |    |       |        |         |

### Office Equipment ACCOUNT NO. 163

| DATE | EXPLANATION | PR | DEBIT | CREDIT | BALANCE |
|------|-------------|----|-------|--------|---------|
| 2011 Dec. 31 | Balance |    |       |        | 18,000 |
|      |             |    |       |        |         |
|      |             |    |       |        |         |

### Accumulated Amortization, Office Equipment          ACCOUNT NO. 164

| DATE | EXPLANATION | PR | DEBIT | CREDIT | BALANCE |
|------|-------------|----|-------|--------|---------|
| 2011 Dec. 31 | Balance | | | | 1,500 |
| | | | | | |

### Computer Equipment          ACCOUNT NO. 167

| DATE | EXPLANATION | PR | DEBIT | CREDIT | BALANCE |
|------|-------------|----|-------|--------|---------|
| 2011 Dec. 31 | Balance | | | | 36,000 |
| | | | | | |

### Accumulated Amortization, Computer Equipment          ACCOUNT NO. 168

| DATE | EXPLANATION | PR | DEBIT | CREDIT | BALANCE |
|------|-------------|----|-------|--------|---------|
| 2011 Dec. 31 | Balance | | | | 2,250 |
| | | | | | |

### Accounts Payable          ACCOUNT NO. 201

| DATE | EXPLANATION | PR | DEBIT | CREDIT | BALANCE |
|------|-------------|----|-------|--------|---------|
| 2011 Dec. 31 | Balance | | | | 2,310 |
| | | | | | |
| | | | | | |
| | | | | | |
| | | | | | |
| | | | | | |
| | | | | | |
| | | | | | |
| | | | | | |
| | | | | | |
| | | | | | |

### Wages Payable          ACCOUNT NO. 210

| DATE | EXPLANATION | PR | DEBIT | CREDIT | BALANCE |
|------|-------------|----|-------|--------|---------|
| 2011 Dec. 31 | Balance | | | | 800 |
| | | | | | |
| | | | | | |

### Unearned Computer Services Revenue     ACCOUNT NO. 236

| DATE | EXPLANATION | PR | DEBIT | CREDIT | BALANCE |
|------|-------------|----|-------|--------|---------|
| 2011 Dec. 31 | Balance | | | | 3,000 |
| | | | | | |
| | | | | | |

### Mary Graham, Capital     ACCOUNT NO. 301

| DATE | EXPLANATION | PR | DEBIT | CREDIT | BALANCE |
|------|-------------|----|-------|--------|---------|
| 2011 Dec. 31 | Balance | | | | 145,860 |
| | | | | | |
| | | | | | |

### Mary Graham, Withdrawals     ACCOUNT NO. 302

| DATE | EXPLANATION | PR | DEBIT | CREDIT | BALANCE |
|------|-------------|----|-------|--------|---------|
| | | | | | |
| | | | | | |

### Computer Services Revenue     ACCOUNT NO. 403

| DATE | EXPLANATION | PR | DEBIT | CREDIT | BALANCE |
|------|-------------|----|-------|--------|---------|
| | | | | | |
| | | | | | |
| | | | | | |
| | | | | | |
| | | | | | |
| | | | | | |

### Sales     ACCOUNT NO. 413

| DATE | EXPLANATION | PR | DEBIT | CREDIT | BALANCE |
|------|-------------|----|-------|--------|---------|
| | | | | | |
| | | | | | |
| | | | | | |
| | | | | | |
| | | | | | |
| | | | | | |
| | | | | | |

### Sales Discounts ACCOUNT NO. 414

| DATE | EXPLANATION | PR | DEBIT | CREDIT | BALANCE |
|------|-------------|----|-------|--------|---------|
|      |             |    |       |        |         |
|      |             |    |       |        |         |
|      |             |    |       |        |         |

### Sales Returns and Allowances ACCOUNT NO. 415

| DATE | EXPLANATION | PR | DEBIT | CREDIT | BALANCE |
|------|-------------|----|-------|--------|---------|
|      |             |    |       |        |         |
|      |             |    |       |        |         |
|      |             |    |       |        |         |

### Cost of Goods Sold ACCOUNT NO. 502

| DATE | EXPLANATION | PR | DEBIT | CREDIT | BALANCE |
|------|-------------|----|-------|--------|---------|
|      |             |    |       |        |         |
|      |             |    |       |        |         |
|      |             |    |       |        |         |
|      |             |    |       |        |         |
|      |             |    |       |        |         |
|      |             |    |       |        |         |
|      |             |    |       |        |         |

### Amortization Expense, Office Equipment ACCOUNT NO. 612

| DATE | EXPLANATION | PR | DEBIT | CREDIT | BALANCE |
|------|-------------|----|-------|--------|---------|
|      |             |    |       |        |         |
|      |             |    |       |        |         |

### Amortization Expense, Computer Equipment ACCOUNT NO. 613

| DATE | EXPLANATION | PR | DEBIT | CREDIT | BALANCE |
|------|-------------|----|-------|--------|---------|
|      |             |    |       |        |         |
|      |             |    |       |        |         |

### Wages Expense ACCOUNT NO. 623

| DATE | EXPLANATION | PR | DEBIT | CREDIT | BALANCE |
|------|-------------|----|-------|--------|---------|
|      |             |    |       |        |         |
|      |             |    |       |        |         |
|      |             |    |       |        |         |
|      |             |    |       |        |         |

### Insurance Expense                                    ACCOUNT NO. 637

| DATE | EXPLANATION | PR | DEBIT | CREDIT | BALANCE |
|------|-------------|-----|-------|--------|---------|
|      |             |     |       |        |         |
|      |             |     |       |        |         |

### Rent Expense                                         ACCOUNT NO. 640

| DATE | EXPLANATION | PR | DEBIT | CREDIT | BALANCE |
|------|-------------|-----|-------|--------|---------|
|      |             |     |       |        |         |
|      |             |     |       |        |         |

### Computer Supplies Expense                            ACCOUNT NO. 652

| DATE | EXPLANATION | P.R. | DEBIT | CREDIT | BALANCE |
|------|-------------|------|-------|--------|---------|
|      |             |      |       |        |         |
|      |             |      |       |        |         |

### Advertising Expense                                  ACCOUNT NO. 655

| DATE | EXPLANATION | PR | DEBIT | CREDIT | BALANCE |
|------|-------------|-----|-------|--------|---------|
|      |             |     |       |        |         |
|      |             |     |       |        |         |
|      |             |     |       |        |         |

### Mileage Expense                                      ACCOUNT NO. 676

| DATE | EXPLANATION | PR | DEBIT | CREDIT | BALANCE |
|------|-------------|-----|-------|--------|---------|
|      |             |     |       |        |         |
|      |             |     |       |        |         |
|      |             |     |       |        |         |
|      |             |     |       |        |         |

### Repairs Expense, Computer                            ACCOUNT NO. 684

| DATE | EXPLANATION | PR | DEBIT | CREDIT | BALANCE |
|------|-------------|-----|-------|--------|---------|
|      |             |     |       |        |         |
|      |             |     |       |        |         |
|      |             |     |       |        |         |

### Charitable Donations Expense                         ACCOUNT NO. 699

| DATE | EXPLANATION | PR | DEBIT | CREDIT | BALANCE |
|------|-------------|-----|-------|--------|---------|
|      |             |     |       |        |         |
|      |             |     |       |        |         |

## ECHO SYSTEMS
## Partial Work Sheet
## For Three Months Ended March 31, 2012

| Acct. No. | Account Title | Unadjusted Trial Balance | | Adjustments | | Adjusted Trial Balance | |
|---|---|---|---|---|---|---|---|
| | | Dr. | Cr. | Dr. | Cr. | Dr. | Cr. |
| 101 | Cash | | | | | | |
| 106.1 | Alamo Engineering Co. | | | | | | |
| 106.2 | Buckman Services | | | | | | |
| 106.3 | Capital Leasing | | | | | | |
| 106.4 | Decker Co. | | | | | | |
| 106.5 | Elite Corporation | | | | | | |
| 106.6 | Fostek Co. | | | | | | |
| 106.7 | Grandview Co. | | | | | | |
| 106.8 | Hacienda Inc. | | | | | | |
| 106.9 | Images Inc. | | | | | | |
| 119 | Merchandise inventory | | | | | | |
| 126 | Computer supplies | | | | | | |
| 128 | Prepaid insurance | | | | | | |
| 131 | Prepaid rent | | | | | | |
| 163 | Office equipment | | | | | | |
| 164 | Accum. amort., office equipment | | | | | | |
| 167 | Computer equipment | | | | | | |
| 168 | Accum. amort., computer equip. | | | | | | |
| 201 | Accounts payable | | | | | | |
| 210 | Wages payable | | | | | | |
| 236 | Unearned computer services rev. | | | | | | |
| 301 | Mary Graham, capital | | | | | | |
| 302 | Mary Graham, withdrawals | | | | | | |
| 403 | Computer services revenue | | | | | | |
| 413 | Sales | | | | | | |
| 414 | Sales discounts | | | | | | |
| 415 | Sales returns and allowances | | | | | | |
| 502 | Cost of goods sold | | | | | | |
| 612 | Amort. exp., office equipment | | | | | | |
| 613 | Amort. exp., computer equipment | | | | | | |
| 623 | Wages expense | | | | | | |
| 637 | Insurance expense | | | | | | |
| 640 | Rent expense | | | | | | |
| 652 | Computer supplies expense | | | | | | |
| 655 | Advertising expense | | | | | | |
| 676 | Mileage expense | | | | | | |
| 684 | Repairs expense, computer | | | | | | |
| 699 | Charitable donations expense | | | | | | |
| | Totals | | | | | | |
| | | | | | | | |
| | | | | | | | |
| | | | | | | | |
| | | | | | | | |
| | | | | | | | |
| | | | | | | | |
| | | | | | | | |
| | | | | | | | |
| | | | | | | | |
| | | | | | | | |

**ECHO SYSTEMS**

**Income Statement**

**For Three Months Ended March 31, 2012**

| | | |
|---|---|---|
| | | |
| | | |
| | | |
| | | |
| | | |
| | | |
| | | |
| | | |
| | | |
| | | |
| | | |
| | | |
| | | |
| | | |
| | | |
| | | |
| | | |
| | | |
| | | |
| | | |
| | | |
| | | |
| | | |
| | | |
| | | |

**Part 5**

**ECHO SYSTEMS**

**Statement of Owner's Equity**

**For Three Months Ended March 31, 2012**

| | | |
|---|---|---|
| | | |
| | | |
| | | |
| | | |
| | | |
| | | |
| | | |
| | | |

## ECHO SYSTEMS
### Balance Sheet
### March 31, 2012

|  |  |  |  |
|---|---|---|---|
|  |  |  |  |
|  |  |  |  |
|  |  |  |  |
|  |  |  |  |
|  |  |  |  |
|  |  |  |  |
|  |  |  |  |
|  |  |  |  |
|  |  |  |  |
|  |  |  |  |
|  |  |  |  |
|  |  |  |  |
|  |  |  |  |
|  |  |  |  |
|  |  |  |  |
|  |  |  |  |
|  |  |  |  |
|  |  |  |  |
|  |  |  |  |
|  |  |  |  |
|  |  |  |  |
|  |  |  |  |
|  |  |  |  |
|  |  |  |  |
|  |  |  |  |
|  |  |  |  |
|  |  |  |  |
|  |  |  |  |
|  |  |  |  |
|  |  |  |  |
|  |  |  |  |
|  |  |  |  |
|  |  |  |  |
|  |  |  |  |
|  |  |  |  |
|  |  |  |  |
|  |  |  |  |
|  |  |  |  |
|  |  |  |  |
|  |  |  |  |
|  |  |  |  |

## GENERAL JOURNAL                                              Page _____

| Date | Account Titles and Explanation | PR | Debit | Credit |
|------|-------------------------------|-----|-------|--------|
|      |                               |     |       |        |
|      |                               |     |       |        |
|      |                               |     |       |        |
|      |                               |     |       |        |
|      |                               |     |       |        |
|      |                               |     |       |        |
|      |                               |     |       |        |
|      |                               |     |       |        |
|      |                               |     |       |        |
|      |                               |     |       |        |
|      |                               |     |       |        |
|      |                               |     |       |        |
|      |                               |     |       |        |
|      |                               |     |       |        |
|      |                               |     |       |        |
|      |                               |     |       |        |
|      |                               |     |       |        |
|      |                               |     |       |        |
|      |                               |     |       |        |
|      |                               |     |       |        |
|      |                               |     |       |        |
|      |                               |     |       |        |
|      |                               |     |       |        |
|      |                               |     |       |        |
|      |                               |     |       |        |
|      |                               |     |       |        |
|      |                               |     |       |        |
|      |                               |     |       |        |
|      |                               |     |       |        |
|      |                               |     |       |        |
|      |                               |     |       |        |
|      |                               |     |       |        |
|      |                               |     |       |        |
|      |                               |     |       |        |
|      |                               |     |       |        |
|      |                               |     |       |        |
|      |                               |     |       |        |
|      |                               |     |       |        |
|      |                               |     |       |        |
|      |                               |     |       |        |
|      |                               |     |       |        |
|      |                               |     |       |        |
|      |                               |     |       |        |
|      |                               |     |       |        |

| Date | | Account Titles and Explanation | PR | Debit | Credit |
|------|---|------|----|----|----|
| | | | | | |
| | | | | | |
| | | | | | |
| | | | | | |
| | | | | | |
| | | | | | |
| | | | | | |
| | | | | | |
| | | | | | |
| | | | | | |
| | | | | | |
| | | | | | |
| | | | | | |
| | | | | | |
| | | | | | |
| | | | | | |
| | | | | | |
| | | | | | |
| | | | | | |
| | | | | | |
| | | | | | |
| | | | | | |
| | | | | | |
| | | | | | |
| | | | | | |
| | | | | | |
| | | | | | |
| | | | | | |
| | | | | | |
| | | | | | |
| | | | | | |
| | | | | | |
| | | | | | |
| | | | | | |
| | | | | | |
| | | | | | |
| | | | | | |
| | | | | | |
| | | | | | |
| | | | | | |
| | | | | | |
| | | | | | |
| | | | | | |
| | | | | | |
| | | | | | |

| Date | Account Titles and Explanation | PR | Debit | Credit |
|------|-------------------------------|----|-------|--------|
|      |                               |    |       |        |
|      |                               |    |       |        |
|      |                               |    |       |        |
|      |                               |    |       |        |
|      |                               |    |       |        |
|      |                               |    |       |        |
|      |                               |    |       |        |
|      |                               |    |       |        |
|      |                               |    |       |        |
|      |                               |    |       |        |
|      |                               |    |       |        |
|      |                               |    |       |        |
|      |                               |    |       |        |
|      |                               |    |       |        |
|      |                               |    |       |        |
|      |                               |    |       |        |
|      |                               |    |       |        |
|      |                               |    |       |        |
|      |                               |    |       |        |
|      |                               |    |       |        |
|      |                               |    |       |        |
|      |                               |    |       |        |
|      |                               |    |       |        |
|      |                               |    |       |        |
|      |                               |    |       |        |
|      |                               |    |       |        |
|      |                               |    |       |        |
|      |                               |    |       |        |
|      |                               |    |       |        |
|      |                               |    |       |        |
|      |                               |    |       |        |
|      |                               |    |       |        |
|      |                               |    |       |        |
|      |                               |    |       |        |
|      |                               |    |       |        |
|      |                               |    |       |        |
|      |                               |    |       |        |
|      |                               |    |       |        |
|      |                               |    |       |        |
|      |                               |    |       |        |
|      |                               |    |       |        |
|      |                               |    |       |        |
|      |                               |    |       |        |

| Date | Account Titles and Explanation | PR | Debit | Credit |
|------|-------------------------------|----|-------|--------|
|      |                               |    |       |        |
|      |                               |    |       |        |
|      |                               |    |       |        |
|      |                               |    |       |        |
|      |                               |    |       |        |
|      |                               |    |       |        |
|      |                               |    |       |        |
|      |                               |    |       |        |
|      |                               |    |       |        |
|      |                               |    |       |        |
|      |                               |    |       |        |
|      |                               |    |       |        |
|      |                               |    |       |        |
|      |                               |    |       |        |
|      |                               |    |       |        |
|      |                               |    |       |        |
|      |                               |    |       |        |
|      |                               |    |       |        |
|      |                               |    |       |        |
|      |                               |    |       |        |
|      |                               |    |       |        |
|      |                               |    |       |        |
|      |                               |    |       |        |
|      |                               |    |       |        |
|      |                               |    |       |        |
|      |                               |    |       |        |
|      |                               |    |       |        |
|      |                               |    |       |        |
|      |                               |    |       |        |
|      |                               |    |       |        |
|      |                               |    |       |        |
|      |                               |    |       |        |
|      |                               |    |       |        |
|      |                               |    |       |        |
|      |                               |    |       |        |
|      |                               |    |       |        |
|      |                               |    |       |        |
|      |                               |    |       |        |
|      |                               |    |       |        |
|      |                               |    |       |        |

## GENERAL LEDGER

Cash       ACCOUNT NO. 101

| DATE | EXPLANATION | PR | DEBIT | CREDIT | BALANCE |
|------|-------------|-----|-------|--------|---------|
| 2011<br>Dec. 31 | Balance | | | | 89,090 |
| | | | | | |
| | | | | | |
| | | | | | |
| | | | | | |
| | | | | | |
| | | | | | |
| | | | | | |
| | | | | | |
| | | | | | |
| | | | | | |
| | | | | | |
| | | | | | |
| | | | | | |
| | | | | | |
| | | | | | |
| | | | | | |
| | | | | | |
| | | | | | |
| | | | | | |
| | | | | | |
| | | | | | |
| | | | | | |
| | | | | | |
| | | | | | |
| | | | | | |
| | | | | | |
| | | | | | |
| | | | | | |
| | | | | | |
| | | | | | |
| | | | | | |
| | | | | | |
| | | | | | |
| | | | | | |
| | | | | | |
| | | | | | |

### Accounts Receivable – Alamo Engineering    ACCOUNT NO. 106.1

| DATE | EXPLANATION | PR | DEBIT | CREDIT | BALANCE |
|---|---|---|---|---|---|
| 2011 Dec. 31 | Balance | | | | -0- |
| | | | | | |
| | | | | | |
| | | | | | |
| | | | | | |

### Accounts Receivable – Buckman Services    ACCOUNT NO. 106.2

| DATE | EXPLANATION | PR | DEBIT | CREDIT | BALANCE |
|---|---|---|---|---|---|
| 2011 Dec. 31 | Balance | | | | -0- |
| | | | | | |
| | | | | | |
| | | | | | |
| | | | | | |

### Accounts Receivable – Capital Leasing    ACCOUNT NO. 106.3

| DATE | EXPLANATION | PR | DEBIT | CREDIT | BALANCE |
|---|---|---|---|---|---|
| 2011 Dec. 31 | Balance | | | | -0- |
| | | | | | |
| | | | | | |
| | | | | | |
| | | | | | |

### Accounts Receivable – Decker Co.    ACCOUNT NO. 106.4

| DATE | EXPLANATION | PR | DEBIT | CREDIT | BALANCE |
|---|---|---|---|---|---|
| 2011 Dec. 31 | Balance | | | | 2,700 |
| | | | | | |
| | | | | | |
| | | | | | |

### Accounts Receivable – Elite Corporation    ACCOUNT NO. 106.5

| DATE | EXPLANATION | PR | DEBIT | CREDIT | BALANCE |
|---|---|---|---|---|---|
| 2011 Dec. 31 | Balance | | | | -0- |
| | | | | | |
| | | | | | |
| | | | | | |
| | | | | | |

### Accounts Receivable – Fostek Co.   ACCOUNT NO. 106.6

| DATE | EXPLANATION | PR | DEBIT | CREDIT | BALANCE |
|---|---|---|---|---|---|
| 2011 Dec. 31 | Balance | | | | 3,000 |
| | | | | | |
| | | | | | |

### Accounts Receivable – Grandview Co.   ACCOUNT NO. 106.7

| DATE | EXPLANATION | PR | DEBIT | CREDIT | BALANCE |
|---|---|---|---|---|---|
| 2011 Dec. 31 | Balance | | | | -0- |
| | | | | | |
| | | | | | |
| | | | | | |

### Accounts Receivable – Hacienda, Inc.   ACCOUNT NO. 106.8

| DATE | EXPLANATION | PR | DEBIT | CREDIT | BALANCE |
|---|---|---|---|---|---|
| 2011 Dec. 31 | Balance | | | | -0- |
| | | | | | |
| | | | | | |

### Accounts Receivable – Images, Inc.   ACCOUNT NO. 106.9

| DATE | EXPLANATION | PR | DEBIT | CREDIT | BALANCE |
|---|---|---|---|---|---|
| 2011 Dec. 31 | Balance | | | | -0- |
| | | | | | |

### Merchandise Inventory   ACCOUNT NO. 119

| DATE | EXPLANATION | PR | DEBIT | CREDIT | BALANCE |
|---|---|---|---|---|---|
| | | | | | |
| | | | | | |
| | | | | | |
| | | | | | |

### Computer Supplies   ACCOUNT NO. 126

| DATE | EXPLANATION | PR | DEBIT | CREDIT | BALANCE |
|---|---|---|---|---|---|
| 2011 Dec. 31 | Balance | | | | 1,440 |
| | | | | | |
| | | | | | |

### Prepaid Insurance                                ACCOUNT NO. 128

| DATE | EXPLANATION | PR | DEBIT | CREDIT | BALANCE |
|------|-------------|----|-------|--------|---------|
| 2011 Dec. 31 | Balance | | | | 3,240 |
| | | | | | |

### Prepaid Rent                                       ACCOUNT NO. 131

| DATE | EXPLANATION | PR | DEBIT | CREDIT | BALANCE |
|------|-------------|----|-------|--------|---------|
| 2011 Dec. 31 | Balance | | | | 2,250 |
| | | | | | |
| | | | | | |

### Office Equipment                                  ACCOUNT NO. 163

| DATE | EXPLANATION | PR | DEBIT | CREDIT | BALANCE |
|------|-------------|----|-------|--------|---------|
| 2011 Dec. 31 | Balance | | | | 18,000 |
| | | | | | |
| | | | | | |

### Accumulated Amortization, Office Equipment        ACCOUNT NO. 164

| DATE | EXPLANATION | PR | DEBIT | CREDIT | BALANCE |
|------|-------------|----|-------|--------|---------|
| 2011 Dec. 31 | Balance | | | | 1,500 |
| | | | | | |

### Computer Equipment                                ACCOUNT NO. 167

| DATE | EXPLANATION | PR | DEBIT | CREDIT | BALANCE |
|------|-------------|----|-------|--------|---------|
| 2011 Dec. 31 | Balance | | | | 36,000 |
| | | | | | |

### Accumulated Amortization, Computer Equipment      ACCOUNT NO. 168

| DATE | EXPLANATION | PR | DEBIT | CREDIT | BALANCE |
|------|-------------|----|-------|--------|---------|
| 2011 Dec. 31 | Balance | | | | 2,250 |
| | | | | | |

### Accounts Payable      ACCOUNT NO. 201

| DATE | EXPLANATION | PR | DEBIT | CREDIT | BALANCE |
|---|---|---|---|---|---|
| 2011 Dec. 31 | Balance | | | | 2,310 |
| | | | | | |
| | | | | | |
| | | | | | |
| | | | | | |
| | | | | | |
| | | | | | |
| | | | | | |
| | | | | | |
| | | | | | |

### Wages Payable      ACCOUNT NO. 210

| DATE | EXPLANATION | PR | DEBIT | CREDIT | BALANCE |
|---|---|---|---|---|---|
| 2011 Dec. 31 | Balance | | | | 800 |
| | | | | | |
| | | | | | |

### Unearned Computer Services Revenue      ACCOUNT NO. 236

| DATE | EXPLANATION | PR | DEBIT | CREDIT | BALANCE |
|---|---|---|---|---|---|
| 2011 Dec. 31 | Balance | | | | 3,000 |
| | | | | | |
| | | | | | |

### Mary Graham, Capital      ACCOUNT NO. 301

| DATE | EXPLANATION | PR | DEBIT | CREDIT | BALANCE |
|---|---|---|---|---|---|
| 2011 Dec. 31 | Balance | | | | 145,860 |
| | | | | | |
| | | | | | |

### Mary Graham, Withdrawals      ACCOUNT NO. 302

| DATE | EXPLANATION | PR | DEBIT | CREDIT | BALANCE |
|---|---|---|---|---|---|
| | | | | | |
| | | | | | |

### Computer Services Revenue                ACCOUNT NO. 403

| DATE | EXPLANATION | PR | DEBIT | CREDIT | BALANCE |
|------|-------------|----|-------|--------|---------|
|      |             |    |       |        |         |
|      |             |    |       |        |         |
|      |             |    |       |        |         |
|      |             |    |       |        |         |
|      |             |    |       |        |         |

### Sales                ACCOUNT NO. 413

| DATE | EXPLANATION | PR | DEBIT | CREDIT | BALANCE |
|------|-------------|----|-------|--------|---------|
|      |             |    |       |        |         |
|      |             |    |       |        |         |
|      |             |    |       |        |         |
|      |             |    |       |        |         |
|      |             |    |       |        |         |
|      |             |    |       |        |         |
|      |             |    |       |        |         |

### Sales Discounts                ACCOUNT NO. 414

| DATE | EXPLANATION | PR | DEBIT | CREDIT | BALANCE |
|------|-------------|----|-------|--------|---------|
|      |             |    |       |        |         |
|      |             |    |       |        |         |
|      |             |    |       |        |         |

### Sales Returns and Allowances                ACCOUNT NO. 415

| DATE | EXPLANATION | PR | DEBIT | CREDIT | BALANCE |
|------|-------------|----|-------|--------|---------|
|      |             |    |       |        |         |
|      |             |    |       |        |         |
|      |             |    |       |        |         |

### Purchases                ACCOUNT NO. 505

| DATE | EXPLANATION | PR | DEBIT | CREDIT | BALANCE |
|------|-------------|----|-------|--------|---------|
|      |             |    |       |        |         |
|      |             |    |       |        |         |
|      |             |    |       |        |         |
|      |             |    |       |        |         |

### Purchase Returns and Allowances        ACCOUNT NO. 506

| DATE | EXPLANATION | PR | DEBIT | CREDIT | BALANCE |
|------|-------------|----|-------|--------|---------|
|      |             |    |       |        |         |
|      |             |    |       |        |         |
|      |             |    |       |        |         |

### Purchase Discounts        ACCOUNT NO. 50

| DATE | EXPLANATION | PR | DEBIT | CREDIT | BALANCE |
|------|-------------|----|-------|--------|---------|
|      |             |    |       |        |         |
|      |             |    |       |        |         |
|      |             |    |       |        |         |
|      |             |    |       |        |         |

### Transportation-In        ACCOUNT NO. 508

| DATE | EXPLANATION | PR | DEBIT | CREDIT | BALANCE |
|------|-------------|----|-------|--------|---------|
|      |             |    |       |        |         |
|      |             |    |       |        |         |
|      |             |    |       |        |         |

### Amortization Expense, Office Equipment        ACCOUNT NO. 612

| DATE | EXPLANATION | PR | DEBIT | CREDIT | BALANCE |
|------|-------------|----|-------|--------|---------|
|      |             |    |       |        |         |
|      |             |    |       |        |         |

### Amortization Expense, Computer Equipment        ACCOUNT NO. 613

| DATE | EXPLANATION | PR | DEBIT | CREDIT | BALANCE |
|------|-------------|----|-------|--------|---------|
|      |             |    |       |        |         |
|      |             |    |       |        |         |

### Wages Expense        ACCOUNT NO. 623

| DATE | EXPLANATION | PR | DEBIT | CREDIT | BALANCE |
|------|-------------|----|-------|--------|---------|
|      |             |    |       |        |         |
|      |             |    |       |        |         |
|      |             |    |       |        |         |
|      |             |    |       |        |         |

### Insurance Expense                                          ACCOUNT NO. 637

| DATE | EXPLANATION | PR | DEBIT | CREDIT | BALANCE |
|------|-------------|----|-------|--------|---------|
|      |             |    |       |        |         |
|      |             |    |       |        |         |

### Rent Expense                                               ACCOUNT NO. 640

| DATE | EXPLANATION | PR | DEBIT | CREDIT | BALANCE |
|------|-------------|----|-------|--------|---------|
|      |             |    |       |        |         |
|      |             |    |       |        |         |

### Computer Supplies Expense                                  ACCOUNT NO. 652

| DATE | EXPLANATION | P.R. | DEBIT | CREDIT | BALANCE |
|------|-------------|------|-------|--------|---------|
|      |             |      |       |        |         |
|      |             |      |       |        |         |

### Advertising Expense                                        ACCOUNT NO. 655

| DATE | EXPLANATION | PR | DEBIT | CREDIT | BALANCE |
|------|-------------|----|-------|--------|---------|
|      |             |    |       |        |         |
|      |             |    |       |        |         |
|      |             |    |       |        |         |

### Mileage Expense                                            ACCOUNT NO. 676

| DATE | EXPLANATION | PR | DEBIT | CREDIT | BALANCE |
|------|-------------|----|-------|--------|---------|
|      |             |    |       |        |         |
|      |             |    |       |        |         |
|      |             |    |       |        |         |
|      |             |    |       |        |         |

### Repairs Expense, Computer                                  ACCOUNT NO. 684

| DATE | EXPLANATION | PR | DEBIT | CREDIT | BALANCE |
|------|-------------|----|-------|--------|---------|
|      |             |    |       |        |         |
|      |             |    |       |        |         |
|      |             |    |       |        |         |

### Charitable Donations Expense                               ACCOUNT NO. 699

| DATE | EXPLANATION | PR | DEBIT | CREDIT | BALANCE |
|------|-------------|----|-------|--------|---------|
|      |             |    |       |        |         |
|      |             |    |       |        |         |

**ECHO SYSTEMS**
**Partial Work Sheet**
**March 31, 2012**

| Acct. No. | Account Title | Unadjusted Trial Balance Debit | Unadjusted Trial Balance Credit | Adjustments Debit | Adjustments Credit | Adjusted Trial Balance Debit | Adjusted Trial Balance Credit |
|---|---|---|---|---|---|---|---|
| 101 | Cash | 117,618 | | | | | |
| 106.1 | Alamo Engineering Co. | 0 | | | | | |
| 106.2 | Buckman Services | 3,600 | | | | | |
| 106.3 | Capital Leasing | 11,800 | | | | | |
| 106.4 | Decker Co. | 7,140 | | | | | |
| 106.5 | Elite Corporation | 0 | | | | | |
| 106.6 | Fostek Co. | 0 | | | | | |
| 106.7 | Grandview Co. | 0 | | | | | |
| 106.8 | Hacienda Inc. | 11,600 | | | | | |
| 106.9 | Images Inc. | 0 | | | | | |
| 119 | Merchandise inventory | 0 | | | | | |
| 126 | Computer supplies | 6,240 | | | | | |
| 128 | Prepaid insurance | 3,240 | | | | | |
| 131 | Prepaid rent | 9,000 | | | | | |
| 163 | Office equipment | 18,000 | | | | | |
| 164 | Accum. amort., office equipment | | 1,500 | | | | |
| 167 | Computer equipment | 36,000 | | | | | |
| 168 | Accum. amort., computer equip. | | 2,250 | | | | |
| 201 | Accounts payable | | 0 | | | | |
| 210 | Wages payable | | 0 | | | | |
| 236 | Unearned computer services rev. | | 0 | | | | |
| 301 | Mary Graham, capital | | 193,860 | | | | |
| 302 | Mary Graham, withdrawals | 9,600 | | | | | |
| 403 | Computer services revenue | | 38,320 | | | | |
| 413 | Sales | | 34,440 | | | | |
| 414 | Sales discounts | 76 | | | | | |
| 415 | Sales returns and allowances | 800 | | | | | |
| 505 | Purchases | 27,200 | | | | | |
| 506 | Purchase returns and allowances | | 792 | | | | |
| 507 | Purchase discounts | | 272 | | | | |
| 508 | Transportation-in | 1,400 | | | | | |
| 612 | Amort. exp., office equipment | 0 | | | | | |
| 613 | Amort. exp., computer equipment | 0 | | | | | |
| 623 | Wages expense | 3,800 | | | | | |
| 637 | Insurance expense | 0 | | | | | |
| 640 | Rent expense | 0 | | | | | |
| 652 | Computer supplies expense | 0 | | | | | |
| 655 | Advertising expense | 1,600 | | | | | |
| 676 | Mileage expense | 1,000 | | | | | |
| 684 | Repairs expense, computer | 1,720 | | | | | |
| 699 | Charitable donations expense | 0 | | | | | |
| | Totals | 271,434 | 271,434 | | | | |

**Parts 4, 5, and 6:  Use the forms provided on pages 432 to 433 Inclusive.**

**1.** _____
_____
_____

**2.** _____
_____
_____

**Quick Study 7-2**

_____
_____
_____
_____
_____

**Quick Study 7-3**

_____
_____
_____
_____
_____
_____

**Quick Study 7-4**

_____
_____
_____
_____
_____

**Quick Study 7-5**

_____
_____
_____
_____
_____
_____
_____
_____
_____
_____

## a.  FIFO Perpetual

| Date | Purchases | Sales (at cost) | Inventory Balance |
|------|-----------|-----------------|-------------------|
|      |           |                 |                   |
|      |           |                 |                   |
|      |           |                 |                   |
|      |           |                 |                   |
|      |           |                 |                   |
|      |           |                 |                   |
|      |           |                 |                   |
|      |           |                 |                   |
|      |           |                 |                   |
|      |           |                 |                   |
|      |           |                 |                   |

## b.  LIFO Perpetual

| Date | Purchases | Sales (at cost) | Inventory Balance |
|------|-----------|-----------------|-------------------|
|      |           |                 |                   |
|      |           |                 |                   |
|      |           |                 |                   |
|      |           |                 |                   |
|      |           |                 |                   |
|      |           |                 |                   |
|      |           |                 |                   |
|      |           |                 |                   |
|      |           |                 |                   |
|      |           |                 |                   |
|      |           |                 |                   |

## c.  Moving Weighted Average Perpetual

| Date | Purchases | Sales (at cost) | Inventory Balance |
|------|-----------|-----------------|-------------------|
|      |           |                 |                   |
|      |           |                 |                   |
|      |           |                 |                   |
|      |           |                 |                   |
|      |           |                 |                   |
|      |           |                 |                   |
|      |           |                 |                   |
|      |           |                 |                   |
|      |           |                 |                   |
|      |           |                 |                   |
|      |           |                 |                   |
|      |           |                 |                   |
|      |           |                 |                   |

| Date | Purchases | Sales (at cost) | Inventory Balance |
|------|-----------|-----------------|-------------------|
|      |           |                 |                   |
|      |           |                 |                   |
|      |           |                 |                   |
|      |           |                 |                   |
|      |           |                 |                   |
|      |           |                 |                   |
|      |           |                 |                   |
|      |           |                 |                   |
|      |           |                 |                   |
|      |           |                 |                   |
|      |           |                 |                   |
|      |           |                 |                   |
|      |           |                 |                   |
|      |           |                 |                   |

## Quick Study 7-8

| Date | Purchases/ Transportation-In/ (Purchase Returns/Discounts) | | | Cost of Goods Sold/ (Returns to Inventory) | | | Balance in Inventory | | |
|------|-------|------------------|----------|-------|------------------|----------|-------|--------------------|----------|
|      | Units | Cost Per Unit | Total $ | Units | Cost Per Unit | Total $ | Units | AvgCost Per Unit | Total $ |
|      |       |                  |          |       |                  |          |       |                    |          |
|      |       |                  |          |       |                  |          |       |                    |          |
|      |       |                  |          |       |                  |          |       |                    |          |
|      |       |                  |          |       |                  |          |       |                    |          |
|      |       |                  |          |       |                  |          |       |                    |          |
|      |       |                  |          |       |                  |          |       |                    |          |

*Calculations:* _____

_____
_____
_____
_____
_____
_____

## Quick Study 7-9

a. _____    c. _____

b. _____    d. _____

### Parts a and b

| Inventory Items | Units on Hand | Per Unit Cost | Per Unit Market | Total Cost | Total Market | LCM applied to: a. Inventory as a Whole | LCM applied to: b. Each Product |
|---|---|---|---|---|---|---|---|
| Aprons | 9 | $6.00 | $5.50 | | | | |
| Bottles | 12 | 3.50 | 4.25 | | | | |
| Candles | 25 | 8.00 | 7.00 | | | | |
| | | | | | | | |

### Part c          GENERAL JOURNAL          Page____

| Date | Account Titles and Explanation | PR | Debit | Credit |
|---|---|---|---|---|
| | | | | |
| | | | | |
| | | | | |
| | | | | |
| | | | | |

### Quick Study 7-11

a. _____
b. _____
c. _____
d. _____
e. _____
f. _____

### Quick Study 7-12

_____
_____
_____
_____
_____
_____
_____
_____
_____
_____
_____
_____
_____
_____
_____
_____
_____

a. _____
_____
_____
_____
_____
_____
_____
_____
_____
_____
_____

b. _____

## Quick Study 7-14

_____
_____
_____
_____
_____
_____
_____
_____
_____
_____
_____

## Quick Study 7-15

_____
_____
_____
_____
_____
_____
_____
_____
_____
_____
_____
_____
_____
_____
_____
_____

_____
_____
_____
_____
_____
_____
_____
_____
_____
_____
_____
_____
_____
_____
_____
_____

**\*Quick Study 7-17**

_____
_____
_____
_____
_____
_____
_____
_____

**\*Quick Study 7-18**

**a. Days' sales in inventory:**

_____
_____
_____
_____
_____
_____
_____

**b. Merchandise turnover:**

_____
_____
_____
_____
_____
_____
_____
_____

*Name* _____

a. FIFO Perpetual

| Date | Purchases | Sales (at cost) | Inventory Balance |
| --- | --- | --- | --- |
| | | | |
| | | | |
| | | | |
| | | | |
| | | | |
| | | | |
| | | | |
| | | | |
| | | | |
| | | | |
| | | | |
| | | | |
| | | | |
| | | | |
| | | | |
| | | | |
| | | | |
| | | | |
| | | | |
| | | | |

**Gross profit calculation under FIFO:**

| | | | |
| --- | --- | --- | --- |
| | | | |
| | | | |
| | | | |
| | | | |
| | | | |
| | | | |

b. Moving weighted Average Perpetual

| Date | Purchases | Sales (at cost) | Inventory Balance |
| --- | --- | --- | --- |
| | | | |
| | | | |
| | | | |
| | | | |
| | | | |
| | | | |
| | | | |
| | | | |
| | | | |
| | | | |
| | | | |
| | | | |
| | | | |
| | | | |
| | | | |
| | | | |
| | | | |

**Gross Profit Calculation under Moving Weighted Average:**

_____
_____
_____
_____
_____
_____

**c.  LIFO Perpetual**

| Date | Purchases | Sales (at cost) | Inventory Balance |
|------|-----------|-----------------|-------------------|
|      |           |                 |                   |
|      |           |                 |                   |
|      |           |                 |                   |
|      |           |                 |                   |
|      |           |                 |                   |
|      |           |                 |                   |
|      |           |                 |                   |
|      |           |                 |                   |
|      |           |                 |                   |
|      |           |                 |                   |
|      |           |                 |                   |
|      |           |                 |                   |
|      |           |                 |                   |
|      |           |                 |                   |
|      |           |                 |                   |
|      |           |                 |                   |
|      |           |                 |                   |
|      |           |                 |                   |

**Gross Profit Calculation Under LIFO:**

_____
_____
_____
_____
_____
_____

## Specific Identification

| Date | Purchases | Sales (at cost) | Inventory Balance |
|------|-----------|-----------------|-------------------|
|      |           |                 |                   |
|      |           |                 |                   |
|      |           |                 |                   |
|      |           |                 |                   |
|      |           |                 |                   |
|      |           |                 |                   |
|      |           |                 |                   |
|      |           |                 |                   |
|      |           |                 |                   |
|      |           |                 |                   |
|      |           |                 |                   |
|      |           |                 |                   |
|      |           |                 |                   |
|      |           |                 |                   |
|      |           |                 |                   |
|      |           |                 |                   |
|      |           |                 |                   |
|      |           |                 |                   |

## Gross Profit Calculation Under Specific Identification:

**1.** _____

_____

_____

_____

_____

_____

_____

_____

**2.** _____

_____

_____

_____

_____

_____

**3(a).  Moving weighted Average Perpetual**

| Date | Purchases | Sales (at cost) | Inventory Balance |
|------|-----------|-----------------|-------------------|
|      |           |                 |                   |

**3(b).  FIFO Perpetual**

| Date | Purchases | Sales (at cost) | Inventory Balance |
| --- | --- | --- | --- |
| | | | |
| | | | |
| | | | |
| | | | |
| | | | |
| | | | |
| | | | |
| | | | |
| | | | |
| | | | |
| | | | |
| | | | |
| | | | |
| | | | |
| | | | |
| | | | |
| | | | |
| | | | |
| | | | |

**3(c).  LIFO Perpetual**

| Date | Purchases | Sales (at cost) | Inventory Balance |
| --- | --- | --- | --- |
| | | | |
| | | | |
| | | | |
| | | | |
| | | | |
| | | | |
| | | | |
| | | | |
| | | | |
| | | | |
| | | | |
| | | | |
| | | | |
| | | | |
| | | | |
| | | | |
| | | | |
| | | | |
| | | | |
| | | | |
| | | | |

**Specific Identification**

| Date | Purchases | Sales (at cost) | Inventory Balance |
|------|-----------|-----------------|-------------------|
|      |           |                 |                   |
|      |           |                 |                   |
|      |           |                 |                   |
|      |           |                 |                   |
|      |           |                 |                   |
|      |           |                 |                   |
|      |           |                 |                   |
|      |           |                 |                   |
|      |           |                 |                   |
|      |           |                 |                   |
|      |           |                 |                   |
|      |           |                 |                   |
|      |           |                 |                   |
|      |           |                 |                   |
|      |           |                 |                   |
|      |           |                 |                   |
|      |           |                 |                   |
|      |           |                 |                   |
|      |           |                 |                   |
|      |           |                 |                   |
|      |           |                 |                   |
|      |           |                 |                   |

| | Specific Identification | Moving Weighted Average | FIFO | LIFO |
|---|---|---|---|---|
| | | | | |
| | | | | |
| | | | | |
| | | | | |
| | | | | |
| | | | | |
| | | | | |
| | | | | |
| | | | | |

Trout, Inc.
Income Statements
For the Year Ended December 31, 2011

1. _____

2. _____

3. _____

## Exercise 7-6

| | Purchases/ Transportation-In/ (Purchase Returns/Discounts) | | | Cost of Goods Sold/ (Returns to Inventory) | | | Balance in Inventory | | |
|---|---|---|---|---|---|---|---|---|---|
| Date | Units | Cost Per Unit | Total $ | Units | Cost Per Unit | Total $ | Units | AvgCost Per Unit | Total $ |
| | | | | | | | | | |
| | | | | | | | | | |
| | | | | | | | | | |
| | | | | | | | | | |
| | | | | | | | | | |
| | | | | | | | | | |

*Calculations:* _____
_____
_____
_____
_____
_____

*Analysis component:* _____
_____
_____
_____

Parts a and b

| Inventory Items | Units on Hand | Per Unit Cost | Per Unit NRV | Total Cost | Total NRV | a. Inventory as a Whole | b. Each Product |
|---|---|---|---|---|---|---|---|
| BB | 22 | $100 | $108 | | | | |
| FM | 15 | 156 | 144 | | | | |
| MB | 36 | 190 | 182 | | | | |
| SL | 40 | 72 | 87 | | | | |
| | | | | | | | |

Part c    GENERAL JOURNAL    Page____

| Date | Account Titles and Explanation | PR | Debit | Credit |
|---|---|---|---|---|
| | | | | |
| | | | | |
| | | | | |
| | | | | |
| | | | | |

1. _____

_____

_____

2.

| For years ended December 31, 2011, 2012, and 2013 Income statement information should have been reported as: | 2011 | Income statement information actually reported for years ended December 31, | 2012 | 2013 |
|---|---|---|---|---|
| Sales | | | | |
| Cost of goods sold: | | | | |
| Beginning inventory | | | | |
| + Purchases | | | | |
| - Ending inventory | | | | |
| = Cost of goods sold | | | | |
| Gross profit | | | | |

_____
_____
_____
_____
_____
_____
_____
_____
_____
_____
_____
_____
_____
_____
_____
_____

## Exercise 7-10

| | *At Cost* | *At Retail* |
|---|---|---|
| | | |
| | | |
| | | |
| | | |
| | | |
| | | |
| | | |
| | | |
| | | |
| | | |
| | | |
| | | |
| | | |

## Exercise 7-11

### a. Estimated cost of physical inventory:

_____
_____

### b. Shrinkage at cost and at retail:

| | At Cost | At Retail |
|---|---|---|
| | | |
| | | |
| | | |
| | | |
| | | |

|  | Ending Inventory | Cost of Goods Sold |
|---|---|---|

**a. Weighted Average Periodic**  _____

_____

_____

_____

_____

**b. FIFO Periodic**  _____

_____

_____

_____

_____

**c. LIFO Periodic**  _____

_____

_____

_____

_____


**Which method provides the lowest net income?**

_____

_____

_____

|  | Ending Inventory | Cost of Goods Sold |
|---|---|---|

**a. FIFO Periodic**

_____
_____
_____
_____

**b. LIFO Periodic**

_____
_____
_____
_____

**c. Weighted Average Periodic**

_____
_____
_____
_____


**Which method provides the lowest net income?**

_____
_____


**\*Exercise 7-14**

_____
_____
_____
_____
_____
_____
_____
_____
_____
_____
_____
_____
_____
_____
_____
_____
_____

**Merchandise turnover (2012):**
_____
_____
_____
_____

**Merchandise turnover (2011):**
_____
_____
_____
_____

**Days' sales in inventory (2012):**
_____
_____
_____
_____

**Days' sales in inventory (2011):**
_____
_____
_____
_____

Comment on Russo's efficiency in using its assets to support increasing sales from 2011 to 2012.
_____
_____
_____
_____

**Problem 7-1A**
**1b. FIFO Perpetual**

| Date | Purchases | Sales (at cost) | Inventory Balance |
|------|-----------|-----------------|-------------------|
|      |           |                 |                   |
|      |           |                 |                   |
|      |           |                 |                   |
|      |           |                 |                   |
|      |           |                 |                   |
|      |           |                 |                   |
|      |           |                 |                   |
|      |           |                 |                   |
|      |           |                 |                   |
|      |           |                 |                   |
|      |           |                 |                   |
|      |           |                 |                   |
|      |           |                 |                   |
|      |           |                 |                   |
|      |           |                 |                   |
|      |           |                 |                   |

**1b. LIFO Perpetual**

| Date | Purchases | Sales (at cost) | Inventory Balance |
| --- | --- | --- | --- |
|  |  |  |  |
|  |  |  |  |
|  |  |  |  |
|  |  |  |  |
|  |  |  |  |
|  |  |  |  |
|  |  |  |  |
|  |  |  |  |
|  |  |  |  |
|  |  |  |  |
|  |  |  |  |
|  |  |  |  |
|  |  |  |  |
|  |  |  |  |
|  |  |  |  |
|  |  |  |  |
|  |  |  |  |
|  |  |  |  |
|  |  |  |  |
|  |  |  |  |

**1c. Moving weighted Average Perpetual**

| Date | Purchase | Cost of Goods Sold | Inventory Balance |
| --- | --- | --- | --- |
|  |  |  |  |
|  |  |  |  |
|  |  |  |  |
|  |  |  |  |
|  |  |  |  |
|  |  |  |  |
|  |  |  |  |
|  |  |  |  |
|  |  |  |  |
|  |  |  |  |
|  |  |  |  |
|  |  |  |  |
|  |  |  |  |
|  |  |  |  |
|  |  |  |  |
|  |  |  |  |
|  |  |  |  |
|  |  |  |  |
|  |  |  |  |
|  |  |  |  |

**2. Specific Identification**

| Date | Purchase | Cost of Goods Sold | Inventory Balance |
|------|----------|--------------------|--------------------|
|      |          |                    |                    |
|      |          |                    |                    |
|      |          |                    |                    |
|      |          |                    |                    |
|      |          |                    |                    |
|      |          |                    |                    |
|      |          |                    |                    |
|      |          |                    |                    |
|      |          |                    |                    |
|      |          |                    |                    |
|      |          |                    |                    |
|      |          |                    |                    |
|      |          |                    |                    |
|      |          |                    |                    |
|      |          |                    |                    |
|      |          |                    |                    |
|      |          |                    |                    |
|      |          |                    |                    |
|      |          |                    |                    |
|      |          |                    |                    |

**3.**                    **GENERAL JOURNAL**                    Page____

| | Date | Account Titles and Explanation | PR | Debit | Credit |
|---|------|-------------------------------|-----|-------|--------|
| a. | | | | | |
| | | | | | |
| | | | | | |
| | | | | | |
| | | | | | |
| | | | | | |
| | | | | | |
| | | | | | |
| | | | | | |
| | | | | | |
| | | | | | |
| | | | | | |
| | | | | | |
| b. | | | | | |
| | | | | | |
| | | | | | |
| | | | | | |
| | | | | | |
| | | | | | |
| | | | | | |
| | | | | | |

## GENERAL JOURNAL                                    Page____

| Date | Account Titles and Explanation | PR | Debit | Credit |
|---|---|---|---|---|
| | | | | |
| | | | | |
| | | | | |
| | | | | |
| | | | | |
| | | | | |
| | | | | |
| | | | | |
| | | | | |
| | | | | |
| | | | | |
| c. | | | | |
| | | | | |
| | | | | |
| | | | | |
| | | | | |
| | | | | |
| | | | | |
| | | | | |
| | | | | |
| | | | | |
| | | | | |
| | | | | |
| | | | | |
| | | | | |
| d. | | | | |
| | | | | |
| | | | | |
| | | | | |
| | | | | |
| | | | | |
| | | | | |
| | | | | |
| | | | | |
| | | | | |
| | | | | |
| | | | | |
| | | | | |
| | | | | |
| | | | | |

**a. FIFO basis:**

_____
_____
_____
_____
_____
_____
_____

**b. LIFO basis:**

_____
_____
_____
_____
_____
_____
_____

**c. Weighted Average basis:**

_____
_____
_____
_____
_____
_____
_____

**Problem 7-3A**

**Calculation of cost of goods available for sale and units available for sale:**

_____
_____
_____
_____
_____
_____
_____

**Calculation of units in ending inventory:**

_____
_____
_____
_____

## 1a. FIFO Perpetual

| Date | Purchase | Cost of Goods Sold | Inventory Balance |
|------|----------|--------------------|--------------------|
|      |          |                    |                    |
|      |          |                    |                    |
|      |          |                    |                    |
|      |          |                    |                    |
|      |          |                    |                    |
|      |          |                    |                    |
|      |          |                    |                    |
|      |          |                    |                    |
|      |          |                    |                    |
|      |          |                    |                    |
|      |          |                    |                    |
|      |          |                    |                    |
|      |          |                    |                    |
|      |          |                    |                    |
|      |          |                    |                    |
|      |          |                    |                    |
|      |          |                    |                    |
|      |          |                    |                    |
|      |          |                    |                    |
|      |          |                    |                    |
|      |          |                    |                    |

## 1b. LIFO Perpetual

| Date | Purchase | Cost of Goods Sold | Inventory Balance |
|------|----------|--------------------|--------------------|
|      |          |                    |                    |
|      |          |                    |                    |
|      |          |                    |                    |
|      |          |                    |                    |
|      |          |                    |                    |
|      |          |                    |                    |
|      |          |                    |                    |
|      |          |                    |                    |
|      |          |                    |                    |
|      |          |                    |                    |
|      |          |                    |                    |
|      |          |                    |                    |
|      |          |                    |                    |
|      |          |                    |                    |
|      |          |                    |                    |
|      |          |                    |                    |
|      |          |                    |                    |
|      |          |                    |                    |
|      |          |                    |                    |

## 1c.  Moving Weighted Average Perpetual

| Date | Purchase | Cost of Goods Sold | Inventory Balance |
|------|----------|--------------------|--------------------|
|      |          |                    |                    |
|      |          |                    |                    |
|      |          |                    |                    |
|      |          |                    |                    |
|      |          |                    |                    |
|      |          |                    |                    |
|      |          |                    |                    |
|      |          |                    |                    |
|      |          |                    |                    |
|      |          |                    |                    |
|      |          |                    |                    |
|      |          |                    |                    |
|      |          |                    |                    |
|      |          |                    |                    |
|      |          |                    |                    |
|      |          |                    |                    |
|      |          |                    |                    |
|      |          |                    |                    |
|      |          |                    |                    |
|      |          |                    |                    |
|      |          |                    |                    |

**2.**

|                       | FIFO | LIFO | Moving Weighted Average |
|-----------------------|------|------|-------------------------|
| Sales....................................... |      |      |                         |
| Cost of goods sold................ |      |      |                         |
| Gross profit........................... |      |      |                         |

*Analysis component:* _____

_____

_____

_____

_____

a. FIFO basis:

_____
_____
_____
_____
_____
_____
_____

b. LIFO basis:

_____
_____
_____
_____
_____
_____
_____

c. Weighted Average basis:

_____
_____
_____
_____
_____
_____
_____

**Fresh Express Company**
**Income Statement Comparing FIFO, LIFO and Moving Weighted Average Cost**
**For Year Ended December 31, 2011**

| | FIFO | LIFO | Moving Weighted Average |
|---|---|---|---|
| Sales | | | |
| Cost of goods sold | | | |
| Gross profit | | | |
| Operating expenses | | | |
| Net income | | | |

**Supporting calculations:**

_____
_____
_____
_____
_____
_____
_____
_____
_____
_____
_____
_____
_____
_____
_____
_____
_____

## 1a. FIFO Perpetual

| Date | Purchase | Cost of Goods Sold | Inventory Balance |
|------|----------|--------------------|--------------------|
|      |          |                    |                    |
|      |          |                    |                    |
|      |          |                    |                    |
|      |          |                    |                    |
|      |          |                    |                    |
|      |          |                    |                    |
|      |          |                    |                    |
|      |          |                    |                    |
|      |          |                    |                    |
|      |          |                    |                    |
|      |          |                    |                    |
|      |          |                    |                    |
|      |          |                    |                    |
|      |          |                    |                    |
|      |          |                    |                    |
|      |          |                    |                    |
|      |          |                    |                    |
|      |          |                    |                    |
|      |          |                    |                    |
|      |          |                    |                    |
|      |          |                    |                    |
|      |          |                    |                    |

## 1b. LIFO Perpetual

| Date | Purchase | Cost of Goods Sold | Inventory Balance |
|------|----------|--------------------|--------------------|
|      |          |                    |                    |
|      |          |                    |                    |
|      |          |                    |                    |
|      |          |                    |                    |
|      |          |                    |                    |
|      |          |                    |                    |
|      |          |                    |                    |
|      |          |                    |                    |
|      |          |                    |                    |
|      |          |                    |                    |
|      |          |                    |                    |
|      |          |                    |                    |
|      |          |                    |                    |
|      |          |                    |                    |
|      |          |                    |                    |
|      |          |                    |                    |
|      |          |                    |                    |
|      |          |                    |                    |

## 1c. Moving Weighted Average Perpetual

| Date | Purchase | Cost of Goods Sold | Inventory Balance |
|------|----------|--------------------|--------------------|
|      |          |                    |                    |
|      |          |                    |                    |
|      |          |                    |                    |
|      |          |                    |                    |
|      |          |                    |                    |
|      |          |                    |                    |
|      |          |                    |                    |
|      |          |                    |                    |
|      |          |                    |                    |
|      |          |                    |                    |
|      |          |                    |                    |
|      |          |                    |                    |
|      |          |                    |                    |
|      |          |                    |                    |
|      |          |                    |                    |
|      |          |                    |                    |
|      |          |                    |                    |
|      |          |                    |                    |
|      |          |                    |                    |
|      |          |                    |                    |
|      |          |                    |                    |

*Analysis component:*

_____
_____
_____
_____
_____
_____
_____
_____

## Fresh Express Company
### Income Statement Comparing FIFO, LIFO and Weighted Average Periodic
### For Year Ended December 31, 2011

|  | FIFO | LIFO | Weighted Average |
|---|---|---|---|
| Sales |  |  |  |
| Cost of goods sold |  |  |  |
| Gross profit |  |  |  |
| Operating expenses |  |  |  |
| Net income |  |  |  |

*Supporting calculations:*

_____
_____
_____
_____
_____
_____
_____
_____
_____
_____
_____
_____
_____
_____
_____
_____
_____
_____
_____
_____
_____

*Name* _____

Part 1

| a.  Cost of Goods Sold: | *2011* | *2012* | *2013* |
|---|---|---|---|
| Reported ...................................... | _____ | _____ | _____ |
| Adjustments:    12/31/2011 error | _____ | _____ | _____ |
|                         12/31/2012 error | _____ | _____ | _____ |
| Corrected ...................................... | _____ | _____ | _____ |

| b.  Net Income: | *2011* | *2012* | *2013* |
|---|---|---|---|
| Reported ...................................... | _____ | _____ | _____ |
| Adjustments:    12/31/2011 error | _____ | _____ | _____ |
|                         12/31/2012 error | _____ | _____ | _____ |
| Corrected ...................................... | _____ | _____ | _____ |

| c.  Total Current Assets: | *2011* | *2012* | *2013* |
|---|---|---|---|
| Reported ...................................... | _____ | _____ | _____ |
| Adjustments:    12/31/2011 error | _____ | _____ | _____ |
|                         12/31/2012 error | _____ | _____ | _____ |
| Corrected ...................................... | _____ | _____ | _____ |

| d.  Owner's Equity: | *2011* | *2012* | *2013* |
|---|---|---|---|
| Reported ...................................... | _____ | _____ | _____ |
| Adjustments:    12/31/2011 error | _____ | _____ | _____ |
|                         12/31/2012 error | _____ | _____ | _____ |
| Corrected ...................................... | _____ | _____ | _____ |

*Analysis component:*

_____
_____
_____
_____
_____
_____
_____
_____
_____
_____
_____
_____
_____
_____
_____
_____

|  | 2011 | 2012 | 2013 |
|---|---|---|---|
| **Corrected Ending Inventory** | | | |
| **Corrected Cost of Goods Sold** | | | |
| **Corrected Net Income** | | | |

## Problem 7-9A

| Inventory Items | Units on Hand | Per Unit Cost | Per Unit Market | Total Cost | Total Market | LCM applied to: a. Whole | b. Major Category | c. Separately to Each Product |
|---|---|---|---|---|---|---|---|---|
| Audio equip: | | | | | | | | |
| Receivers | 335 | $180 | $ 196 | | | | | |
| CD players | 250 | 222 | 200 | | | | | |
| Cassette decks | 316 | 172 | 190 | | | | | |
| Turntables | 194 | 104 | 82 | | | | | |
| | | | | | | | | |
| Video: | | | | | | | | |
| Televisions | 470 | 300 | 250 | | | | | |
| VCRs | 281 | 186 | 168 | | | | | |
| Video cameras | 202 | 620 | 644 | | | | | |
| | | | | | | | | |
| Car Audio: | | | | | | | | |
| Cassette radios | 175 | 140 | 168 | | | | | |
| CD radios | 160 | 194 | 210 | | | | | |
| | | | | | | | | |
| | | | | | | | | |

_____

**Problem 7-11A**

_____

**Part 1**

Earthly Goods
Estimated Inventory
December 31, 2011

|  | *At Cost* | *At Retail* |
|---|---|---|
|  |  |  |
|  |  |  |
|  |  |  |
|  |  |  |
|  |  |  |
|  |  |  |
|  |  |  |
|  |  |  |
|  |  |  |
|  |  |  |
|  |  |  |
|  |  |  |
|  |  |  |
|  |  |  |

**Part 2**

Earthly Goods
Inventory Shortage
December 31, 2011

|  | *At Cost* | *At Retail* |
|---|---|---|
|  |  |  |
|  |  |  |
|  |  |  |
|  |  |  |
|  |  |  |
|  |  |  |

**Part 1**

|  | At Cost | At Retail |
|---|---|---|
|  |  |  |

**Part 2**

**\*Problem 7-14A**

**Part 1**

**Part 2**
**a. FIFO basis:**

_____
_____
_____
_____
_____
_____
_____
_____

**b. LIFO basis:**

_____
_____
_____
_____
_____
_____
_____
_____

**c. Weighted Average basis:**

_____
_____
_____
_____
_____
_____
_____
_____

Name _____

## 1a.  FIFO Perpetual

| Date | Purchases | Sales (at cost) | Inventory Balance |
|------|-----------|-----------------|-------------------|
|      |           |                 |                   |

## 1b.  LIFO Perpetual

| Date | Purchases | Sales (at cost) | Inventory Balance |
|------|-----------|-----------------|-------------------|
|      |           |                 |                   |

## 1c. Moving weighted Average Perpetual

| Date | Purchase | Cost of Goods Sold | Inventory Balance |
|------|----------|--------------------|--------------------|
|      |          |                    |                    |
|      |          |                    |                    |
|      |          |                    |                    |
|      |          |                    |                    |
|      |          |                    |                    |
|      |          |                    |                    |
|      |          |                    |                    |
|      |          |                    |                    |
|      |          |                    |                    |
|      |          |                    |                    |
|      |          |                    |                    |
|      |          |                    |                    |
|      |          |                    |                    |
|      |          |                    |                    |
|      |          |                    |                    |
|      |          |                    |                    |
|      |          |                    |                    |
|      |          |                    |                    |
|      |          |                    |                    |
|      |          |                    |                    |
|      |          |                    |                    |

## 2. Specific Identification

| Date | Purchase | Cost of Goods Sold | Inventory Balance |
|------|----------|--------------------|--------------------|
|      |          |                    |                    |
|      |          |                    |                    |
|      |          |                    |                    |
|      |          |                    |                    |
|      |          |                    |                    |
|      |          |                    |                    |
|      |          |                    |                    |
|      |          |                    |                    |
|      |          |                    |                    |
|      |          |                    |                    |
|      |          |                    |                    |
|      |          |                    |                    |
|      |          |                    |                    |
|      |          |                    |                    |
|      |          |                    |                    |
|      |          |                    |                    |

3.                              **GENERAL JOURNAL**                      Page____

| Date | Account Titles and Explanation | PR | Debit | Credit |
|------|-------------------------------|-----|-------|--------|
| a. | | | | |
| | | | | |
| | | | | |
| | | | | |
| | | | | |
| | | | | |
| | | | | |
| | | | | |
| | | | | |
| | | | | |
| | | | | |
| | | | | |
| b. | | | | |
| | | | | |
| | | | | |
| | | | | |
| | | | | |
| | | | | |
| | | | | |
| | | | | |
| | | | | |
| | | | | |
| | | | | |
| c. | | | | |
| | | | | |
| | | | | |
| | | | | |
| | | | | |
| | | | | |
| | | | | |
| | | | | |
| | | | | |
| | | | | |
| | | | | |

## GENERAL JOURNAL                                              Page____

| Date | | Account Titles and Explanation | PR | Debit | | | Credit | | |
|------|--|-------------------------------|----|-------|--|--|--------|--|--|
| d. | | | | | | | | | |
| | | | | | | | | | |
| | | | | | | | | | |
| | | | | | | | | | |
| | | | | | | | | | |
| | | | | | | | | | |
| | | | | | | | | | |
| | | | | | | | | | |
| | | | | | | | | | |
| | | | | | | | | | |
| | | | | | | | | | |
| | | | | | | | | | |
| | | | | | | | | | |
| | | | | | | | | | |
| | | | | | | | | | |
| | | | | | | | | | |

### *Problem 7-2B

**a. FIFO basis:**

_____

_____

_____

_____

_____

_____

_____

**b. LIFO basis:**

_____

_____

_____

_____

_____

_____

_____

**c. Weighted Average basis:**

_____

_____

_____

_____

_____

_____

## 1a.  FIFO Perpetual

| Date | Purchase | Cost of Goods Sold | Inventory Balance |
|------|----------|--------------------|-------------------|
|      |          |                    |                   |

## 1b.  LIFO Perpetual

| Date | Purchase | Cost of Goods Sold | Inventory Balance |
|------|----------|--------------------|-------------------|
|      |          |                    |                   |

## 1c.  Moving Weighted Average Perpetual

| Date | Purchase | Cost of Goods Sold | Inventory Balance |
|------|----------|--------------------|-------------------|
|      |          |                    |                   |
|      |          |                    |                   |
|      |          |                    |                   |
|      |          |                    |                   |
|      |          |                    |                   |
|      |          |                    |                   |
|      |          |                    |                   |
|      |          |                    |                   |
|      |          |                    |                   |
|      |          |                    |                   |
|      |          |                    |                   |
|      |          |                    |                   |
|      |          |                    |                   |
|      |          |                    |                   |
|      |          |                    |                   |
|      |          |                    |                   |
|      |          |                    |                   |

## 2.

|  | FIFO | LIFO | Moving Weighted Average |
|------|------|------|-------------------------|
| Sales................................. |  |  |  |
| Cost of goods sold............... |  |  |  |
| Gross profit.......................... |  |  |  |

*Analysis component:* _____

_____

_____

_____

_____

_____

*Problem 7-4B

a.  FIFO basis:

_____

_____

_____

_____

_____

_____

_____

b. LIFO basis:

_____
_____
_____
_____
_____
_____
_____
_____

c. Weighted Average basis:

_____
_____
_____
_____
_____
_____
_____
_____

## Problem 7-5B

### The Denney Company
### Income Statement Comparing FIFO, LIFO and Moving Weighted Average Cost
### For Year Ended December 31, 2011

|  | FIFO | LIFO | Moving Weighted Average |
|---|---|---|---|
| Sales |  |  |  |
| Cost of goods sold |  |  |  |
| Gross profit |  |  |  |
| Operating expenses |  |  |  |
| Net income |  |  |  |

Supporting calculations:

_____
_____
_____
_____
_____
_____
_____
_____
_____
_____
_____
_____
_____
_____

## 1a.  FIFO Perpetual

| Date | Purchase | Cost of Goods Sold | Inventory Balance |
|------|----------|--------------------|--------------------|
|      |          |                    |                    |

## 1b.  LIFO Perpetual

| Date | Purchase | Cost of Goods Sold | Inventory Balance |
|------|----------|--------------------|--------------------|
|      |          |                    |                    |

## 1c.  Moving Weighted Average Perpetual

| Date | Purchase | Cost of Goods Sold | Inventory Balance |
|------|----------|--------------------|--------------------|
|      |          |                    |                    |
|      |          |                    |                    |
|      |          |                    |                    |
|      |          |                    |                    |
|      |          |                    |                    |
|      |          |                    |                    |
|      |          |                    |                    |
|      |          |                    |                    |
|      |          |                    |                    |
|      |          |                    |                    |
|      |          |                    |                    |
|      |          |                    |                    |
|      |          |                    |                    |
|      |          |                    |                    |
|      |          |                    |                    |
|      |          |                    |                    |
|      |          |                    |                    |
|      |          |                    |                    |
|      |          |                    |                    |

*Analysis component:*

_____

_____

_____

_____

_____

_____

_____

_____

## The Denney Company
### Income Statement Comparing FIFO, LIFO and Weighted Average Periodic
### For Year Ended December 31, 2011

|  | FIFO | LIFO | Weighted Average |
|---|---|---|---|
| Sales |  |  |  |
| Cost of goods sold |  |  |  |
| Gross profit |  |  |  |
| Operating expenses |  |  |  |
| Net income |  |  |  |

Supporting calculations:

_____
_____
_____
_____
_____
_____
_____
_____
_____
_____
_____

a.  FIFO Periodic

_____
_____
_____
_____
_____
_____
_____
_____
_____
_____

b.  LIFO Periodic

_____
_____
_____
_____
_____
_____
_____
_____
_____
_____

## c. Weighted Average Periodic

_____

_____

_____

_____

_____

_____

_____

_____

_____

_____

Part 1

| a.  Cost of Goods Sold: | 2011 | 2012 | 2013 |
|---|---|---|---|
| Reported ..................................... | _____ | _____ | _____ |
| Adjustments:    12/31/2011 error | _____ | _____ | _____ |
| 12/31/2012 error | _____ | _____ | _____ |
| Corrected ..................................... | _____ | _____ | _____ |

| b.  Net Income: | 2011 | 2012 | 2013 |
|---|---|---|---|
| Reported ..................................... | _____ | _____ | _____ |
| Adjustments:    12/31/2011 error | _____ | _____ | _____ |
| 12/31/2012 error | _____ | _____ | _____ |
| Corrected ..................................... | _____ | _____ | _____ |

| c.  Total Current Assets: | 2011 | 2012 | 2013 |
|---|---|---|---|
| Reported ..................................... | _____ | _____ | _____ |
| Adjustments:    12/31/2011 error | _____ | _____ | _____ |
| 12/31/2012 error | _____ | _____ | _____ |
| Corrected ..................................... | _____ | _____ | _____ |

| d.  Owner's Equity: | 2011 | 2012 | 2013 |
|---|---|---|---|
| Reported ..................................... | _____ | _____ | _____ |
| Adjustments:    12/31/2011 error | _____ | _____ | _____ |
| 12/31/2012 error | _____ | _____ | _____ |
| Corrected ..................................... | _____ | _____ | _____ |

*Analysis component:*

_____
_____
_____
_____
_____
_____
_____
_____
_____
_____
_____
_____
_____
_____
_____
_____
_____

Part 1

|  | Incorrect Income Statement Information For Years Ended December 31 | | | | Corrected Income Statement Information For Years Ended December 31 | | | |
|  | 2011 | % | 2012 | % | 2011 | % | 2012 | % |
|---|---|---|---|---|---|---|---|---|
| Sales ......................... |  |  |  |  |  |  |  |  |
| Cost of goods sold ... |  |  |  |  |  |  |  |  |
| Gross profit .............. |  |  |  |  |  |  |  |  |

Part 2    _____

_____

_____

_____

## Problem 7-9B

| Inventory Items | Units on Hand | Per Unit | | Total Cost | Total Market | LCM applied to: | | |
|  |  | Cost | Market |  |  | a. Whole | b. Major Category | c. Separately to Each Product |
|---|---|---|---|---|---|---|---|---|
| **Office furniture:** |  |  |  |  |  |  |  |  |
| Desks | 436 | $261 | $305 |  |  |  |  |  |
| Credenzas | 295 | 227 | 256 |  |  |  |  |  |
| Chairs | 587 | 49 | 43 |  |  |  |  |  |
| Bookshelves | 321 | 93 | 82 |  |  |  |  |  |
|  |  |  |  |  |  |  |  |  |
| **Filing cabinets:** |  |  |  |  |  |  |  |  |
| Two-drawer | 214 | 81 | 70 |  |  |  |  |  |
| Four-drawer | 398 | 135 | 122 |  |  |  |  |  |
| Lateral | 175 | 104 | 118 |  |  |  |  |  |
|  |  |  |  |  |  |  |  |  |
| **Office Equip.:** |  |  |  |  |  |  |  |  |
| Fax machines | 430 | 168 | 200 |  |  |  |  |  |
| Copiers | 545 | 317 | 288 |  |  |  |  |  |
| Typewriters | 352 | 125 | 117 |  |  |  |  |  |
|  |  |  |  |  |  |  |  |  |
|  |  |  |  |  |  |  |  |  |

**Problem 7-11B**

**Part 1**

### THE R.E. McFADDEN CO.
### Estimated Inventory
### December 31, 2011

| | *At Cost* | *At Retail* |
| --- | --- | --- |
| | | |
| | | |
| | | |
| | | |
| | | |
| | | |
| | | |
| | | |
| | | |
| | | |
| | | |
| | | |
| | | |
| | | |
| | | |
| | | |
| | | |
| | | |
| | | |
| | | |
| | | |

**Part 2**

### THE R.E. McFADDEN CO.
### Inventory Shortage
### December 31, 2011

| | *At Cost* | *At Retail* |
| --- | --- | --- |
| | | |
| | | |
| | | |
| | | |
| | | |
| | | |
| | | |

Chapter 7    Problem 7-13B         *Name*

Part 1

| | At Cost | At Retail |
| --- | --- | --- |
| | | |
| | | |
| | | |
| | | |
| | | |
| | | |
| | | |
| | | |
| | | |
| | | |
| | | |
| | | |
| | | |
| | | |
| | | |
| | | |
| | | |
| | | |

Part 2

*Problem 7-14B

Part 1

**Part 2**
**a. FIFO basis:**

_____
_____
_____
_____
_____
_____
_____
_____

**b. LIFO basis:**

_____
_____
_____
_____
_____
_____
_____
_____

**c. Weighted Average basis:**

_____
_____
_____
_____
_____
_____
_____
_____

1.                                          3.
2.                                          4.

## Quick Study 8-2

1.                                          5.
2.                                          6.
3.                                          7.
4.                                          8.

## Quick Study 8-3

a.                                          e.
b.                                          f.
c.                                          g.
d.

## Quick Study 8-4

### GENERAL JOURNAL                                          Page____

| Date | Account Titles and Explanation | PR | Debit | Credit |
|------|-------------------------------|----|----|----|
|  |  |  |  |  |
|  |  |  |  |  |
|  |  |  |  |  |
|  |  |  |  |  |
|  |  |  |  |  |
|  |  |  |  |  |
|  |  |  |  |  |
|  |  |  |  |  |
|  |  |  |  |  |
|  |  |  |  |  |
|  |  |  |  |  |
|  |  |  |  |  |
|  |  |  |  |  |
|  |  |  |  |  |
|  |  |  |  |  |
|  |  |  |  |  |
|  |  |  |  |  |
|  |  |  |  |  |

1. _____      5. _____
2. _____      6. _____
3. _____      7. _____
4. _____

## Quick Study 8-6

1. _____      5. _____
2. _____      6. _____
3. _____      7. _____
4. _____

## Quick Study 8-7

| | | | | Sales Journal | Page |
|---|---|---|---|---|---|
| Date | Account Debited | Invoice Number | PR | Accounts Receivable Dr. Sales Cr. | Cost of Goods Sold Dr. Merchandise Inventory Cr. |
| | | | | | |
| | | | | | |
| | | | | | |
| | | | | | |
| | | | | | |

## Quick Study 8-8

| | | | | | | | | | |
|---|---|---|---|---|---|---|---|---|---|
| | | | Cash Receipts Journal | | | | | | Page |
| Date | Account Credited | PR | Explanation | Cash Dr. | Sales Disc. Dr. | Accts. Rec. Cr. | Sales Cr. | Other Accts. Cr. | COGS Dr. Merch. Inv. Cr. |
| | | | | | | | | | |
| | | | | | | | | | |
| | | | | | | | | | |
| | | | | | | | | | |
| | | | | | | | | | |

## Quick Study 8-9

| | | | | | Purchases Journal | | | Page |
|---|---|---|---|---|---|---|---|---|
| Date | Account Credited | Date of Invoice | Terms | PR | Accounts Payable Cr. | Merch. Inventory Dr. | Office Supplies Dr. | Other Accounts Dr. |
| | | | | | | | | |
| | | | | | | | | |
| | | | | | | | | |
| | | | | | | | | |
| | | | | | | | | |

| | | | | | | | | |
|---|---|---|---|---|---|---|---|---|
| | | | Cash Disbursements Journal | | | | | Page |
| Date | Ch. No. | Payee | Account Debited | PR | Cash Cr. | Merch. Inventory Cr. | Other Accounts Dr. | Accounts Payable Dr. |
| | | | | | | | | |
| | | | | | | | | |
| | | | | | | | | |
| | | | | | | | | |
| | | | | | | | | |

## Exercise 8-1

| | | | | | |
|---|---|---|---|---|---|
| | | | Sales Journal | | Page |
| Date | Account Debited | Invoice Number | PR | Accounts Receivable Dr. Sales Cr. | Cost of Goods Sold Dr. Merchandise Inventory Cr. |
| | | | | | |
| | | | | | |
| | | | | | |
| | | | | | |
| | | | | | |

## *Exercise 8-2

| | | | | |
|---|---|---|---|---|
| | | Sales Journal | | Page |
| Date | Account Debited | Invoice No. | PR | Accounts Receivable Dr. Sales Cr. |
| | | | | |
| | | | | |
| | | | | |
| | | | | |
| | | | | |

## Exercise 8-3

| | | | | | | | | | |
|---|---|---|---|---|---|---|---|---|---|
| | | | | Cash Receipts Journal | | | | | Page |
| Date | Account Credited | PR | Explanation | Cash Dr. | Sales Disc. Dr. | Accts. Rec. Cr. | Sales Cr. | Other Accts. Cr. | COGS Dr. Merch. Inv. Cr. |
| | | | | | | | | | |
| | | | | | | | | | |
| | | | | | | | | | |
| | | | | | | | | | |
| | | | | | | | | | |
| | | | | | | | | | |

### Cash Receipts Journal                    Page

| Date | Account Credited | PR | Explanation | Cash Dr. | Sales Disc. Dr. | Accts. Rec. Cr. | Sales Cr. | Other Accts. Cr. |
|------|------------------|----|-----|------|------|------|------|------|
|      |                  |    |     |      |      |      |      |      |
|      |                  |    |     |      |      |      |      |      |
|      |                  |    |     |      |      |      |      |      |
|      |                  |    |     |      |      |      |      |      |
|      |                  |    |     |      |      |      |      |      |

## Exercise 8-5

### Purchases Journal                    Page

| Date | Account Credited | Date of Invoice | Terms | PR | Accounts Payable Cr. | Merch. Inventory Dr. | Office Supplies Dr. | Other Accounts Dr. |
|------|------------------|-----------------|-------|----|------|------|------|------|
|      |                  |                 |       |    |      |      |      |      |
|      |                  |                 |       |    |      |      |      |      |
|      |                  |                 |       |    |      |      |      |      |
|      |                  |                 |       |    |      |      |      |      |
|      |                  |                 |       |    |      |      |      |      |

## *Exercise 8-6

### Purchases Journal                    Page

| Date | Account Credited | Date of Invoice | Terms | PR | Accts. Payable Cr. | Purchases Dr. | Office Supplies Dr. | Other Accts. Dr. |
|------|------------------|-----------------|-------|----|------|------|------|------|
|      |                  |                 |       |    |      |      |      |      |
|      |                  |                 |       |    |      |      |      |      |
|      |                  |                 |       |    |      |      |      |      |
|      |                  |                 |       |    |      |      |      |      |
|      |                  |                 |       |    |      |      |      |      |

## Exercise 8-7

### Cash Disbursements Journal                    Page

| Date | Ch. No. | Payee | Account Debited | PR | Cash Cr. | Merch. Inventory Cr. | Other Accounts Dr. | Accounts Payable Dr. |
|------|---------|-------|-----------------|----|------|------|------|------|
|      |         |       |                 |    |      |      |      |      |
|      |         |       |                 |    |      |      |      |      |
|      |         |       |                 |    |      |      |      |      |
|      |         |       |                 |    |      |      |      |      |
|      |         |       |                 |    |      |      |      |      |
|      |         |       |                 |    |      |      |      |      |
|      |         |       |                 |    |      |      |      |      |

| Cash Disbursements Journal | | | | | | | | Page |
|---|---|---|---|---|---|---|---|---|
| Date | Ch. No. | Payee | Account Debited | PR | Cash Cr. | Purch. Disc. Cr. | Other Accounts Dr. | Accts. Payable Dr. |
| | | | | | | | | |
| | | | | | | | | |
| | | | | | | | | |
| | | | | | | | | |
| | | | | | | | | |
| | | | | | | | | |
| | | | | | | | | |

## Exercise 8-9

## Part 1 – Wilson Purchasing

| Purchases Journal | | | | | | | | Page |
|---|---|---|---|---|---|---|---|---|
| Date | Account Credited | Date of Invoice | Terms | PR | Accounts Payable Cr. | Merch. Inventory Dr. | Office Supplies Dr. | Other Accounts Dr. |
| | | | | | | | | |
| | | | | | | | | |
| | | | | | | | | |

| Cash Disbursements Journal | | | | | | | | Page |
|---|---|---|---|---|---|---|---|---|
| Date | Ch. No. | Payee | Account Debited | PR | Cash Cr. | Merch. Inventory Cr. | Other Accounts Dr. | Accounts Payable Dr. |
| | | | | | | | | |
| | | | | | | | | |
| | | | | | | | | |
| | | | | | | | | |

### GENERAL JOURNAL                                     Page____

| Date | Account Titles and Explanation | PR | Debit | Credit |
|---|---|---|---|---|
| | | | | |
| | | | | |
| | | | | |
| | | | | |
| | | | | |

## Part 2 – Hostel Sales

| Sales Journal | | | | Accounts Receivable Dr. Sales Cr. | Cost of Goods Sold Dr. Merchandise Inventory Cr. | Page |
|---|---|---|---|---|---|---|
| Date | Account Debited | Invoice Number | PR | | | |
| | | | | | | |
| | | | | | | |
| | | | | | | |

| Cash Receipts Journal | | | | | | | | | Page |
|---|---|---|---|---|---|---|---|---|---|
| Date | Account Credited | PR | Explanation | Cash Dr. | Sales Disc. Dr. | Accts. Rec. Cr. | Sales Cr. | Other Accts. Cr. | COGS Dr. Merch. Inv. Cr. |
| | | | | | | | | | |
| | | | | | | | | | |
| | | | | | | | | | |

### GENERAL JOURNAL                                                    Page____

| Date | Account Titles and Explanation | PR | Debit | Credit |
|---|---|---|---|---|
| | | | | |
| | | | | |
| | | | | |
| | | | | |
| | | | | |
| | | | | |
| | | | | |
| | | | | |
| | | | | |
| | | | | |
| | | | | |

## *Exercise 8-10

## Part 1 – Wilson Purchasing

| Purchases Journal | | | | | Accts. Payable Cr. | Purchases Dr. | Office Supplies Dr. | Other Accts. Dr. | Page |
|---|---|---|---|---|---|---|---|---|---|
| Date | Account Credited | Date of Invoice | Terms | PR | | | | | |
| | | | | | | | | | |
| | | | | | | | | | |
| | | | | | | | | | |
| | | | | | | | | | |
| | | | | | | | | | |

| Cash Disbursements Journal | | | | | | | | Page |
|---|---|---|---|---|---|---|---|---|
| Date | Ch. No. | Payee | Account Debited | PR | Cash Cr. | Purch. Disc. Cr. | Other Accounts Dr. | Accts. Payable Dr. |
|  |  |  |  |  |  |  |  |  |
|  |  |  |  |  |  |  |  |  |
|  |  |  |  |  |  |  |  |  |
|  |  |  |  |  |  |  |  |  |
|  |  |  |  |  |  |  |  |  |

### GENERAL JOURNAL    Page____

| Date | Account Titles and Explanation | PR | Debit | Credit |
|---|---|---|---|---|
|  |  |  |  |  |
|  |  |  |  |  |
|  |  |  |  |  |
|  |  |  |  |  |

## Part 2 – Hostel Sales

| Sales Journal | | | | Page |
|---|---|---|---|---|
| Date | Account Debited | Invoice No. | PR | Accounts Receivable Dr. Sales Cr. |
|  |  |  |  |  |
|  |  |  |  |  |
|  |  |  |  |  |
|  |  |  |  |  |
|  |  |  |  |  |

| Cash Receipts Journal | | | | | | | | Page |
|---|---|---|---|---|---|---|---|---|
| Date | Account Credited | PR | Explanation | Cash Dr. | Sales Disc. Dr. | Accts. Rec. Cr. | Sales Cr. | Other Accts. Cr. |
|  |  |  |  |  |  |  |  |  |
|  |  |  |  |  |  |  |  |  |
|  |  |  |  |  |  |  |  |  |
|  |  |  |  |  |  |  |  |  |
|  |  |  |  |  |  |  |  |  |

### GENERAL JOURNAL    Page____

| Date | Account Titles and Explanation | PR | Debit | Credit |
|---|---|---|---|---|
|  |  |  |  |  |
|  |  |  |  |  |
|  |  |  |  |  |
|  |  |  |  |  |

_____
_____
_____
_____
_____
_____
_____
_____
_____
_____
_____
_____
_____
_____

## Exercise 8-12

a. _____

b. _____

c. _____

d. _____

e. _____

_____

## Exercise 8-13

**Part 1**                **ACCOUNTS RECEIVABLE SUBLEDGER**

| Sanders Farrell | Don Holland | Brad Smithers |
|:---:|:---:|:---:|
|  |  |  |

**Part 2**                **GENERAL LEDGER**

| Accounts Receivable | Sales | Sales Returns and Allowances |
|:---:|:---:|:---:|
|  |  |  |

Part 3

## Schedule of Accounts Receivable

| | | |
|---|---|---|
| | | |
| | | |
| | | |
| | | |
| | | |
| | | |
| | | |
| | | |
| | | |
| | | |
| | | |

*Exercise 8-14

Parts 1 and 2

## GENERAL LEDGER

| Cash | Accounts Payable | Sales Returns and Allowances |
|---|---|---|
| | | |

| Accts. Receivable | Notes Payable | Purchases |
|---|---|---|
| | | |

| Prepaid Insurance | Sales | Purchase Discounts |
|---|---|---|
| | | |

| Store Equipment | Sales Discounts | Purchase Returns and Allowances |
|---|---|---|
| | | |

## ACCOUNTS RECEIVABLE SUBLEDGER

| Jack Hertz | Trudy Stone | Dave Waylon |
|---|---|---|
| | | |

## ACCOUNTS PAYABLE SUBLEDGER

| Grass Corp. | McGrew Company | Sulter Inc. |
|---|---|---|
| | | |

**\*Exercise 8-15**

**Part 1**

### ACCOUNTS RECEIVABLE SUBLEDGER

| Adrian Carr | Lisa Mack |
|---|---|
| | |

| Jay Newton | Kathy Olivas |
|---|---|
| | |

**Part 2**                    **GENERAL JOURNAL**                    Page____

| Date | Account Titles and Explanation | PR | Debit | Credit |
|---|---|---|---|---|
| | | | | |
| | | | | |
| | | | | |
| | | | | |
| | | | | |
| | | | | |

Part 3                        GENERAL LEDGER

| Accounts Receivable | Sales |
|---|---|
| | |

Part 4

## Schedule of Accounts Receivable

| | | |
|---|---|---|
| | | |
| | | |
| | | |
| | | |
| | | |
| | | |
| | | |
| | | |
| | | |
| | | |

## *Exercise 8-16

| | | | | | | | | |
|---|---|---|---|---|---|---|---|---|
| **Sales Journal** | | | | | | | | **Page** |
| Date | Account Debited | Invoice No. | PR | Acct. Rec. Dr. | PST Payable Cr. | GST Payable Cr. | Sales Cr. | COGS Dr. Merch. Inv. Cr. |
| | | | | | | | | |
| | | | | | | | | |
| | | | | | | | | |
| | | | | | | | | |

| | | | | | | | | | | | |
|---|---|---|---|---|---|---|---|---|---|---|---|
| **Cash Receipts Journal** | | | | | | | | | | | **Page** |
| Date | Account Credited | Explanation | PR | Cash Dr. | Sales Disc. Dr. | Accts. Rec. Cr. | Sales Cr. | Other Accts. Cr. | PST Payable Cr. | GST Payable Cr. | COGS Dr. Merch. Inv. Cr. |
| | | | | | | | | | | | |
| | | | | | | | | | | | |
| | | | | | | | | | | | |
| | | | | | | | | | | | |

| Purchases Journal | | | | | | | | Page |
|---|---|---|---|---|---|---|---|---|
| Date | Account Credited | Terms | PR | Accounts Payable Cr. | Merch. Inventory Dr. | Other Accounts Dr. | GST Receivable Dr. | |
| | | | | | | | | |
| | | | | | | | | |
| | | | | | | | | |
| | | | | | | | | |

| Cash Disbursements Journal | | | | | | | | Page |
|---|---|---|---|---|---|---|---|---|
| Date | Ch No | Account Debited | PR | Cash Cr. | Merch. Inventory Cr. | Other Accounts Dr. | GST Receivable Dr. | Accts. Payable Dr. |
| | | | | | | | | |
| | | | | | | | | |
| | | | | | | | | |

## *Exercise 8-17

| Sales Journal | | | | | | | Page |
|---|---|---|---|---|---|---|---|
| Date | Account Debited | Invoice No. | PR | Accounts Receivable Dr. | PST Payable Cr. | GST Payable Cr. | Sales Cr. |
| | | | | | | | |
| | | | | | | | |
| | | | | | | | |
| | | | | | | | |

| Cash Receipts Journal | | | | | | | | | Page |
|---|---|---|---|---|---|---|---|---|---|
| Date | Account Credited | PR | Explanation | Cash Dr. | Sales Disc. Dr. | Accts. Rec. Cr. | Sales Cr. | Other Accts. Cr. | |
| | | | | | | | | | |
| | | | | | | | | | |
| | | | | | | | | | |
| | | | | | | | | | |

| Purchases Journal | | | | | | | | Page |
|---|---|---|---|---|---|---|---|---|
| Date | Account Credited | Date of Invoice | Terms | PR | Accts. Payable Cr. | Purchases Dr. | Other Accounts Dr. | GST Rec'ble Dr. |
| | | | | | | | | |
| | | | | | | | | |
| | | | | | | | | |
| | | | | | | | | |

| Cash Disbursements Journal | | | | | | | | | Page |
|---|---|---|---|---|---|---|---|---|---|
| Date | Ch No | Payee | Account Debited | PR | Other Accts. Dr. | GST Rec'ble Dr. | Accts. Payable Dr. | Pur. Disc. Cr. | Cash Cr. |
| | | | | | | | | | |
| | | | | | | | | | |
| | | | | | | | | | |

| Special Journal | | Subledger | |
| --- | --- | --- | --- |
| Sales........................... | S | Accounts Receivable.... | AR |
| Purchases ................... | P | Accounts Payable......... | AP |
| Cash Receipts.............. | CR | No Effect....................... | NE |
| Cash Disbursements... | CD | | |
| General Journal .......... | G | | |

| Date | Transaction | Special Journal | Subledger |
| --- | --- | --- | --- |
| *Mar. 1* | *Sold merchandise on credit.* | *S* | *AR/MI* |
| 2 | Defective merchandise sold on March 1 was returned by the customer. It was scrapped. | | |
| 3 | Purchased office equipment on credit. | | |
| 5 | Received payment regarding the March 1 sale. | | |
| 10 | Received a credit memorandum from the supplier regarding defective equipment purchased on March 3. | | |
| 14 | Sold merchandise for cash. | | |
| 16 | Purchased merchandise inventory on credit; terms 1/5, n30. | | |
| 17 | Paid the balance owing regarding the March 3 transaction. | | |
| 18 | Purchased merchandise inventory for cash. | | |
| 21 | Paid for the merchandise purchased on March 16. | | |
| 22 | Sold old equipment for cash. | | |
| 30 | Paid salaries for the month of March. | | |
| 30 | Accrued utilities for the month of March. | | |
| 30 | Closed the credit balance in the income summary to capital. | | |

| Sales Journal | | | | | Page 3 |
|---|---|---|---|---|---|
| Date | Account Debited | Invoice Number | PR | Accounts Receivable Dr. Sales Cr. | Cost of Goods Sold Dr. Merchandise Inventory Cr. |
| | | | | | |
| | | | | | |
| | | | | | |
| | | | | | |
| | | | | | |
| | | | | | |
| | | | | | |
| | | | | | |

| Cash Receipts Journal | | | | | | | | | Page 3 |
|---|---|---|---|---|---|---|---|---|---|
| Date | Account Credited | PR | Explanation | Cash Dr. | Sales Disc. Dr. | Accts. Rec. Cr. | Sales Cr. | Other Accts. Cr. | COGS Dr. Merch. Inv. Cr. |
| | | | | | | | | | |
| | | | | | | | | | |
| | | | | | | | | | |
| | | | | | | | | | |
| | | | | | | | | | |
| | | | | | | | | | |
| | | | | | | | | | |

| Purchases Journal | | | | | | | | Page 3 |
|---|---|---|---|---|---|---|---|---|
| Date | Account | Date of Invoice | Terms | PR | Accounts Payable Cr. | Merch. Inventory Dr. | Office Supplies Dr. | Other Accounts Dr. |
| | | | | | | | | |
| | | | | | | | | |
| | | | | | | | | |
| | | | | | | | | |
| | | | | | | | | |
| | | | | | | | | |

| Cash Disbursements Journal | | | | | | | | Page 3 |
|---|---|---|---|---|---|---|---|---|
| Date | Ch. No. | Payee | Account Debited | PR | Cash Cr. | Merch. Inventory Cr. | Other Accounts Dr. | Accounts Payable Dr. |
| | | | | | | | | |
| | | | | | | | | |
| | | | | | | | | |
| | | | | | | | | |
| | | | | | | | | |
| | | | | | | | | |
| | | | | | | | | |

## GENERAL JOURNAL                                    Page____

| Date | Account Titles and Explanation | PR | Debit | Credit |
|------|-------------------------------|----|-------|--------|
|      |                               |    |       |        |
|      |                               |    |       |        |
|      |                               |    |       |        |
|      |                               |    |       |        |
|      |                               |    |       |        |
|      |                               |    |       |        |
|      |                               |    |       |        |
|      |                               |    |       |        |
|      |                               |    |       |        |
|      |                               |    |       |        |

## Problem 8-3A    Part 1

### ACCOUNTS RECEIVABLE SUBLEDGER

Paul Abrams                                      ACCOUNT NO. 106-1

| DATE | EXPLANATION | PR | DEBIT | CREDIT | BALANCE |
|------|-------------|----|-------|--------|---------|
|      |             |    |       |        |         |
|      |             |    |       |        |         |
|      |             |    |       |        |         |
|      |             |    |       |        |         |

Linda Hobart                                     ACCOUNT NO. 106-2

| DATE | EXPLANATION | PR | DEBIT | CREDIT | BALANCE |
|------|-------------|----|-------|--------|---------|
|      |             |    |       |        |         |
|      |             |    |       |        |         |
|      |             |    |       |        |         |
|      |             |    |       |        |         |
|      |             |    |       |        |         |

Kelly Schaefer                                   ACCOUNT NO. 106-3

| DATE | EXPLANATION | PR | DEBIT | CREDIT | BALANCE |
|------|-------------|----|-------|--------|---------|
|      |             |    |       |        |         |
|      |             |    |       |        |         |
|      |             |    |       |        |         |
|      |             |    |       |        |         |

Part 2                    ACCOUNTS PAYABLE SUBLEDGER

### Frank's Supply                                        ACCOUNT NO. 201-1

| DATE | EXPLANATION | PR | DEBIT | CREDIT | BALANCE |
|------|-------------|----|-------|--------|---------|
|      |             |    |       |        |         |
|      |             |    |       |        |         |
|      |             |    |       |        |         |

### Baskin Company                                        ACCOUNT NO. 201-2

| DATE | EXPLANATION | PR | DEBIT | CREDIT | BALANCE |
|------|-------------|----|-------|--------|---------|
|      |             |    |       |        |         |
|      |             |    |       |        |         |
|      |             |    |       |        |         |
|      |             |    |       |        |         |

### Sprocket Company                                      ACCOUNT NO. 201-3

| DATE | EXPLANATION | PR | DEBIT | CREDIT | BALANCE |
|------|-------------|----|-------|--------|---------|
|      |             |    |       |        |         |
|      |             |    |       |        |         |
|      |             |    |       |        |         |
|      |             |    |       |        |         |

### Eau Claire Inc.                                       ACCOUNT NO. 201-4

| DATE | EXPLANATION | PR | DEBIT | CREDIT | BALANCE |
|------|-------------|----|-------|--------|---------|
|      |             |    |       |        |         |
|      |             |    |       |        |         |
|      |             |    |       |        |         |

Part 3

| Sales Journal | | | | | Page |
|---|---|---|---|---|---|
| Date | Account Debited | Invoice Number | PR | Accounts Receivable Dr. Sales Cr. | Cost of Goods Sold Dr. Merchandise Inventory Cr. |
|  |  |  |  |  |  |
|  |  |  |  |  |  |
|  |  |  |  |  |  |
|  |  |  |  |  |  |
|  |  |  |  |  |  |
|  |  |  |  |  |  |
|  |  |  |  |  |  |
|  |  |  |  |  |  |
|  |  |  |  |  |  |
|  |  |  |  |  |  |
|  |  |  |  |  |  |
|  |  |  |  |  |  |

| Cash Receipts Journal | | | | | | | | | Page |
|---|---|---|---|---|---|---|---|---|---|
| Date | Accounts Credited | PR | Explanation | Cash Dr. | Sales Disc. Dr. | Accts. Rec. Cr. | Sales Cr. | Other Accts. Cr. | COGS Dr. Merch. Inv. Cr. |
|  |  |  |  |  |  |  |  |  |  |
|  |  |  |  |  |  |  |  |  |  |
|  |  |  |  |  |  |  |  |  |  |
|  |  |  |  |  |  |  |  |  |  |
|  |  |  |  |  |  |  |  |  |  |
|  |  |  |  |  |  |  |  |  |  |
|  |  |  |  |  |  |  |  |  |  |
|  |  |  |  |  |  |  |  |  |  |
|  |  |  |  |  |  |  |  |  |  |
|  |  |  |  |  |  |  |  |  |  |
|  |  |  |  |  |  |  |  |  |  |

| | | | | | Accounts Payable Cr. | Merch. Inventory Dr. | Office Supplies Dr. | Other Accounts Dr. |
|---|---|---|---|---|---|---|---|---|
| Date | Account Credited | Date of Invoice | Terms | PR | | | | |
| | | | | | | | | |
| | | | | | | | | |
| | | | | | | | | |
| | | | | | | | | |
| | | | | | | | | |
| | | | | | | | | |
| | | | | | | | | |
| | | | | | | | | |
| | | | | | | | | |
| | | | | | | | | |
| | | | | | | | | |
| | | | | | | | | |

**Purchases Journal** — Page

| Date | Ch. No. | Payee | Account Debited | PR | Cash Cr. | Merch. Inventory Cr. | Other Accounts Dr. | Accounts Payable Dr. |
|---|---|---|---|---|---|---|---|---|
| | | | | | | | | |
| | | | | | | | | |
| | | | | | | | | |
| | | | | | | | | |
| | | | | | | | | |
| | | | | | | | | |
| | | | | | | | | |
| | | | | | | | | |
| | | | | | | | | |
| | | | | | | | | |
| | | | | | | | | |
| | | | | | | | | |

**Cash Disbursements Journal** — Page

## GENERAL JOURNAL     Page____

| Date | Account Titles and Explanation | PR | Debit | Credit |
|---|---|---|---|---|
| | | | | |
| | | | | |
| | | | | |
| | | | | |
| | | | | |
| | | | | |
| | | | | |
| | | | | |
| | | | | |
| | | | | |

## GENERAL LEDGER

### Cash      ACCOUNT NO. 101

| DATE | EXPLANATION | PR | DEBIT | CREDIT | BALANCE |
|------|-------------|----|-------|--------|---------|
| 2011 | | | | | |
| Mar. 31 | Balance brought forward | | | | 167,000 |
| | | | | | |
| | | | | | |

### Accounts Receivable      ACCOUNT NO. 106

| DATE | EXPLANATION | PR | DEBIT | CREDIT | BALANCE |
|------|-------------|----|-------|--------|---------|
| | | | | | |
| | | | | | |
| | | | | | |

### Merchandise Inventory      ACCOUNT NO. 119

| DATE | EXPLANATION | PR | DEBIT | CREDIT | BALANCE |
|------|-------------|----|-------|--------|---------|
| 2011 | | | | | |
| Mar. 31 | Balance brought forward | | | | 95,000 |
| | | | | | |
| | | | | | |
| | | | | | |
| | | | | | |
| | | | | | |

### Office Supplies      ACCOUNT NO. 124

| DATE | EXPLANATION | PR | DEBIT | CREDIT | BALANCE |
|------|-------------|----|-------|--------|---------|
| | | | | | |
| | | | | | |
| | | | | | |

### Store Supplies      ACCOUNT NO. 125

| DATE | EXPLANATION | PR | DEBIT | CREDIT | BALANCE |
|------|-------------|----|-------|--------|---------|
| | | | | | |
| | | | | | |
| | | | | | |

### Store Equipment      ACCOUNT NO. 165

| DATE | EXPLANATION | PR | DEBIT | CREDIT | BALANCE |
|------|-------------|----|-------|--------|---------|
| | | | | | |
| | | | | | |
| | | | | | |

### Accounts Payable                                   ACCOUNT NO. 201

| DATE | EXPLANATION | PR | DEBIT | CREDIT | BALANCE |
|------|-------------|----|-------|--------|---------|
|      |             |    |       |        |         |
|      |             |    |       |        |         |
|      |             |    |       |        |         |
|      |             |    |       |        |         |
|      |             |    |       |        |         |

### Long-Term Notes Payable                             ACCOUNT NO. 251

| DATE | EXPLANATION | PR | DEBIT | CREDIT | BALANCE |
|------|-------------|----|-------|--------|---------|
| 2011 |             |    |       |        |         |
| Mar. 31 | Balance brought forward |    |       |        | 167,000 |
|      |             |    |       |        |         |

### Jeff Newton, Capital                                ACCOUNT NO. 301

| DATE | EXPLANATION | PR | DEBIT | CREDIT | BALANCE |
|------|-------------|----|-------|--------|---------|
| 2011 |             |    |       |        |         |
| Mar. 31 | Balance brought forward |    |       |        | 95,000 |
|      |             |    |       |        |         |

### Sales                                               ACCOUNT NO. 413

| DATE | EXPLANATION | PR | DEBIT | CREDIT | BALANCE |
|------|-------------|----|-------|--------|---------|
|      |             |    |       |        |         |
|      |             |    |       |        |         |
|      |             |    |       |        |         |

### Sales Discounts                                     ACCOUNT NO. 415

| DATE | EXPLANATION | PR | DEBIT | CREDIT | BALANCE |
|------|-------------|----|-------|--------|---------|
|      |             |    |       |        |         |
|      |             |    |       |        |         |
|      |             |    |       |        |         |

### Cost of Goods Sold                                  ACCOUNT NO. 502

| DATE | EXPLANATION | PR | DEBIT | CREDIT | BALANCE |
|------|-------------|----|-------|--------|---------|
|      |             |    |       |        |         |
|      |             |    |       |        |         |
|      |             |    |       |        |         |

### Sales Salaries Expense                              ACCOUNT NO. 621

| DATE | EXPLANATION | PR | DEBIT | CREDIT | BALANCE |
|------|-------------|----|-------|--------|---------|
|      |             |    |       |        |         |
|      |             |    |       |        |         |
|      |             |    |       |        |         |

| | Advertising Expense | | | | ACCOUNT NO. 655 |
|---|---|---|---|---|---|
| DATE | EXPLANATION | PR | DEBIT | CREDIT | BALANCE |
| | | | | | |
| | | | | | |
| | | | | | |

**NOTE:** *For Parts 2 and 3, journalizing and posting, continue journalizing the transactions in the journals provided in Problem 8-3A.*

**Part 5**

### Trial Balance

| | Debit | Credit |
|---|---|---|
| | | |
| | | |
| | | |
| | | |
| | | |
| | | |
| | | |
| | | |
| | | |
| | | |
| | | |
| | | |
| | | |
| | | |
| | | |
| | | |
| | | |
| | | |
| | | |
| | | |
| | | |
| | | |
| | | |
| | | |
| | | |
| | | |
| | | |

## Schedule of Accounts Receivable

| | | |
|---|---|---|
| | | |
| | | |
| | | |
| | | |
| | | |
| | | |

## Schedule of Accounts Payable

| | | |
|---|---|---|
| | | |
| | | |
| | | |
| | | |
| | | |
| | | |

*Analysis component:*

_____
_____
_____
_____
_____
_____
_____
_____
_____
_____
_____
_____
_____

# Problem 8-5A

## Parts 1, 2, 3

| Sales Journal | | | | | Page 3 |
|---|---|---|---|---|---|
| Date | Account Debited | Invoice Number | PR | Accounts Receivable Dr. Sales Cr. | Cost of Goods Sold Dr. Merchandise Inventory Cr. |
| 2011 | | | | | |
| Oct. 6 | M. Craig | 913 | √ | 3,300 | 1,600 |
| 12 | V. Foresman | 914 | √ | 3,650 | 1,900 |
| 15 | A. Ihrig | 915 | √ | 3,100 | 1,700 |
| | | | | | |
| | | | | | |
| | | | | | |
| | | | | | |
| | | | | | |

| Purchases Journal | | | | | | | | Page 2 |
|---|---|---|---|---|---|---|---|---|
| Date | Account | Date of Invoice | Terms | PR | Accounts Payable Cr. | Merch. Inventory Dr. | Office Supplies Dr. | Other Accounts Dr. |
| 2011 | | | | | | | | |
| Oct. 2 | Shore Co. | 12/2 | 2/10,n/60 | √ | 3,200 | 3,200 | | |
| 5 | Brown Sup. | 12/3 | n/10,EOM | √ | 1,300 | 1,300 | | |
| 15 | Shore Co. | 12/15 | 2/10,n/60 | √ | 3,990 | 3,990 | | |
| 15 | Sunshine Co | 12/15 | 2/10,n/60 | √ | 2,650 | 2,650 | | |
| | | | | | | | | |
| | | | | | | | | |
| | | | | | | | | |
| | | | | | | | | |
| | | | | | | | | |
| | | | | | | | | |
| | | | | | | | | |
| | | | | | | | | |

| | | | | Cash Receipts Journal | | | | | Page 3 |
|---|---|---|---|---|---|---|---|---|---|
| Date | Account Credited | PR | Explanation | Cash Dr. | Sales Disc. Dr. | Accts. Rec. Cr. | Sales Cr. | Other Accts. Cr. | COGS Dr. Merch. Inv. Cr. |
| 2011 | | | | | | | | | |
| Oct. 2 | B. Grigsby | √ | Inv. 11/23 | 4,116 | 84 | 4,200 | | | |
| 15 | Sales | | Cash sales | 38,830 | | | 38,830 | | 21,400 |
| 15 | M. Craig | √ | Inv. 12/6 | 2,401 | 49 | 2,450 | | | |
| | | | | | | | | | |
| | | | | | | | | | |
| | | | | | | | | | |
| | | | | | | | | | |
| | | | | | | | | | |
| | | | | | | | | | |
| | | | | | | | | | |
| | | | | | | | | | |
| | | | | | | | | | |
| | | | | | | | | | |

| | | | | Cash Disbursements Journal | | | | Page 4 |
|---|---|---|---|---|---|---|---|---|
| Date | Ch. No. | Payee | Account Debited | PR | Cash Cr. | Merch. Inventory Cr. | Other Accounts Dr. | Accounts Payable Dr. |
| 2011 | | | | | | | | |
| Oct. 2 | 619 | Omni Realty | Rent Exp. | 640 | 2,250 | | 2,250 | |
| 6 | 620 | Fireside Co. | Fireside Co. | √ | 3,724 | 76 | | 3,800 |
| 12 | 621 | Shore Co. | Shore Co. | √ | 3,136 | 64 | | 3,200 |
| 15 | 622 | Jamie Green | Sales Sal. Exp. | 621 | 2,020 | | 2,020 | |
| | | | | | | | | |
| | | | | | | | | |
| | | | | | | | | |
| | | | | | | | | |
| | | | | | | | | |
| | | | | | | | | |
| | | | | | | | | |
| | | | | | | | | |
| | | | | | | | | |
| | | | | | | | | |

## GENERAL JOURNAL

Page 2

| Date | | Account Titles and Explanation | PR | Debit | Credit |
|---|---|---|---|---|---|
| 2011 | | | | | |
| Oct. | 4 | Accounts Payable—Fireside Company | 201/√ | 460 | |
| | | Merchandise Inventory | 119 | | 460 |
| | | *Received a credit memo for returns.* | | | |
| | | | | | |
| | 9 | Sales Returns and Allowances | 414 | 850 | |
| | | Accounts Receivable—Marge Craig | 106/√ | | 850 |
| | | *Issued a credit memorandum.* | | | |
| | | | | | |
| | 9 | Merchandise Inventory | 119 | 430 | |
| | | Cost of Goods Sold | 502 | | 430 |
| | | *Merchandise returned to inventory.* | | | |
| | | | | | |
| | | | | | |
| | | | | | |
| | | | | | |
| | | | | | |
| | | | | | |
| | | | | | |
| | | | | | |
| | | | | | |
| | | | | | |
| | | | | | |
| | | | | | |
| | | | | | |
| | | | | | |

## ACCOUNTS RECEIVABLE SUBLEDGER

### Marge Craig

| DATE | | EXPLANATION | PR | DEBIT | CREDIT | BALANCE |
|---|---|---|---|---|---|---|
| 2011 | | | | | | |
| Oct. | 6 | | S3 | 3,300 | | 3,300 |
| | 9 | | G2 | | 8,50 | 2,450 |
| | 15 | | CR3 | | 2,450 | -0- |
| | | | | | | |

### Vickie Foresman

| DATE | | EXPLANATION | PR | DEBIT | CREDIT | BALANCE |
|---|---|---|---|---|---|---|
| 2011 | | | | | | |
| Oct. | 12 | | S3 | 3,650 | | 3,650 |
| | | | | | | |
| | | | | | | |

**Parts 2 and 3**

### Bill Grigsby

| DATE | | EXPLANATION | PR | DEBIT | CREDIT | BALANCE |
|---|---|---|---|---|---|---|
| 2011 | | | | | | |
| Sept | 23 | | S2 | 4,200 | | 4,200 |
| Oct. | 2 | | CR3 | | 4,200 | -0- |
| | | | | | | |

### Amy Ihrig

| DATE | | EXPLANATION | PR | DEBIT | CREDIT | BALANCE |
|---|---|---|---|---|---|---|
| 2011 | | | | | | |
| Oct. | 15 | | S3 | 3,100 | | 3,100 |
| | | | | | | |
| | | | | | | |

### ACCOUNTS PAYABLE SUBLEDGER

### Fireside Company

| DATE | | EXPLANATION | PR | DEBIT | CREDIT | BALANCE |
|---|---|---|---|---|---|---|
| 2011 | | | | | | |
| Sept | 28 | | P1 | | 4,260 | 4,260 |
| Oct. | 4 | | G2 | 460 | | 3,800 |
| | 6 | | CD4 | 3,800 | | -0- |
| | | | | | | |

### Brown Supply Company

| DATE | | EXPLANATION | PR | DEBIT | CREDIT | BALANCE |
|---|---|---|---|---|---|---|
| 2011 | | | | | | |
| Oct. | 5 | | P2 | | 1,300 | 1,300 |
| | | | | | | |
| | | | | | | |
| | | | | | | |

### Sunshine Company

| DATE | | EXPLANATION | PR | DEBIT | CREDIT | BALANCE |
|---|---|---|---|---|---|---|
| 2011 | | | | | | |
| Oct. | 15 | | P2 | | 2,650 | 2,650 |
| | | | | | | |
| | | | | | | |

## Parts 2 and 3   (Cont'd.)

### Shore Company

| DATE | | EXPLANATION | PR | DEBIT | CREDIT | BALANCE |
|---|---|---|---|---|---|---|
| 2011 | | | | | | |
| Oct. | 2 | | P2 | | 3,200 | 3,200 |
| | 12 | | CD4 | 3,200 | | -0- |
| | 15 | | P2 | | 3,990 | 3,990 |
| | | | | | | |
| | | | | | | |
| | | | | | | |

**Parts 2 and 3**                    **GENERAL LEDGER**

### Cash                                    ACCOUNT NO. 101

| DATE | | EXPLANATION | PR | DEBIT | CREDIT | BALANCE |
|---|---|---|---|---|---|---|
| 2011 | | | | | | |
| Sept | 30 | Balance | | | | 5,361 |
| | | | | | | |
| | | | | | | |
| | | | | | | |

### Accounts Receivable                    ACCOUNT NO. 106

| DATE | | EXPLANATION | PR | DEBIT | CREDIT | BALANCE |
|---|---|---|---|---|---|---|
| 2011 | | | | | | |
| Sept | 30 | Balance | | | | 4,200 |
| Oct. | 9 | | G2 | | 850 | 3,350 |
| | | | | | | |
| | | | | | | |
| | | | | | | |
| | | | | | | |

### Merchandise Inventory                    ACCOUNT NO. 119

| DATE | | EXPLANATION | PR | DEBIT | CREDIT | BALANCE |
|---|---|---|---|---|---|---|
| 2011 | | | | | | |
| Sept | 30 | Balance | | | | 66,970 |
| Oct. | 4 | | G2 | | 460 | 66,510 |
| | 9 | | G2 | 430 | | 66,940 |
| | | | | | | |
| | | | | | | |
| | | | | | | |
| | | | | | | |
| | | | | | | |
| | | | | | | |

## Office Supplies                                   ACCOUNT NO. 124

| DATE | | EXPLANATION | PR | DEBIT | CREDIT | BALANCE |
|---|---|---|---|---|---|---|
| 2011 | | | | | | |
| Sept | 30 | Balance | | | | 607 |
| | | | | | | |
| | | | | | | |
| | | | | | | |

## Store Supplies                                   ACCOUNT NO. 125

| DATE | | EXPLANATION | PR | DEBIT | CREDIT | BALANCE |
|---|---|---|---|---|---|---|
| 2011 | | | | | | |
| Sept | 30 | Balance | | | | 346 |
| | | | | | | |

## Store Equipment                                   ACCOUNT NO. 165

| DATE | | EXPLANATION | PR | DEBIT | CREDIT | BALANCE |
|---|---|---|---|---|---|---|
| 2011 | | | | | | |
| Sept | 30 | Balance | | | | 42,129 |
| | | | | | | |

## Accumulated Amortization, Store Equipment         ACCOUNT NO. 166

| DATE | | EXPLANATION | PR | DEBIT | CREDIT | BALANCE |
|---|---|---|---|---|---|---|
| 2011 | | | | | | |
| Sept | 30 | Balance | | | | 9,153 |
| | | | | | | |

## Accounts Payable                                  ACCOUNT NO. 201

| DATE | | EXPLANATION | PR | DEBIT | CREDIT | BALANCE |
|---|---|---|---|---|---|---|
| 2011 | | | | | | |
| Sept | 30 | Balance | | | | 4,260 |
| Oct. | 4 | | G2 | 460 | | 3,800 |
| | | | | | | |
| | | | | | | |
| | | | | | | |
| | | | | | | |

## Ken Shaw, Capital                                 ACCOUNT NO. 301

| DATE | | EXPLANATION | PR | DEBIT | CREDIT | BALANCE |
|---|---|---|---|---|---|---|
| 2011 | | | | | | |
| Sept | 30 | Balance | | | | 106,200 |
| | | | | | | |

### Ken Shaw, Withdrawals                        ACCOUNT NO. 302

| DATE | EXPLANATION | PR | DEBIT | CREDIT | BALANCE |
|------|-------------|----|-------|--------|---------|
|      |             |    |       |        |         |
|      |             |    |       |        |         |
|      |             |    |       |        |         |

### Sales                        ACCOUNT NO. 413

| DATE | EXPLANATION | PR | DEBIT | CREDIT | BALANCE |
|------|-------------|----|-------|--------|---------|
| 2011 |             |    |       |        |         |
|      |             |    |       |        |         |
|      |             |    |       |        |         |

### Sales Returns and Allowances                        ACCOUNT NO. 414

| DATE | EXPLANATION | PR | DEBIT | CREDIT | BALANCE |
|------|-------------|----|-------|--------|---------|
| 2011 |             |    |       |        |         |
| Oct.  9 |          | G2 | 850   |        | 850     |
|      |             |    |       |        |         |

### Sales Discounts                        ACCOUNT NO. 415

| DATE | EXPLANATION | PR | DEBIT | CREDIT | BALANCE |
|------|-------------|----|-------|--------|---------|
| 2011 |             |    |       |        |         |
|      |             |    |       |        |         |

### Cost of Goods Sold                        ACCOUNT NO. 502

| DATE | EXPLANATION | PR | DEBIT | CREDIT | BALANCE |
|------|-------------|----|-------|--------|---------|
| 2011 |             |    |       |        |         |
| Oct.  9 |          | G2 |       | 430    | (430)   |
|      |             |    |       |        |         |
|      |             |    |       |        |         |

### Sales Salaries Expense                        ACCOUNT NO. 621

| DATE | EXPLANATION | PR | DEBIT | CREDIT | BALANCE |
|------|-------------|----|-------|--------|---------|
| 2011 |             |    |       |        |         |
| Oct. 15 |          | CD4 | 2,020 |      | 2,020   |
|      |             |    |       |        |         |

### Rent Expense                        ACCOUNT NO. 640

| DATE | EXPLANATION | PR | DEBIT | CREDIT | BALANCE |
|------|-------------|----|-------|--------|---------|
| 2011 |             |    |       |        |         |
| Oct.  2 |          | CD4 | 2,250 |      | 2,250   |
|      |             |    |       |        |         |

### Utilities Expense                    ACCOUNT NO. 690

| DATE | EXPLANATION | PR | DEBIT | CREDIT | BALANCE |
|------|-------------|----|-------|--------|---------|
| 2011 | | | | | |
| | | | | | |

## Part 4

### SASKAN ENTERPRISES
### Trial Balance
### October 31, 2011

| | | |
|---|---|---|
| | | |
| | | |
| | | |
| | | |
| | | |
| | | |
| | | |
| | | |
| | | |
| | | |
| | | |
| | | |
| | | |
| | | |
| | | |
| | | |
| | | |
| | | |
| | | |
| | | |
| | | |
| | | |
| | | |
| | | |
| | | |
| | | |
| | | |
| | | |
| | | |
| | | |
| | | |
| | | |
| | | |
| | | |

Problem 8-5A (concl'd.)     *Name* _____

## SASKAN ENTERPRISES
### Schedule of Accounts Receivable
### October 31, 2011

| | | |
|---|---|---|
| | | |
| | | |
| | | |
| | | |
| | | |
| | | |
| | | |

## SASKAN ENTERPRISES
### Schedule of Accounts Payable
### October 31, 2011

| | | |
|---|---|---|
| | | |
| | | |
| | | |
| | | |
| | | |
| | | |
| | | |

## Problem 8-6A

| Sales Journal | | | | | | | Page |
|---|---|---|---|---|---|---|---|
| Date | Account Debited | Invoice Number | PR | Accounts Receivable Dr. Sales Cr. | PR | Cost of Goods Sold Dr. Merch. Inventory Cr. | |
| | | | | | | | |
| | | | | | | | |
| | | | | | | | |
| | | | | | | | |
| | | | | | | | |
| | | | | | | | |

| Purchases Journal | | | | | | | | | Page |
|---|---|---|---|---|---|---|---|---|---|
| Date | Account | Date of Invoice | Terms | PR | Accts. Payable Cr. | PR | Merch. Inventory Dr. | Office Supplies Dr. | Other Accounts Dr. |
| | | | | | | | | | |
| | | | | | | | | | |
| | | | | | | | | | |
| | | | | | | | | | |

*NOTE: An additional PR column has been added to both journals to facilitate the referencing of inventory entries into the inventory subsidiary ledger.*

| Date | PR | Purchases | Sales (at cost) | Inventory Balance |
|------|----|-----------|-----------------|-------------------|
|      |    |           |                 |                   |
|      |    |           |                 |                   |
|      |    |           |                 |                   |
|      |    |           |                 |                   |
|      |    |           |                 |                   |
|      |    |           |                 |                   |
|      |    |           |                 |                   |
|      |    |           |                 |                   |
|      |    |           |                 |                   |
|      |    |           |                 |                   |
|      |    |           |                 |                   |
|      |    |           |                 |                   |
|      |    |           |                 |                   |
|      |    |           |                 |                   |
|      |    |           |                 |                   |
|      |    |           |                 |                   |
|      |    |           |                 |                   |
|      |    |           |                 |                   |
|      |    |           |                 |                   |
|      |    |           |                 |                   |
|      |    |           |                 |                   |
|      |    |           |                 |                   |

*Note: An additional PR column has been added to the Inventory Subledger Record to facilitate referencing of inventory entries.*

*Problem 8-7A

Part 1                    ACCOUNTS RECEIVABLE SUBLEDGER

|  |  | Paul Abrams |  |  | ACCOUNT NO. 106-1 | |
|--|--|-------------|--|--|-------------------|--|

| DATE | EXPLANATION | PR | DEBIT | CREDIT | BALANCE |
|------|-------------|----|-------|--------|---------|
|      |             |    |       |        |         |
|      |             |    |       |        |         |
|      |             |    |       |        |         |
|      |             |    |       |        |         |

### Linda Hobart                                    ACCOUNT NO. 106-2

| DATE | EXPLANATION | PR | DEBIT | CREDIT | BALANCE |
|------|-------------|----|-------|--------|---------|
|      |             |    |       |        |         |
|      |             |    |       |        |         |
|      |             |    |       |        |         |
|      |             |    |       |        |         |
|      |             |    |       |        |         |

### Kelly Schaefer                                  ACCOUNT NO. 106-3

| DATE | EXPLANATION | PR | DEBIT | CREDIT | BALANCE |
|------|-------------|----|-------|--------|---------|
|      |             |    |       |        |         |
|      |             |    |       |        |         |
|      |             |    |       |        |         |
|      |             |    |       |        |         |

**Part 2**                    ACCOUNTS PAYABLE SUBLEDGER

### Frank's Supply                                  ACCOUNT NO. 201-1

| DATE | EXPLANATION | PR | DEBIT | CREDIT | BALANCE |
|------|-------------|----|-------|--------|---------|
|      |             |    |       |        |         |
|      |             |    |       |        |         |
|      |             |    |       |        |         |
|      |             |    |       |        |         |

### Baskin Company                                  ACCOUNT NO. 201-2

| DATE | EXPLANATION | PR | DEBIT | CREDIT | BALANCE |
|------|-------------|----|-------|--------|---------|
|      |             |    |       |        |         |
|      |             |    |       |        |         |
|      |             |    |       |        |         |
|      |             |    |       |        |         |
|      |             |    |       |        |         |

### Sprocket Company                                ACCOUNT NO. 201-3

| DATE | EXPLANATION | PR | DEBIT | CREDIT | BALANCE |
|------|-------------|----|-------|--------|---------|
|      |             |    |       |        |         |
|      |             |    |       |        |         |
|      |             |    |       |        |         |
|      |             |    |       |        |         |
|      |             |    |       |        |         |

| Eau Claire Inc. | | | | | ACCOUNT NO. 201-4 |
| --- | --- | --- | --- | --- | --- |
| DATE | EXPLANATION | PR | DEBIT | CREDIT | BALANCE |
|  |  |  |  |  |  |
|  |  |  |  |  |  |
|  |  |  |  |  |  |
|  |  |  |  |  |  |

## Part 3

| Sales Journal | | | | | Page |
| --- | --- | --- | --- | --- | --- |
| Date | Account Debited | Invoice No. | PR | Accounts Receivable Dr. Sales Cr. | |
|  |  |  |  |  | |
|  |  |  |  |  | |
|  |  |  |  |  | |
|  |  |  |  |  | |
|  |  |  |  |  | |
|  |  |  |  |  | |
|  |  |  |  |  | |
|  |  |  |  |  | |
|  |  |  |  |  | |
|  |  |  |  |  | |
|  |  |  |  |  | |

| Cash Receipts Journal | | | | | | | | Page |
| --- | --- | --- | --- | --- | --- | --- | --- | --- |
| Date | Account Credited | PR | Explanation | Cash Dr. | Sales Disc. Dr. | Accts. Rec. Cr. | Sales Cr. | Other Accts. Cr. |
|  |  |  |  |  |  |  |  |  |
|  |  |  |  |  |  |  |  |  |
|  |  |  |  |  |  |  |  |  |
|  |  |  |  |  |  |  |  |  |
|  |  |  |  |  |  |  |  |  |
|  |  |  |  |  |  |  |  |  |
|  |  |  |  |  |  |  |  |  |
|  |  |  |  |  |  |  |  |  |
|  |  |  |  |  |  |  |  |  |
|  |  |  |  |  |  |  |  |  |
|  |  |  |  |  |  |  |  |  |

| Purchases Journal | | | | | | | | Page |
|---|---|---|---|---|---|---|---|---|
| Date | Account Credited | Date of Invoice | Terms | PR | Accts. Payable Cr. | Purchases Dr. | Office Supplies Dr. | Other Accts. Dr. |
| | | | | | | | | |
| | | | | | | | | |
| | | | | | | | | |
| | | | | | | | | |
| | | | | | | | | |
| | | | | | | | | |
| | | | | | | | | |
| | | | | | | | | |
| | | | | | | | | |
| | | | | | | | | |

| Cash Disbursements Journal | | | | | | | | Page |
|---|---|---|---|---|---|---|---|---|
| Date | Ch. No. | Payee | Account Debited | PR | Cash Cr. | Purch. Disc. Cr. | Other Accounts Dr. | Accts. Payable Dr. |
| | | | | | | | | |
| | | | | | | | | |
| | | | | | | | | |
| | | | | | | | | |
| | | | | | | | | |
| | | | | | | | | |
| | | | | | | | | |
| | | | | | | | | |
| | | | | | | | | |

## GENERAL JOURNAL                                     Page____

| Date | Account Titles and Explanation | PR | Debit | Credit |
|---|---|---|---|---|
| | | | | |
| | | | | |
| | | | | |
| | | | | |
| | | | | |
| | | | | |
| | | | | |
| | | | | |
| | | | | |
| | | | | |
| | | | | |
| | | | | |
| | | | | |
| | | | | |

Parts 1 and 4                    GENERAL LEDGER

### Cash                                                        ACCOUNT NO. 101

| DATE | EXPLANATION | PR | DEBIT | CREDIT | BALANCE |
|---|---|---|---|---|---|
| 2011 | | | | | |
| Mar. 31 | | | | | 167,000 |
| | | | | | |
| | | | | | |

### Accounts Receivable                                        ACCOUNT NO. 106

| DATE | EXPLANATION | PR | DEBIT | CREDIT | BALANCE |
|---|---|---|---|---|---|
| | | | | | |
| | | | | | |
| | | | | | |

### Merchandise Inventory                                      ACCOUNT NO. 119

| DATE | EXPLANATION | PR | DEBIT | CREDIT | BALANCE |
|---|---|---|---|---|---|
| 2011 | | | | | |
| Mar. 31 | | | | | 95,000 |
| | | | | | |

### Office Supplies                                            ACCOUNT NO. 124

| DATE | EXPLANATION | PR | DEBIT | CREDIT | BALANCE |
|---|---|---|---|---|---|
| | | | | | |
| | | | | | |
| | | | | | |

### Store Supplies                                             ACCOUNT NO. 125

| DATE | EXPLANATION | PR | DEBIT | CREDIT | BALANCE |
|---|---|---|---|---|---|
| | | | | | |
| | | | | | |
| | | | | | |

### Store Equipment                                            ACCOUNT NO. 165

| DATE | EXPLANATION | PR | DEBIT | CREDIT | BALANCE |
|---|---|---|---|---|---|
| | | | | | |
| | | | | | |
| | | | | | |

### Accounts Payable                                           ACCOUNT NO. 201

| DATE | EXPLANATION | PR | DEBIT | CREDIT | BALANCE |
|---|---|---|---|---|---|
| | | | | | |
| | | | | | |
| | | | | | |
| | | | | | |

## Notes Payable                                                    ACCOUNT NO. 251

| DATE | EXPLANATION | PR | DEBIT | CREDIT | BALANCE |
|------|-------------|----|-------|--------|---------|
| 2011 | | | | | |
| Mar. 31 | | | | | 167,000 |
| | | | | | |

## Jeff Newton, Capital                                              ACCOUNT NO. 301

| DATE | EXPLANATION | PR | DEBIT | CREDIT | BALANCE |
|------|-------------|----|-------|--------|---------|
| 2011 | | | | | |
| Mar. 31 | | | | | 95,000 |
| | | | | | |

## Sales                                                              ACCOUNT NO. 413

| DATE | EXPLANATION | PR | DEBIT | CREDIT | BALANCE |
|------|-------------|----|-------|--------|---------|
| | | | | | |
| | | | | | |
| | | | | | |

## Sales Discounts                                                    ACCOUNT NO. 415

| DATE | EXPLANATION | PR | DEBIT | CREDIT | BALANCE |
|------|-------------|----|-------|--------|---------|
| | | | | | |
| | | | | | |
| | | | | | |

## Purchases                                                          ACCOUNT NO. 505

| DATE | EXPLANATION | PR | DEBIT | CREDIT | BALANCE |
|------|-------------|----|-------|--------|---------|
| | | | | | |
| | | | | | |
| | | | | | |

## Purchases Discounts                                                ACCOUNT NO. 506

| DATE | EXPLANATION | PR | DEBIT | CREDIT | BALANCE |
|------|-------------|----|-------|--------|---------|
| | | | | | |
| | | | | | |
| | | | | | |

## Purchases Returns and Allowances                                   ACCOUNT NO. 507

| DATE | EXPLANATION | PR | DEBIT | CREDIT | BALANCE |
|------|-------------|----|-------|--------|---------|
| | | | | | |
| | | | | | |
| | | | | | |

## Sales Salaries Expense    ACCOUNT NO. 621

| DATE | EXPLANATION | PR | DEBIT | CREDIT | BALANCE |
|------|-------------|----|-------|--------|---------|
|      |             |    |       |        |         |
|      |             |    |       |        |         |
|      |             |    |       |        |         |

## Advertising Expense    ACCOUNT NO. 655

| DATE | EXPLANATION | PR | DEBIT | CREDIT | BALANCE |
|------|-------------|----|-------|--------|---------|
|      |             |    |       |        |         |
|      |             |    |       |        |         |
|      |             |    |       |        |         |

NOTE:  For Parts 2 and 3, journalizing and posting, continue journalizing the transactions in the journals provided in *Problem 8-7A.

Part 5

## Trial Balance

|  | Debit | Credit |
|--|-------|--------|
|  |       |        |
|  |       |        |
|  |       |        |
|  |       |        |
|  |       |        |
|  |       |        |
|  |       |        |
|  |       |        |
|  |       |        |
|  |       |        |
|  |       |        |
|  |       |        |
|  |       |        |
|  |       |        |
|  |       |        |
|  |       |        |
|  |       |        |
|  |       |        |
|  |       |        |
|  |       |        |
|  |       |        |
|  |       |        |
|  |       |        |
|  |       |        |

## Schedule of Accounts Receivable

| | | |
|---|---|---|
| | | |
| | | |
| | | |
| | | |
| | | |

## Schedule of Accounts Payable

| | | |
|---|---|---|
| | | |
| | | |
| | | |
| | | |

## *Problem 8-9A (Perpetual)

### Part 1

#### GENERAL LEDGER

**Cash**                                    **ACCOUNT NO. 101**

| DATE | EXPLANATION | PR | DEBIT | CREDIT | BALANCE |
|---|---|---|---|---|---|
| | | | | | |
| | | | | | |
| | | | | | |

**Accounts Receivable**                     **ACCOUNT NO. 106**

| DATE | EXPLANATION | PR | DEBIT | CREDIT | BALANCE |
|---|---|---|---|---|---|
| | | | | | |
| | | | | | |
| | | | | | |

**GST Receivable**                          **ACCOUNT NO. 108**

| DATE | EXPLANATION | PR | DEBIT | CREDIT | BALANCE |
|---|---|---|---|---|---|
| | | | | | |
| | | | | | |
| | | | | | |

### Merchandise Inventory                          ACCOUNT NO. 119

| DATE | EXPLANATION | PR | DEBIT | CREDIT | BALANCE |
|---|---|---|---|---|---|
| 2011 | | | | | |
| Feb. 28 | Balance brought forward | | | | 250,000 |
| | | | | | |
| | | | | | |
| | | | | | |
| | | | | | |
| | | | | | |
| | | | | | |

### Office Supplies                               ACCOUNT NO. 124

| DATE | EXPLANATION | PR | DEBIT | CREDIT | BALANCE |
|---|---|---|---|---|---|
| | | | | | |
| | | | | | |
| | | | | | |

### Store Supplies                               ACCOUNT NO. 125

| DATE | EXPLANATION | PR | DEBIT | CREDIT | BALANCE |
|---|---|---|---|---|---|
| | | | | | |
| | | | | | |
| | | | | | |

### Office Equipment                             ACCOUNT NO. 163

| DATE | EXPLANATION | PR | DEBIT | CREDIT | BALANCE |
|---|---|---|---|---|---|
| | | | | | |
| | | | | | |
| | | | | | |

### Accounts Payable                             ACCOUNT NO. 201

| DATE | EXPLANATION | PR | DEBIT | CREDIT | BALANCE |
|---|---|---|---|---|---|
| | | | | | |
| | | | | | |
| | | | | | |
| | | | | | |
| | | | | | |

### PST Payable                                  ACCOUNT NO. 224

| DATE | EXPLANATION | PR | DEBIT | CREDIT | BALANCE |
|---|---|---|---|---|---|
| | | | | | |
| | | | | | |
| | | | | | |

### GST Payable                                          ACCOUNT NO. 225

| DATE | EXPLANATION | PR | DEBIT | CREDIT | BALANCE |
|------|-------------|----|-------|--------|---------|
|      |             |    |       |        |         |
|      |             |    |       |        |         |
|      |             |    |       |        |         |
|      |             |    |       |        |         |
|      |             |    |       |        |         |
|      |             |    |       |        |         |

### Long-Term Notes Payable                              ACCOUNT NO. 251

| DATE | EXPLANATION | PR | DEBIT | CREDIT | BALANCE |
|------|-------------|----|-------|--------|---------|
|      |             |    |       |        |         |
|      |             |    |       |        |         |
|      |             |    |       |        |         |

### George Bledsoe, Capital                              ACCOUNT NO. 301

| DATE | EXPLANATION | PR | DEBIT | CREDIT | BALANCE |
|------|-------------|----|-------|--------|---------|
| 2011 |             |    |       |        |         |
| Feb. 28 | Balance brought forward |  |    |        | 250,000 |
|      |             |    |       |        |         |

### Sales                                                ACCOUNT NO. 413

| DATE | EXPLANATION | PR | DEBIT | CREDIT | BALANCE |
|------|-------------|----|-------|--------|---------|
|      |             |    |       |        |         |
|      |             |    |       |        |         |
|      |             |    |       |        |         |
|      |             |    |       |        |         |

### Sales Discounts                                      ACCOUNT NO. 415

| DATE | EXPLANATION | PR | DEBIT | CREDIT | BALANCE |
|------|-------------|----|-------|--------|---------|
|      |             |    |       |        |         |
|      |             |    |       |        |         |
|      |             |    |       |        |         |

### Cost of Goods Sold                                   ACCOUNT NO. 502

| DATE | EXPLANATION | PR | DEBIT | CREDIT | BALANCE |
|------|-------------|----|-------|--------|---------|
|      |             |    |       |        |         |
|      |             |    |       |        |         |
|      |             |    |       |        |         |

### Sales Salaries Expense — ACCOUNT NO. 621

| DATE | EXPLANATION | PR | DEBIT | CREDIT | BALANCE |
|------|-------------|----|-------|--------|---------|
|      |             |    |       |        |         |
|      |             |    |       |        |         |
|      |             |    |       |        |         |

## Part 2  ACCOUNTS RECEIVABLE SUBLEDGER

### Marjorie Coble — ACCOUNT NO. 106-1

| DATE | EXPLANATION | PR | DEBIT | CREDIT | BALANCE |
|------|-------------|----|-------|--------|---------|
|      |             |    |       |        |         |
|      |             |    |       |        |         |
|      |             |    |       |        |         |
|      |             |    |       |        |         |
|      |             |    |       |        |         |

### Leroy Hackett — ACCOUNT NO. 106-2

| DATE | EXPLANATION | PR | DEBIT | CREDIT | BALANCE |
|------|-------------|----|-------|--------|---------|
|      |             |    |       |        |         |
|      |             |    |       |        |         |
|      |             |    |       |        |         |
|      |             |    |       |        |         |

### Sam Snickers — ACCOUNT NO. 106-3

| DATE | EXPLANATION | PR | DEBIT | CREDIT | BALANCE |
|------|-------------|----|-------|--------|---------|
|      |             |    |       |        |         |
|      |             |    |       |        |         |
|      |             |    |       |        |         |
|      |             |    |       |        |         |
|      |             |    |       |        |         |

## Part 3  ACCOUNTS PAYABLE SUBLEDGER

### Arndt Company — 201-1

| DATE | EXPLANATION | PR | DEBIT | CREDIT | BALANCE |
|------|-------------|----|-------|--------|---------|
|      |             |    |       |        |         |
|      |             |    |       |        |         |
|      |             |    |       |        |         |
|      |             |    |       |        |         |

### Defore Industries     ACCOUNT NO. 201-2

| DATE | EXPLANATION | PR | DEBIT | CREDIT | BALANCE |
|------|-------------|----|-------|--------|---------|
|      |             |    |       |        |         |
|      |             |    |       |        |         |
|      |             |    |       |        |         |
|      |             |    |       |        |         |

### Jett Supply     ACCOUNT NO. 201-3

| DATE | EXPLANATION | PR | DEBIT | CREDIT | BALANCE |
|------|-------------|----|-------|--------|---------|
|      |             |    |       |        |         |
|      |             |    |       |        |         |
|      |             |    |       |        |         |
|      |             |    |       |        |         |

### Welch Company     ACCOUNT NO. 201-4

| DATE | EXPLANATION | PR | DEBIT | CREDIT | BALANCE |
|------|-------------|----|-------|--------|---------|
|      |             |    |       |        |         |
|      |             |    |       |        |         |
|      |             |    |       |        |         |
|      |             |    |       |        |         |
|      |             |    |       |        |         |

### Part 4

| | | | | | Sales Journal | | | | Page |
|------|-------------------|----------------|----|------------------|----------------------|----------------------|-----------|------------------------------|
| Date | Account Debited | Invoice No. | PR | Acct. Rec. Dr. | PST Payable Cr. | GST Payable Cr. | Sales Cr. | COGS Dr. Merch. Inv. Cr. |
|      |                   |                |    |                  |                      |                      |           |                              |
|      |                   |                |    |                  |                      |                      |           |                              |
|      |                   |                |    |                  |                      |                      |           |                              |
|      |                   |                |    |                  |                      |                      |           |                              |
|      |                   |                |    |                  |                      |                      |           |                              |
|      |                   |                |    |                  |                      |                      |           |                              |
|      |                   |                |    |                  |                      |                      |           |                              |
|      |                   |                |    |                  |                      |                      |           |                              |
|      |                   |                |    |                  |                      |                      |           |                              |

## Cash Receipts Journal    Page ____

| Date | Account Credited | Explanation | PR | Cash Dr. | Sales Disc. Dr. | Accts. Rec. Cr. | Sales Cr. | Other Accts. Cr. | PST Payable Cr. | GST Payable Cr. | COGS Dr. Merch. Inv. Cr. |
|------|------------------|-------------|----|----------|-----------------|-----------------|-----------|------------------|-----------------|-----------------|--------------------------|
|      |                  |             |    |          |                 |                 |           |                  |                 |                 |                          |
|      |                  |             |    |          |                 |                 |           |                  |                 |                 |                          |
|      |                  |             |    |          |                 |                 |           |                  |                 |                 |                          |
|      |                  |             |    |          |                 |                 |           |                  |                 |                 |                          |
|      |                  |             |    |          |                 |                 |           |                  |                 |                 |                          |
|      |                  |             |    |          |                 |                 |           |                  |                 |                 |                          |
|      |                  |             |    |          |                 |                 |           |                  |                 |                 |                          |
|      |                  |             |    |          |                 |                 |           |                  |                 |                 |                          |
|      |                  |             |    |          |                 |                 |           |                  |                 |                 |                          |

## Purchases Journal    Page ____

| Date | Account Credited | Terms | PR | Accounts Payable Cr. | Merch. Inventory Dr. | Other Accounts Dr. | GST Receivable Dr. |
|------|------------------|-------|----|----------------------|----------------------|--------------------|--------------------|
|      |                  |       |    |                      |                      |                    |                    |
|      |                  |       |    |                      |                      |                    |                    |
|      |                  |       |    |                      |                      |                    |                    |
|      |                  |       |    |                      |                      |                    |                    |
|      |                  |       |    |                      |                      |                    |                    |
|      |                  |       |    |                      |                      |                    |                    |
|      |                  |       |    |                      |                      |                    |                    |
|      |                  |       |    |                      |                      |                    |                    |
|      |                  |       |    |                      |                      |                    |                    |

## Cash Disbursements Journal    Page ____

| Date | Ch. No. | Account Debited | PR | Cash Cr. | Merch. Inventory Cr. | Other Accounts Dr. | GST Receivable Dr. | Accts. Payable Dr. |
|------|---------|-----------------|----|----------|----------------------|--------------------|--------------------|--------------------|
|      |         |                 |    |          |                      |                    |                    |                    |
|      |         |                 |    |          |                      |                    |                    |                    |
|      |         |                 |    |          |                      |                    |                    |                    |
|      |         |                 |    |          |                      |                    |                    |                    |
|      |         |                 |    |          |                      |                    |                    |                    |
|      |         |                 |    |          |                      |                    |                    |                    |
|      |         |                 |    |          |                      |                    |                    |                    |
|      |         |                 |    |          |                      |                    |                    |                    |

## GENERAL JOURNAL                                    Page____

| Date | Account Titles and Explanation | PR | Debit | Credit |
|------|-------------------------------|----|-------|--------|
|      |                               |    |       |        |
|      |                               |    |       |        |
|      |                               |    |       |        |
|      |                               |    |       |        |
|      |                               |    |       |        |
|      |                               |    |       |        |
|      |                               |    |       |        |
|      |                               |    |       |        |
|      |                               |    |       |        |
|      |                               |    |       |        |
|      |                               |    |       |        |
|      |                               |    |       |        |

**Part 5**

### THE BLEDSOE COMPANY
### Trial Balance
### March 31, 2011

|  | Debit | Credit |
|--|-------|--------|
|  |       |        |
|  |       |        |
|  |       |        |
|  |       |        |
|  |       |        |
|  |       |        |
|  |       |        |
|  |       |        |
|  |       |        |
|  |       |        |
|  |       |        |
|  |       |        |
|  |       |        |
|  |       |        |
|  |       |        |
|  |       |        |
|  |       |        |
|  |       |        |
|  |       |        |
|  |       |        |
|  |       |        |
|  |       |        |

### THE BLEDSOE COMPANY
### Schedule of Accounts Receivable
### March 31, 2011

|  |  |  |
|---|---|---|
|  |  |  |
|  |  |  |
|  |  |  |
|  |  |  |

### THE BLEDSOE COMPANY
### Schedule of Accounts Payable
### March 31, 2011

|  |  |  |
|---|---|---|
|  |  |  |
|  |  |  |
|  |  |  |
|  |  |  |

## *Problem 8-9A (Periodic)

### Part 1

### GENERAL LEDGER

#### Cash                                    ACCOUNT NO. 101

| DATE | EXPLANATION | PR | DEBIT | CREDIT | BALANCE |
|---|---|---|---|---|---|
|  |  |  |  |  |  |
|  |  |  |  |  |  |
|  |  |  |  |  |  |
|  |  |  |  |  |  |

#### Accounts Receivable                    ACCOUNT NO. 106

| DATE | EXPLANATION | PR | DEBIT | CREDIT | BALANCE |
|---|---|---|---|---|---|
|  |  |  |  |  |  |
|  |  |  |  |  |  |
|  |  |  |  |  |  |

#### GST Receivable                         ACCOUNT NO. 108

| DATE | EXPLANATION | PR | DEBIT | CREDIT | BALANCE |
|---|---|---|---|---|---|
|  |  |  |  |  |  |
|  |  |  |  |  |  |
|  |  |  |  |  |  |

## Merchandise Inventory                    ACCOUNT NO. 119

| DATE | EXPLANATION | PR | DEBIT | CREDIT | BALANCE |
|------|-------------|----|----|------|------|
| 2011 | | | | | |
| Feb. 28 | Balance brought forward | | | | 250,000 |
| | | | | | |

## Office Supplies                    ACCOUNT NO. 124

| DATE | EXPLANATION | PR | DEBIT | CREDIT | BALANCE |
|------|-------------|----|----|------|------|
| | | | | | |
| | | | | | |
| | | | | | |

## Store Supplies                    ACCOUNT NO. 125

| DATE | EXPLANATION | PR | DEBIT | CREDIT | BALANCE |
|------|-------------|----|----|------|------|
| | | | | | |
| | | | | | |
| | | | | | |

## Office Equipment                    ACCOUNT NO. 163

| DATE | EXPLANATION | PR | DEBIT | CREDIT | BALANCE |
|------|-------------|----|----|------|------|
| | | | | | |
| | | | | | |
| | | | | | |

## Accounts Payable                    ACCOUNT NO. 201

| DATE | EXPLANATION | PR | DEBIT | CREDIT | BALANCE |
|------|-------------|----|----|------|------|
| | | | | | |
| | | | | | |
| | | | | | |
| | | | | | |
| | | | | | |

## PST Payable                    ACCOUNT NO. 224

| DATE | EXPLANATION | PR | DEBIT | CREDIT | BALANCE |
|------|-------------|----|----|------|------|
| | | | | | |
| | | | | | |
| | | | | | |

### GST Payable                                    ACCOUNT NO. 225

| DATE | EXPLANATION | PR | DEBIT | CREDIT | BALANCE |
|------|-------------|-----|-------|--------|---------|
|      |             |     |       |        |         |
|      |             |     |       |        |         |
|      |             |     |       |        |         |
|      |             |     |       |        |         |
|      |             |     |       |        |         |
|      |             |     |       |        |         |

### Long-Term Notes Payable                        ACCOUNT NO. 251

| DATE | EXPLANATION | PR | DEBIT | CREDIT | BALANCE |
|------|-------------|-----|-------|--------|---------|
|      |             |     |       |        |         |
|      |             |     |       |        |         |
|      |             |     |       |        |         |

### George Bledsoe, Capital                        ACCOUNT NO. 301

| DATE | EXPLANATION | PR | DEBIT | CREDIT | BALANCE |
|------|-------------|-----|-------|--------|---------|
| 2011 |             |     |       |        |         |
| Feb. 28 | Balance brought forward |  |    |        | 250,000 |
|      |             |     |       |        |         |

### Sales                                          ACCOUNT NO. 413

| DATE | EXPLANATION | PR | DEBIT | CREDIT | BALANCE |
|------|-------------|-----|-------|--------|---------|
|      |             |     |       |        |         |
|      |             |     |       |        |         |
|      |             |     |       |        |         |

### Sales Discounts                                ACCOUNT NO. 415

| DATE | EXPLANATION | PR | DEBIT | CREDIT | BALANCE |
|------|-------------|-----|-------|--------|---------|
|      |             |     |       |        |         |
|      |             |     |       |        |         |
|      |             |     |       |        |         |

### Purchases                                      ACCOUNT NO. 505

| DATE | EXPLANATION | PR | DEBIT | CREDIT | BALANCE |
|------|-------------|-----|-------|--------|---------|
|      |             |     |       |        |         |
|      |             |     |       |        |         |
|      |             |     |       |        |         |

### Purchase Returns and Allowances                ACCOUNT NO. 506

| DATE | EXPLANATION | PR | DEBIT | CREDIT | BALANCE |
|------|-------------|-----|-------|--------|---------|
|      |             |     |       |        |         |
|      |             |     |       |        |         |
|      |             |     |       |        |         |

### Purchase Discounts        ACCOUNT NO. 507

| DATE | EXPLANATION | PR | DEBIT | CREDIT | BALANCE |
|------|-------------|----|-------|--------|---------|
|      |             |    |       |        |         |
|      |             |    |       |        |         |
|      |             |    |       |        |         |

### Sales Salaries Expense        ACCOUNT NO. 621

| DATE | EXPLANATION | PR | DEBIT | CREDIT | BALANCE |
|------|-------------|----|-------|--------|---------|
|      |             |    |       |        |         |
|      |             |    |       |        |         |
|      |             |    |       |        |         |

NOTE: For Parts 2, 3, and 5, use the respective forms provided in *Problem 8-9A (Perpetual).

Part 4

| | | | | Sales Journal | | | Page |
|--|--|--|--|--|--|--|--|
| Date | Account Debited | Invoice No. | PR | Accounts Receivable Dr. | PST Payable Cr. | GST Payable Cr. | Sales Cr. |
|      |                 |             |    |                         |                 |                 |           |
|      |                 |             |    |                         |                 |                 |           |
|      |                 |             |    |                         |                 |                 |           |
|      |                 |             |    |                         |                 |                 |           |
|      |                 |             |    |                         |                 |                 |           |
|      |                 |             |    |                         |                 |                 |           |
|      |                 |             |    |                         |                 |                 |           |
|      |                 |             |    |                         |                 |                 |           |
|      |                 |             |    |                         |                 |                 |           |

| | | | | Cash Receipts Journal | | | | Page |
|--|--|--|--|--|--|--|--|--|
| Date | Account Credited | PR | Explanation | Cash Dr. | Sales Disc. Dr. | Accts. Rec. Cr. | Sales Cr. | Other Accts. Cr. |
|      |                  |    |             |          |                 |                 |           |                  |
|      |                  |    |             |          |                 |                 |           |                  |
|      |                  |    |             |          |                 |                 |           |                  |
|      |                  |    |             |          |                 |                 |           |                  |
|      |                  |    |             |          |                 |                 |           |                  |
|      |                  |    |             |          |                 |                 |           |                  |
|      |                  |    |             |          |                 |                 |           |                  |
|      |                  |    |             |          |                 |                 |           |                  |

| | | Purchases Journal | | | | | | Page | |
|---|---|---|---|---|---|---|---|---|---|
| Date | Account Credited | Date of Invoice | Terms | PR | Accts. Payable Cr. | Purchases Dr. | Other Accounts Dr. | GST Rec'ble Dr. |
| | | | | | | | | |
| | | | | | | | | |
| | | | | | | | | |
| | | | | | | | | |
| | | | | | | | | |
| | | | | | | | | |
| | | | | | | | | |
| | | | | | | | | |
| | | | | | | | | |

| | | | Cash Disbursements Journal | | | | | | Page | |
|---|---|---|---|---|---|---|---|---|---|---|
| Date | Ch No | Payee | Account Debited | PR | Other Accts. Dr. | GST Rec'ble Dr. | Accts. Payable Dr. | Pur. Disc. Cr. | Cash Cr. |
| | | | | | | | | | |
| | | | | | | | | | |
| | | | | | | | | | |
| | | | | | | | | | |
| | | | | | | | | | |
| | | | | | | | | | |
| | | | | | | | | | |
| | | | | | | | | | |

## GENERAL JOURNAL                    Page____

| Date | Account Titles and Explanation | PR | Debit | Credit |
|---|---|---|---|---|
| | | | | |
| | | | | |
| | | | | |
| | | | | |
| | | | | |
| | | | | |
| | | | | |
| | | | | |
| | | | | |
| | | | | |
| | | | | |
| | | | | |
| | | | | |
| | | | | |

## Sales Journal                                                                 Page _____

| Date | Account Debited | Invoice No. | PR | Acct. Rec. Dr. | PST Payable Cr. | GST Payable Cr. | Sales Cr. | COGS Dr. Merch. Inv. Cr. |
|------|-----------------|-------------|----|----------------|-----------------|-----------------|-----------|--------------------------|
|      |                 |             |    |                |                 |                 |           |                          |
|      |                 |             |    |                |                 |                 |           |                          |
|      |                 |             |    |                |                 |                 |           |                          |
|      |                 |             |    |                |                 |                 |           |                          |
|      |                 |             |    |                |                 |                 |           |                          |

## Cash Receipts Journal                                                          Page _____

| Date | Account Credited | Explanation | PR | Cash Dr. | Sales Disc. Dr. | Accts. Rec. Cr. | Sales Cr. | Other Accts. Cr. | PST Payable Cr. | GST Payable Cr. | COGS Dr. Merch. Inv. Cr. |
|------|------------------|-------------|----|----------|-----------------|-----------------|-----------|------------------|-----------------|-----------------|--------------------------|
|      |                  |             |    |          |                 |                 |           |                  |                 |                 |                          |
|      |                  |             |    |          |                 |                 |           |                  |                 |                 |                          |
|      |                  |             |    |          |                 |                 |           |                  |                 |                 |                          |
|      |                  |             |    |          |                 |                 |           |                  |                 |                 |                          |
|      |                  |             |    |          |                 |                 |           |                  |                 |                 |                          |

## Purchases Journal                                                              Page _____

| Date | Account Credited | Terms | PR | Accounts Payable Cr. | Merch. Inventory Dr. | Other Accounts Dr. | GST Receivable Dr. |
|------|------------------|-------|----|----------------------|----------------------|--------------------|--------------------|
|      |                  |       |    |                      |                      |                    |                    |
|      |                  |       |    |                      |                      |                    |                    |
|      |                  |       |    |                      |                      |                    |                    |
|      |                  |       |    |                      |                      |                    |                    |
|      |                  |       |    |                      |                      |                    |                    |

## Cash Disbursements Journal                                                     Page _____

| Date | Ch. No. | Account Debited | PR | Cash Cr. | Merch. Inventory Cr. | Other Accounts Dr. | GST Receivable Dr. | Accts. Payable Dr. |
|------|---------|-----------------|----|----------|----------------------|--------------------|--------------------|--------------------|
|      |         |                 |    |          |                      |                    |                    |                    |
|      |         |                 |    |          |                      |                    |                    |                    |
|      |         |                 |    |          |                      |                    |                    |                    |
|      |         |                 |    |          |                      |                    |                    |                    |
|      |         |                 |    |          |                      |                    |                    |                    |

## Sales Journal                                                    Page ____

| Date | Account Debited | Invoice No. | PR | Accounts Receivable Dr. | PST Payable Cr. | GST Payable Cr. | Sales Cr. |
|------|-----------------|-------------|----|-----------------------|-----------------|-----------------|-----------|
|      |                 |             |    |                       |                 |                 |           |
|      |                 |             |    |                       |                 |                 |           |
|      |                 |             |    |                       |                 |                 |           |
|      |                 |             |    |                       |                 |                 |           |
|      |                 |             |    |                       |                 |                 |           |

## Cash Receipts Journal                                            Page ____

| Date | Account Credited | PR | Explanation | Cash Dr. | Sales Disc. Dr. | Accts. Rec. Cr. | Sales Cr. | Other Accts. Cr. |
|------|------------------|----|-------------|----------|-----------------|-----------------|-----------|------------------|
|      |                  |    |             |          |                 |                 |           |                  |
|      |                  |    |             |          |                 |                 |           |                  |
|      |                  |    |             |          |                 |                 |           |                  |
|      |                  |    |             |          |                 |                 |           |                  |
|      |                  |    |             |          |                 |                 |           |                  |

## Purchases Journal                                                Page ____

| Date | Account Credited | Date of Invoice | Terms | PR | Accts. Payable Cr. | Purchases Dr. | Other Accounts Dr. | GST Rec'ble Dr. |
|------|------------------|-----------------|-------|----|--------------------|---------------|--------------------|-----------------|
|      |                  |                 |       |    |                    |               |                    |                 |
|      |                  |                 |       |    |                    |               |                    |                 |
|      |                  |                 |       |    |                    |               |                    |                 |
|      |                  |                 |       |    |                    |               |                    |                 |
|      |                  |                 |       |    |                    |               |                    |                 |

## Cash Disbursements Journal                                       Page ____

| Date | Ch No | Payee | Account Debited | PR | Other Accts. Dr. | GST Rec'ble Dr. | Accts. Payable Dr. | Pur. Disc. Cr. | Cash Cr. |
|------|-------|-------|-----------------|----|------------------|-----------------|--------------------|----------------|----------|
|      |       |       |                 |    |                  |                 |                    |                |          |
|      |       |       |                 |    |                  |                 |                    |                |          |
|      |       |       |                 |    |                  |                 |                    |                |          |
|      |       |       |                 |    |                  |                 |                    |                |          |
|      |       |       |                 |    |                  |                 |                    |                |          |

| Special Journal | | Subledger | |
|---|---|---|---|
| Sales............................. | S | Accounts Receivable.... | AR |
| Purchases .................... | P | Accounts Payable......... | AP |
| Cash Receipts.............. | CR | No Effect....................... | NE |
| Cash Disbursements ... | CD | | |
| General Journal ........... | G | | |

| Date | Transaction | Special Journal | Subledger |
|---|---|---|---|
| May 1 | The owner invested an automobile into the business. | | |
| 2 | Sold merchandise and received cash. | | |
| 3 | Purchased merchandise inventory on credit. | | |
| 4 | Sold merchandise on terms of 1/10, n30. | | |
| 5 | The customer of May 4 returned defective merchandise. | | |
| 6 | Regarding the May 3 purchase, received a credit memorandum from the supplier granting an allowance. | | |
| 15 | Paid mid-month salaries. | | |
| 17 | Purchased office supplies on credit. | | |
| 19 | Paid for the balance owing on the May 3 purchase. | | |
| 22 | Received payment on the May 4 sale. | | |
| 25 | Borrowed money from bank. | | |
| 29 | Purchased merchandise inventory; paid cash. | | |
| 30 | Accrued interest revenue. | | |
| 30 | Closed all revenue accounts to the Income Summary account. | | |

| Sales Journal | | | | | Page 3 |
|---|---|---|---|---|---|
| Date | Account Debited | Invoice Number | PR | Accounts Receivable Dr. Sales Cr. | Cost of Goods Sold Dr. Merchandise Inventory Cr. |
| | | | | | |
| | | | | | |
| | | | | | |
| | | | | | |
| | | | | | |
| | | | | | |

| Cash Receipts Journal | | | | | | | | | Page 3 |
|---|---|---|---|---|---|---|---|---|---|
| Date | Accounts Credited | PR | Explanation | Cash Dr. | Sales Disc. Dr. | Accts. Rec. Cr. | Sales Cr. | Other Accts. Cr. | COGS Dr. Merch. Inv. Cr. |
| | | | | | | | | | |
| | | | | | | | | | |
| | | | | | | | | | |
| | | | | | | | | | |
| | | | | | | | | | |

| Purchases Journal | | | | | | | | Page 3 |
|---|---|---|---|---|---|---|---|---|
| Date | Account | Date of Invoice | Terms | PR | Accounts Payable Cr. | Merch. Inventory Dr. | Office Supplies Dr. | Other Accounts Dr. |
| | | | | | | | | |
| | | | | | | | | |
| | | | | | | | | |
| | | | | | | | | |
| | | | | | | | | |

| Cash Disbursements Journal | | | | | | | | Page 3 |
|---|---|---|---|---|---|---|---|---|
| Date | Ch. No. | Payee | Account Debited | PR | Cash Cr. | Merch. Inventory Cr. | Other Accounts Dr. | Accounts Payable Dr. |
| | | | | | | | | |
| | | | | | | | | |
| | | | | | | | | |
| | | | | | | | | |
| | | | | | | | | |

## GENERAL JOURNAL                                    Page____

| Date | Account Titles and Explanation | PR | Debit | Credit |
|------|-------------------------------|----|----|----|
|  |  |  |  |  |
|  |  |  |  |  |
|  |  |  |  |  |
|  |  |  |  |  |
|  |  |  |  |  |
|  |  |  |  |  |
|  |  |  |  |  |
|  |  |  |  |  |
|  |  |  |  |  |
|  |  |  |  |  |
|  |  |  |  |  |
|  |  |  |  |  |
|  |  |  |  |  |

## Problem 8-3B     Parts 2, 3, 5

### Part 1                         ACCOUNTS RECEIVABLE SUBLEDGER

#### Kelly Grody                              ACCOUNT NO. 106-1

| DATE | EXPLANATION | PR | DEBIT | CREDIT | BALANCE |
|------|-------------|----|----|----|----|
|  |  |  |  |  |  |
|  |  |  |  |  |  |
|  |  |  |  |  |  |
|  |  |  |  |  |  |

#### Karen Harden                            ACCOUNT NO. 106-2

| DATE | EXPLANATION | PR | DEBIT | CREDIT | BALANCE |
|------|-------------|----|----|----|----|
|  |  |  |  |  |  |
|  |  |  |  |  |  |
|  |  |  |  |  |  |

#### Paul Kane                               ACCOUNT NO. 106-3

| DATE | EXPLANATION | PR | DEBIT | CREDIT | BALANCE |
|------|-------------|----|----|----|----|
|  |  |  |  |  |  |
|  |  |  |  |  |  |
|  |  |  |  |  |  |

Part 2                            ACCOUNTS PAYABLE SUBLEDGER
                                  Beech Company                    ACCOUNT NO. 201-1

| DATE | EXPLANATION | PR | DEBIT | CREDIT | BALANCE |
|------|-------------|----|-------|--------|---------|
|      |             |    |       |        |         |
|      |             |    |       |        |         |
|      |             |    |       |        |         |
|      |             |    |       |        |         |
|      |             |    |       |        |         |

Blackwater Inc.                    ACCOUNT NO. 201-2

| DATE | EXPLANATION | PR | DEBIT | CREDIT | BALANCE |
|------|-------------|----|-------|--------|---------|
|      |             |    |       |        |         |
|      |             |    |       |        |         |
|      |             |    |       |        |         |
|      |             |    |       |        |         |

Poppe's Supply                     ACCOUNT NO. 201-3

| DATE | EXPLANATION | PR | DEBIT | CREDIT | BALANCE |
|------|-------------|----|-------|--------|---------|
|      |             |    |       |        |         |
|      |             |    |       |        |         |
|      |             |    |       |        |         |
|      |             |    |       |        |         |

Sprague Company                    ACCOUNT NO. 201-4

| DATE | EXPLANATION | PR | DEBIT | CREDIT | BALANCE |
|------|-------------|----|-------|--------|---------|
|      |             |    |       |        |         |
|      |             |    |       |        |         |
|      |             |    |       |        |         |
|      |             |    |       |        |         |

Part 3

| | | | | Sales Journal | Page |
|------|-------------------|-------------------|----|-------------------------------------|-------------------------------------------------------|
| Date | Account Debited | Invoice Number | PR | Accounts Receivable Dr. Sales Cr. | Cost of Goods Sold Dr. Merchandise Inventory Cr. |
|      |                   |                   |    |                                     |                                                       |
|      |                   |                   |    |                                     |                                                       |
|      |                   |                   |    |                                     |                                                       |
|      |                   |                   |    |                                     |                                                       |
|      |                   |                   |    |                                     |                                                       |
|      |                   |                   |    |                                     |                                                       |
|      |                   |                   |    |                                     |                                                       |
|      |                   |                   |    |                                     |                                                       |

## Cash Receipts Journal       Page

| Date | Account Credited | PR | Explanation | Cash Dr. | Sales Disc. Dr. | Accts. Rec. Cr. | Sales Cr. | Other Accts. Cr. | COGS Dr. Merch. Inv. Cr. |
|------|------------------|----|-------------|----------|-----------------|-----------------|-----------|------------------|--------------------------|
|      |                  |    |             |          |                 |                 |           |                  |                          |
|      |                  |    |             |          |                 |                 |           |                  |                          |
|      |                  |    |             |          |                 |                 |           |                  |                          |
|      |                  |    |             |          |                 |                 |           |                  |                          |
|      |                  |    |             |          |                 |                 |           |                  |                          |
|      |                  |    |             |          |                 |                 |           |                  |                          |
|      |                  |    |             |          |                 |                 |           |                  |                          |
|      |                  |    |             |          |                 |                 |           |                  |                          |
|      |                  |    |             |          |                 |                 |           |                  |                          |
|      |                  |    |             |          |                 |                 |           |                  |                          |
|      |                  |    |             |          |                 |                 |           |                  |                          |

## Purchases Journal       Page

| Date | Account Credited | Date of Invoice | Terms | PR | Accounts Payable Cr. | Merch. Inventory Dr. | Office Supplies Dr. | Other Accounts Dr. |
|------|------------------|-----------------|-------|----|----------------------|----------------------|---------------------|--------------------|
|      |                  |                 |       |    |                      |                      |                     |                    |
|      |                  |                 |       |    |                      |                      |                     |                    |
|      |                  |                 |       |    |                      |                      |                     |                    |
|      |                  |                 |       |    |                      |                      |                     |                    |
|      |                  |                 |       |    |                      |                      |                     |                    |
|      |                  |                 |       |    |                      |                      |                     |                    |
|      |                  |                 |       |    |                      |                      |                     |                    |
|      |                  |                 |       |    |                      |                      |                     |                    |
|      |                  |                 |       |    |                      |                      |                     |                    |
|      |                  |                 |       |    |                      |                      |                     |                    |

## Cash Disbursements Journal       Page

| Date | Ch No | Payee | Account Debited | PR | Cash Cr. | Merch. Inventory Cr. | Other Accounts Dr. | Accounts Payable Dr. |
|------|-------|-------|-----------------|----|----------|----------------------|--------------------|----------------------|
|      |       |       |                 |    |          |                      |                    |                      |
|      |       |       |                 |    |          |                      |                    |                      |
|      |       |       |                 |    |          |                      |                    |                      |
|      |       |       |                 |    |          |                      |                    |                      |
|      |       |       |                 |    |          |                      |                    |                      |
|      |       |       |                 |    |          |                      |                    |                      |
|      |       |       |                 |    |          |                      |                    |                      |
|      |       |       |                 |    |          |                      |                    |                      |
|      |       |       |                 |    |          |                      |                    |                      |

## GENERAL JOURNAL                                        Page____

| Date | Account Titles and Explanation | PR | Debit | Credit |
|------|-------------------------------|----|-------|--------|
|      |                               |    |       |        |
|      |                               |    |       |        |
|      |                               |    |       |        |
|      |                               |    |       |        |
|      |                               |    |       |        |
|      |                               |    |       |        |
|      |                               |    |       |        |
|      |                               |    |       |        |
|      |                               |    |       |        |
|      |                               |    |       |        |
|      |                               |    |       |        |
|      |                               |    |       |        |
|      |                               |    |       |        |
|      |                               |    |       |        |

## Problem 8-4B

### Part 1                          GENERAL LEDGER

**Cash**                                            ACCOUNT NO. 101

| DATE | EXPLANATION | PR | DEBIT | CREDIT | BALANCE |
|------|-------------|----|-------|--------|---------|
| 2011 |             |    |       |        |         |
| Jun. 30 | Balance brought forward |  |   |        | 95,000 |
|      |             |    |       |        |         |
|      |             |    |       |        |         |

**Accounts Receivable**                             ACCOUNT NO. 106

| DATE | EXPLANATION | PR | DEBIT | CREDIT | BALANCE |
|------|-------------|----|-------|--------|---------|
|      |             |    |       |        |         |
|      |             |    |       |        |         |
|      |             |    |       |        |         |

**Merchandise Inventory**                           ACCOUNT NO. 119

| DATE | EXPLANATION | PR | DEBIT | CREDIT | BALANCE |
|------|-------------|----|-------|--------|---------|
| 2011 |             |    |       |        |         |
| Jun. 30 | Balance brought forward |  |   |        | 167,000 |
|      |             |    |       |        |         |
|      |             |    |       |        |         |
|      |             |    |       |        |         |
|      |             |    |       |        |         |
|      |             |    |       |        |         |

## Office Supplies                                    ACCOUNT NO. 124

| DATE | EXPLANATION | PR | DEBIT | CREDIT | BALANCE |
|------|-------------|----|-------|--------|---------|
|      |             |    |       |        |         |
|      |             |    |       |        |         |
|      |             |    |       |        |         |

## Store Supplies                                    ACCOUNT NO. 125

| DATE | EXPLANATION | PR | DEBIT | CREDIT | BALANCE |
|------|-------------|----|-------|--------|---------|
|      |             |    |       |        |         |
|      |             |    |       |        |         |
|      |             |    |       |        |         |

## Store Equipment                                   ACCOUNT NO. 165

| DATE | EXPLANATION | PR | DEBIT | CREDIT | BALANCE |
|------|-------------|----|-------|--------|---------|
|      |             |    |       |        |         |
|      |             |    |       |        |         |
|      |             |    |       |        |         |

## Accounts Payable                                  ACCOUNT NO. 201

| DATE | EXPLANATION | PR | DEBIT | CREDIT | BALANCE |
|------|-------------|----|-------|--------|---------|
|      |             |    |       |        |         |
|      |             |    |       |        |         |
|      |             |    |       |        |         |
|      |             |    |       |        |         |
|      |             |    |       |        |         |

## Long-Term Notes Payable                           ACCOUNT NO. 251

| DATE | EXPLANATION | PR | DEBIT | CREDIT | BALANCE |
|------|-------------|----|-------|--------|---------|
| 2011 |             |    |       |        |         |
| Jun. 30 | Balance brought forward |    |       |        | 167,000 |
|      |             |    |       |        |         |

## Gene Eldridge, Capital                            ACCOUNT NO. 301

| DATE | EXPLANATION | PR | DEBIT | CREDIT | BALANCE |
|------|-------------|----|-------|--------|---------|
| 2011 |             |    |       |        |         |
| Jun. 30 | Balance brought forward |    |       |        | 95,000 |
|      |             |    |       |        |         |

Sales                                    ACCOUNT NO. 413

| DATE | EXPLANATION | PR | DEBIT | CREDIT | BALANCE |
|------|-------------|----|-------|--------|---------|
|      |             |    |       |        |         |
|      |             |    |       |        |         |
|      |             |    |       |        |         |

Sales Discounts                          ACCOUNT NO. 1415

| DATE | EXPLANATION | PR | DEBIT | CREDIT | BALANCE |
|------|-------------|----|-------|--------|---------|
|      |             |    |       |        |         |
|      |             |    |       |        |         |
|      |             |    |       |        |         |

Cost of Goods Sold                       ACCOUNT NO. 502

| DATE | EXPLANATION | PR | DEBIT | CREDIT | BALANCE |
|------|-------------|----|-------|--------|---------|
|      |             |    |       |        |         |
|      |             |    |       |        |         |
|      |             |    |       |        |         |

Sales Salaries Expense                   ACCOUNT NO. 621

| DATE | EXPLANATION | PR | DEBIT | CREDIT | BALANCE |
|------|-------------|----|-------|--------|---------|
|      |             |    |       |        |         |
|      |             |    |       |        |         |
|      |             |    |       |        |         |

Advertising Expense                      ACCOUNT NO. 655

| DATE | EXPLANATION | PR | DEBIT | CREDIT | BALANCE |
|------|-------------|----|-------|--------|---------|
|      |             |    |       |        |         |
|      |             |    |       |        |         |
|      |             |    |       |        |         |

**NOTE:  For Parts 2 and 3, journalizing and posting, continue journalizing the transactions in the accounts provided in Problem 8-3A.**

**Part 5**

### ELDRIDGE INDUSTRIES
### Trial Balance
### July 31, 2011

| | Debit | Credit |
|---|---|---|
| | | |
| | | |
| | | |
| | | |
| | | |
| | | |
| | | |
| | | |
| | | |
| | | |
| | | |
| | | |
| | | |
| | | |
| | | |
| | | |
| | | |
| | | |
| | | |

### ELDRIDGE INDUSTRIES
### Schedule of Accounts Receivable
### July 31, 2011

| | | |
|---|---|---|
| | | |
| | | |
| | | |
| | | |
| | | |

### ELDRIDGE INDUSTRIES
### Schedule of Accounts Payable
### July 31, 2011

| | | |
|---|---|---|
| | | |
| | | |
| | | |
| | | |
| | | |
| | | |

*Analysis component:* _____

_____
_____
_____
_____
_____
_____
_____
_____

## Problem 8-5B

### Part 1

| Sales Journal | | | | | Page 3 |
|---|---|---|---|---|---|
| **Date** | **Account Debited** | **Invoice Number** | **PR** | **Accounts Receivable Dr. Sales Cr.** | **Cost of Goods Sold Dr. Merchandise Inventory Cr.** |
| 2011 | | | | | |
| Oct. 6 | M. Craig | 913 | √ | 3,300 | 1,800 |
| 12 | H. Flatt | 914 | √ | 3,650 | 2,000 |
| 15 | A. Izon | 915 | √ | 3,100 | 1,700 |
| | | | | | |
| | | | | | |
| | | | | | |
| | | | | | |

| Cash Receipts Journal | | | | | | | | | Page 3 |
|---|---|---|---|---|---|---|---|---|---|
| **Date** | **Account Credited** | **PR** | **Explanation** | **Cash Dr.** | **Sales Disc. Dr.** | **Accts. Rec. Cr.** | **Sales Cr.** | **Other Accts. Cr.** | **COGS Dr. Merch. Inv. Cr.** |
| 2011 | | | | | | | | | |
| Oct. 2 | J. Wildman | √ | Inv. 11/23 | 4,116 | 84 | 4,200 | | | |
| 15 | Sales | | Cash sales | 38,830 | | | 38,830 | | 21,400 |
| 15 | M. Craig | √ | Inv. 12/6 | 2,401 | 49 | 2,450 | | | |
| | | | | | | | | | |
| | | | | | | | | | |
| | | | | | | | | | |
| | | | | | | | | | |
| | | | | | | | | | |
| | | | | | | | | | |

| Purchases Journal | | | | | | | | Page 2 |
|---|---|---|---|---|---|---|---|---|
| Date | Account | Date of Invoice | Terms | PR | Accounts Payable Cr. | Merch. Inventory Dr. | Office Supplies Dr. | Other Accounts Dr. |
| 2011 | | | | | | | | |
| Oct. 2 | Walters Co. | 12/2 | 2/10,n/60 | √ | 3,200 | 3,200 | | |
| 5 | Green Supply | 12/3 | n/10,EOM | √ | 1,300 | 1,300 | | |
| 15 | Walters Co. | 12/15 | 2/10,n/60 | √ | 3,990 | 3,990 | | |
| 15 | Sunshine Co. | 12/15 | 2/10,n/60 | √ | 2,650 | 2,650 | | |
| | | | | | | | | |
| | | | | | | | | |
| | | | | | | | | |
| | | | | | | | | |
| | | | | | | | | |

| Cash Disbursements Journal | | | | | | | | Page 3 |
|---|---|---|---|---|---|---|---|---|
| Date | Ch. No. | Payee | Account Debited | PR | Cash Cr. | Merch. Inventory Cr. | Other Accounts Dr. | Accounts Payable Dr. |
| 2011 | | | | | | | | |
| Oct. 2 | 619 | Omni Realty | Rent Exp. | 640 | 2,250 | | 2,250 | |
| 6 | 620 | Fireside Co. | Fireside Co. | √ | 3,724 | 76 | | 3,800 |
| 12 | 621 | Walters Co. | Walters Co. | √ | 3,136 | 64 | | 3,200 |
| 15 | 622 | Jamie Ford | Sales Sal. Exp. | 621 | 2,620 | | 2,620 | |
| | | | | | | | | |
| | | | | | | | | |
| | | | | | | | | |
| | | | | | | | | |
| | | | | | | | | |
| | | | | | | | | |
| | | | | | | | | |

## GENERAL JOURNAL

| Date | | Account Titles and Explanation | PR | Debit | Credit |
|---|---|---|---|---|---|
| 2011 | | | | | |
| Oct. | 4 | Accounts Payable—Fireside Company | 201/√ | 460 | |
| | | Merchandise Inventory | 119 | | 460 |
| | | *Received a credit memo for returns.* | | | |
| | | | | | |
| | 9 | Sales Returns and Allowances | 414 | 850 | |
| | | Accounts Receivable—Marge Craig | 106/√ | | 850 |
| | | *Issued a credit memorandum.* | | | |
| | | | | | |
| | | | | | |
| | | | | | |
| | | | | | |
| | | | | | |
| | | | | | |
| | | | | | |
| | | | | | |
| | | | | | |
| | | | | | |
| | | | | | |
| | | | | | |
| | | | | | |
| | | | | | |
| | | | | | |

## ACCOUNTS RECEIVABLE SUBLEDGER

### Marge Craig

| DATE | | EXPLANATION | PR | DEBIT | CREDIT | BALANCE |
|---|---|---|---|---|---|---|
| 2011 | | | | | | |
| Oct. | 6 | | S3 | 3,300 | | 3,300 |
| | 9 | | G2 | | 850 | 2,450 |
| | 15 | | CR3 | | 2,450 | -0- |
| | | | | | | |

### Heather Flatt

| DATE | | EXPLANATION | PR | DEBIT | CREDIT | BALANCE |
|---|---|---|---|---|---|---|
| 2011 | | | | | | |
| Oct. | 12 | | S3 | 3,650 | | 3,650 |
| | | | | | | |
| | | | | | | |

## Amy Izon

| DATE | | EXPLANATION | PR | DEBIT | CREDIT | BALANCE |
|---|---|---|---|---|---|---|
| 2011 | | | | | | |
| Oct. | 15 | | S3 | 3,100 | | 3,100 |
| | | | | | | |
| | | | | | | |

## Jan Wildman

| DATE | | EXPLANATION | PR | DEBIT | CREDIT | BALANCE |
|---|---|---|---|---|---|---|
| 2011 | | | | | | |
| Sept | 23 | | S2 | 4,200 | | 4,200 |
| Oct. | 2 | | CR3 | | 4,200 | -0- |
| | | | | | | |

## ACCOUNTS PAYABLE SUBLEDGER

### Fireside Company

| DATE | | EXPLANATION | PR | DEBIT | CREDIT | BALANCE |
|---|---|---|---|---|---|---|
| 2011 | | | | | | |
| Sept | 28 | | P1 | | 4,260 | 4,260 |
| Oct. | 4 | | G2 | 460 | | 3,800 |
| | 6 | | CD4 | 3,800 | | -0- |
| | | | | | | |

### Green Supply Company

| DATE | | EXPLANATION | PR | DEBIT | CREDIT | BALANCE |
|---|---|---|---|---|---|---|
| 2011 | | | | | | |
| Oct. | 5 | | P2 | | 1,300 | 1,300 |
| | | | | | | |
| | | | | | | |
| | | | | | | |

### Sunshine Company

| DATE | | EXPLANATION | PR | DEBIT | CREDIT | BALANCE |
|---|---|---|---|---|---|---|
| 2011 | | | | | | |
| Oct. | 15 | | P2 | | 2,650 | 2,650 |
| | | | | | | |

## Walters Company

| DATE | | EXPLANATION | PR | DEBIT | CREDIT | BALANCE |
|---|---|---|---|---|---|---|
| 2011 | | | | | | |
| Oct. | 2 | | P2 | | 3,200 | 3,200 |
| | 12 | | CD4 | 3,200 | | -0- |
| | 15 | | P2 | | 3,990 | 3,990 |
| | | | | | | |
| | | | | | | |
| | | | | | | |

Parts 2 and 3                    GENERAL LEDGER

Cash                                            ACCOUNT NO. 101

| DATE | | EXPLANATION | PR | DEBIT | CREDIT | BALANCE |
|---|---|---|---|---|---|---|
| 2011 | | | | | | |
| Sept | 30 | Balance | | | | 5,361 |
| | | | | | | |
| | | | | | | |

Accounts Receivable                    ACCOUNT NO. 106

| DATE | | EXPLANATION | PR | DEBIT | CREDIT | BALANCE |
|---|---|---|---|---|---|---|
| 2011 | | | | | | |
| Sept | 30 | Balance | | | | 4,200 |
| Oct. | 9 | | G2 | | 850 | 3,350 |
| | | | | | | |
| | | | | | | |
| | | | | | | |

Merchandise Inventory                    ACCOUNT NO. 119

| DATE | | EXPLANATION | PR | DEBIT | CREDIT | BALANCE |
|---|---|---|---|---|---|---|
| 2011 | | | | | | |
| Sept | 30 | Balance | | | | 66,970 |
| Oct. | 4 | | G2 | | 460 | 66,510 |
| | | | | | | |
| | | | | | | |
| | | | | | | |
| | | | | | | |

## Office Supplies                    ACCOUNT NO. 124

| DATE | | EXPLANATION | PR | DEBIT | CREDIT | BALANCE |
|---|---|---|---|---|---|---|
| 2011 | | | | | | |
| Sept | 30 | Balance | | | | 607 |
| | | | | | | |
| | | | | | | |

## Store Supplies                    ACCOUNT NO. 125

| DATE | | EXPLANATION | PR | DEBIT | CREDIT | BALANCE |
|---|---|---|---|---|---|---|
| 2011 | | | | | | |
| Sept | 30 | Balance | | | | 346 |
| | | | | | | |
| | | | | | | |

## Store Equipment                    ACCOUNT NO. 165

| DATE | | EXPLANATION | PR | DEBIT | CREDIT | BALANCE |
|---|---|---|---|---|---|---|
| 2011 | | | | | | |
| Sept | 30 | Balance | | | | 42,129 |
| | | | | | | |
| | | | | | | |

## Accumulated Amortization, Store Equipment    ACCOUNT NO. 166

| DATE | | EXPLANATION | PR | DEBIT | CREDIT | BALANCE |
|---|---|---|---|---|---|---|
| 2011 | | | | | | |
| Sept | 30 | Balance | | | | 9,153 |
| | | | | | | |

## Accounts Payable                    ACCOUNT NO. 201

| DATE | | EXPLANATION | PR | DEBIT | CREDIT | BALANCE |
|---|---|---|---|---|---|---|
| 2011 | | | | | | |
| Sept | 30 | Balance | | | | 4,260 |
| Oct. | 4 | | G2 | 460 | | 3,800 |
| | | | | | | |
| | | | | | | |
| | | | | | | |

### Marlee Levin, Capital                    ACCOUNT NO. 301

| DATE | EXPLANATION | PR | DEBIT | CREDIT | BALANCE |
|------|-------------|----|-------|--------|---------|
| 2011 | | | | | |
| Sept 30 | Balance | | | | 106,200 |
| | | | | | |

### Marlee Levin, Withdrawals               ACCOUNT NO. 302

| DATE | EXPLANATION | PR | DEBIT | CREDIT | BALANCE |
|------|-------------|----|-------|--------|---------|
| 2011 | | | | | |
| | | | | | |
| | | | | | |

### Sales                                   ACCOUNT NO. 413

| DATE | EXPLANATION | PR | DEBIT | CREDIT | BALANCE |
|------|-------------|----|-------|--------|---------|
| 2011 | | | | | |
| | | | | | |
| | | | | | |

### Sales Returns and Allowances            ACCOUNT NO. 414

| DATE | EXPLANATION | PR | DEBIT | CREDIT | BALANCE |
|------|-------------|----|-------|--------|---------|
| 2011 | | | | | |
| Oct. 9 | | G2 | 850 | | 850 |
| | | | | | |

### Sales Discounts                         ACCOUNT NO. 415

| DATE | EXPLANATION | PR | DEBIT | CREDIT | BALANCE |
|------|-------------|----|-------|--------|---------|
| 2011 | | | | | |
| | | | | | |
| | | | | | |

### Cost of Goods Sold                      ACCOUNT NO. 502

| DATE | EXPLANATION | PR | DEBIT | CREDIT | BALANCE |
|------|-------------|----|-------|--------|---------|
| 2011 | | | | | |
| | | | | | |
| | | | | | |

### Sales Salaries Expense                  ACCOUNT NO. 621

| DATE | EXPLANATION | PR | DEBIT | CREDIT | BALANCE |
|------|-------------|----|-------|--------|---------|
| 2011 | | | | | |
| Oct. 15 | | CD4 | 2,620 | | 2,620 |
| | | | | | |

### Rent Expense — ACCOUNT NO. 640

| DATE | EXPLANATION | PR | DEBIT | CREDIT | BALANCE |
|------|-------------|----|-------|--------|---------|
| 2011 | | | | | |
| Oct. 2 | | CD4 | 2,250 | | 2,250 |
| | | | | | |

### Utilities Expense — ACCOUNT NO. 690

| DATE | EXPLANATION | PR | DEBIT | CREDIT | BALANCE |
|------|-------------|----|-------|--------|---------|
| 2011 | | | | | |
| | | | | | |
| | | | | | |

## Part 4

### STARSHINE PRODUCTS
### Trial Balance
### October 31, 2011

| | Debit | Credit |
|---|-------|--------|
| | | |
| | | |
| | | |
| | | |
| | | |
| | | |
| | | |
| | | |
| | | |
| | | |
| | | |
| | | |
| | | |
| | | |
| | | |
| | | |
| | | |
| | | |
| | | |
| | | |
| | | |
| | | |
| | | |
| | | |
| | | |

### STARSHINE PRODUCTS
#### Schedule of Accounts Receivable
#### October 31, 2011

| | | |
|---|---|---|
| | | |
| | | |
| | | |
| | | |
| | | |

### STARSHINE PRODUCTS
#### Schedule of Accounts Payable
#### October 31, 2011

| | | |
|---|---|---|
| | | |
| | | |
| | | |
| | | |
| | | |
| | | |

## Problem 8-6B

| | | | | Sales Journal | | | Page |
|---|---|---|---|---|---|---|---|
| Date | Account Debited | Invoice Number | PR | Accounts Receivable Dr. Sales Cr. | PR | Cost of Goods Sold Dr. Merch. Inventory Cr. |
| | | | | | | |
| | | | | | | |
| | | | | | | |
| | | | | | | |
| | | | | | | |
| | | | | | | |

| | | | | | Purchases Journal | | | | Page |
|---|---|---|---|---|---|---|---|---|---|
| Date | Account | Date of Invoice | Terms | PR | Accts. Payable Cr. | PR | Merch. Inventory Dr. | Office Supplies Dr. | Other Accounts Dr. |
| | | | | | | | | | |
| | | | | | | | | | |
| | | | | | | | | | |
| | | | | | | | | | |

*NOTE: An additional PR column has been added to both journals to facilitate the referencing of inventory entries into the inventory subledger.*

| Date | PR | Purchases | Sales (at cost) | Inventory Balance |
|------|----|-----------|-----------------|-------------------|
|      |    |           |                 |                   |
|      |    |           |                 |                   |
|      |    |           |                 |                   |
|      |    |           |                 |                   |
|      |    |           |                 |                   |
|      |    |           |                 |                   |
|      |    |           |                 |                   |
|      |    |           |                 |                   |
|      |    |           |                 |                   |
|      |    |           |                 |                   |
|      |    |           |                 |                   |
|      |    |           |                 |                   |
|      |    |           |                 |                   |
|      |    |           |                 |                   |
|      |    |           |                 |                   |
|      |    |           |                 |                   |
|      |    |           |                 |                   |
|      |    |           |                 |                   |
|      |    |           |                 |                   |
|      |    |           |                 |                   |
|      |    |           |                 |                   |
|      |    |           |                 |                   |

*Note: An additional PR column has been added to the Inventory Subledger Record to facilitate referencing of inventory entries.*

*Problem 8-7B

Part 1                          ACCOUNTS RECEIVABLE SUBLEDGER
                                      Kelly Grody                          ACCOUNT NO. 106-1

| DATE | EXPLANATION | PR | DEBIT | CREDIT | BALANCE |
|------|-------------|----|-------|--------|---------|
|      |             |    |       |        |         |
|      |             |    |       |        |         |
|      |             |    |       |        |         |
|      |             |    |       |        |         |

                                      Karen Harden                        ACCOUNT NO. 106-2

| DATE | EXPLANATION | PR | DEBIT | CREDIT | BALANCE |
|------|-------------|----|-------|--------|---------|
|      |             |    |       |        |         |
|      |             |    |       |        |         |
|      |             |    |       |        |         |

Paul Kane                                    ACCOUNT NO. 106-3

| DATE | EXPLANATION | PR | DEBIT | CREDIT | BALANCE |
|------|-------------|-----|-------|--------|---------|
|      |             |     |       |        |         |
|      |             |     |       |        |         |
|      |             |     |       |        |         |
|      |             |     |       |        |         |

Part 2                    ACCOUNTS PAYABLE SUBLEDGER

Beech Company                                ACCOUNT NO. 201-1

| DATE | EXPLANATION | PR | DEBIT | CREDIT | BALANCE |
|------|-------------|-----|-------|--------|---------|
|      |             |     |       |        |         |
|      |             |     |       |        |         |
|      |             |     |       |        |         |
|      |             |     |       |        |         |
|      |             |     |       |        |         |

Blackwater Inc.                              ACCOUNT NO. 201-2

| DATE | EXPLANATION | PR | DEBIT | CREDIT | BALANCE |
|------|-------------|-----|-------|--------|---------|
|      |             |     |       |        |         |
|      |             |     |       |        |         |
|      |             |     |       |        |         |
|      |             |     |       |        |         |

Poppe's Supply                               ACCOUNT NO. 201-3

| DATE | EXPLANATION | PR | DEBIT | CREDIT | BALANCE |
|------|-------------|-----|-------|--------|---------|
|      |             |     |       |        |         |
|      |             |     |       |        |         |
|      |             |     |       |        |         |
|      |             |     |       |        |         |

Sprague Company                              ACCOUNT NO. 201-4

| DATE | EXPLANATION | PR | DEBIT | CREDIT | BALANCE |
|------|-------------|-----|-------|--------|---------|
|      |             |     |       |        |         |
|      |             |     |       |        |         |
|      |             |     |       |        |         |
|      |             |     |       |        |         |

## Part 3

| Sales Journal | | | | Page |
|---|---|---|---|---|
| Date | Account Debited | Invoice No. | PR | Accounts Receivable Dr. Sales Cr. |
|  |  |  |  |  |
|  |  |  |  |  |
|  |  |  |  |  |
|  |  |  |  |  |
|  |  |  |  |  |
|  |  |  |  |  |
|  |  |  |  |  |
|  |  |  |  |  |
|  |  |  |  |  |

| Cash Receipts Journal | | | | | | | | Page |
|---|---|---|---|---|---|---|---|---|
| Date | Account Credited | PR | Explanation | Cash Dr. | Sales Disc. Dr. | Accts. Rec. Cr. | Sales Cr. | Other Accts. Cr. |
|  |  |  |  |  |  |  |  |  |
|  |  |  |  |  |  |  |  |  |
|  |  |  |  |  |  |  |  |  |
|  |  |  |  |  |  |  |  |  |
|  |  |  |  |  |  |  |  |  |
|  |  |  |  |  |  |  |  |  |
|  |  |  |  |  |  |  |  |  |
|  |  |  |  |  |  |  |  |  |
|  |  |  |  |  |  |  |  |  |
|  |  |  |  |  |  |  |  |  |
|  |  |  |  |  |  |  |  |  |

| Purchases Journal | | | | | | | Page |
|---|---|---|---|---|---|---|---|
| Date | Account Credited | Date of Invoice | Terms | PR | Accts. Payable Cr. | Purchases Dr. | Office Supplies Dr. | Other Accts. Dr. |
|  |  |  |  |  |  |  |  |  |
|  |  |  |  |  |  |  |  |  |
|  |  |  |  |  |  |  |  |  |
|  |  |  |  |  |  |  |  |  |
|  |  |  |  |  |  |  |  |  |
|  |  |  |  |  |  |  |  |  |
|  |  |  |  |  |  |  |  |  |
|  |  |  |  |  |  |  |  |  |

## Cash Disbursements Journal                    Page ____

| Date | Ch. No. | Payee | Account Debited | PR | Cash Cr. | Purch. Disc. Cr. | Other Accounts Dr. | Accts. Payable Dr. |
|------|---------|-------|-----------------|----|----------|------------------|--------------------|--------------------|
|      |         |       |                 |    |          |                  |                    |                    |
|      |         |       |                 |    |          |                  |                    |                    |
|      |         |       |                 |    |          |                  |                    |                    |
|      |         |       |                 |    |          |                  |                    |                    |
|      |         |       |                 |    |          |                  |                    |                    |
|      |         |       |                 |    |          |                  |                    |                    |
|      |         |       |                 |    |          |                  |                    |                    |
|      |         |       |                 |    |          |                  |                    |                    |

## GENERAL JOURNAL                               Page ____

| Date | Account Titles and Explanation | PR | Debit | Credit |
|------|--------------------------------|----|-------|--------|
|      |                                |    |       |        |
|      |                                |    |       |        |
|      |                                |    |       |        |
|      |                                |    |       |        |
|      |                                |    |       |        |
|      |                                |    |       |        |
|      |                                |    |       |        |
|      |                                |    |       |        |
|      |                                |    |       |        |
|      |                                |    |       |        |
|      |                                |    |       |        |
|      |                                |    |       |        |

## *Problem 8-8B

Part 1                          GENERAL LEDGER

Cash                                            ACCOUNT NO. 101

| DATE | EXPLANATION | PR | DEBIT | CREDIT | BALANCE |
|------|-------------|----|-------|--------|---------|
| 2011 |             |    |       |        |         |
| Jun. 30 | Balance brought forward |  |  |  | 95,000 |
|      |             |    |       |        |         |
|      |             |    |       |        |         |

Accounts Receivable                             ACCOUNT NO. 106

| DATE | EXPLANATION | PR | DEBIT | CREDIT | BALANCE |
|------|-------------|----|-------|--------|---------|
|      |             |    |       |        |         |
|      |             |    |       |        |         |
|      |             |    |       |        |         |

## Merchandise Inventory     ACCOUNT NO. 119

| DATE | EXPLANATION | PR | DEBIT | CREDIT | BALANCE |
|------|-------------|----|-------|--------|---------|
| 2011 | | | | | |
| Jun. 30 | Balance brought forward | | | | 167,000 |
| | | | | | |
| | | | | | |
| | | | | | |
| | | | | | |

## Office Supplies     ACCOUNT NO. 124

| DATE | EXPLANATION | PR | DEBIT | CREDIT | BALANCE |
|------|-------------|----|-------|--------|---------|
| | | | | | |
| | | | | | |

## Store Supplies     ACCOUNT NO. 125

| DATE | EXPLANATION | PR | DEBIT | CREDIT | BALANCE |
|------|-------------|----|-------|--------|---------|
| | | | | | |
| | | | | | |

## Store Equipment     ACCOUNT NO. 165

| DATE | EXPLANATION | PR | DEBIT | CREDIT | BALANCE |
|------|-------------|----|-------|--------|---------|
| | | | | | |
| | | | | | |

## Accounts Payable     ACCOUNT NO. 201

| DATE | EXPLANATION | PR | DEBIT | CREDIT | BALANCE |
|------|-------------|----|-------|--------|---------|
| | | | | | |
| | | | | | |
| | | | | | |
| | | | | | |

## Long-Term Notes Payable     ACCOUNT NO. 251

| DATE | EXPLANATION | PR | DEBIT | CREDIT | BALANCE |
|------|-------------|----|-------|--------|---------|
| 2011 | | | | | |
| Jun. 30 | Balance brought forward | | | | 167,000 |
| | | | | | |

## Gene Eldridge, Capital                    ACCOUNT NO. 301

| DATE | EXPLANATION | PR | DEBIT | CREDIT | BALANCE |
|------|-------------|-----|-------|--------|---------|
| 2011 | | | | | |
| Jun. 30 | Balance brought forward | | | | 95,000 |
| | | | | | |

## Sales                                      ACCOUNT NO. 413

| DATE | EXPLANATION | PR | DEBIT | CREDIT | BALANCE |
|------|-------------|-----|-------|--------|---------|
| | | | | | |
| | | | | | |
| | | | | | |

## Sales Discounts                            ACCOUNT NO. 1415

| DATE | EXPLANATION | PR | DEBIT | CREDIT | BALANCE |
|------|-------------|-----|-------|--------|---------|
| | | | | | |
| | | | | | |
| | | | | | |

## Purchases                                  ACCOUNT NO. 505

| DATE | EXPLANATION | PR | DEBIT | CREDIT | BALANCE |
|------|-------------|-----|-------|--------|---------|
| | | | | | |
| | | | | | |
| | | | | | |

## Purchase Discounts                         ACCOUNT NO. 506

| DATE | EXPLANATION | PR | DEBIT | CREDIT | BALANCE |
|------|-------------|-----|-------|--------|---------|
| | | | | | |
| | | | | | |
| | | | | | |

## Purchase Returns and Allowances            ACCOUNT NO. 507

| DATE | EXPLANATION | PR | DEBIT | CREDIT | BALANCE |
|------|-------------|-----|-------|--------|---------|
| | | | | | |
| | | | | | |
| | | | | | |

### Sales Salaries Expense                                          ACCOUNT NO. 621

| DATE | EXPLANATION | PR | DEBIT | CREDIT | BALANCE |
|------|-------------|----|-------|--------|---------|
|      |             |    |       |        |         |
|      |             |    |       |        |         |
|      |             |    |       |        |         |

### Advertising Expense                                          ACCOUNT NO. 655

| DATE | EXPLANATION | PR | DEBIT | CREDIT | BALANCE |
|------|-------------|----|-------|--------|---------|
|      |             |    |       |        |         |
|      |             |    |       |        |         |
|      |             |    |       |        |         |

*NOTE:  For Parts 2 and 3, journalizing and posting, continue journalizing the transactions in the accounts provided in *Problem 8-7B.*

## Part 5

### ELDRIDGE INDUSTRIES
### Trial Balance
### July 31, 2011

|  | Debit | Credit |
|--|-------|--------|
|  |       |        |
|  |       |        |
|  |       |        |
|  |       |        |
|  |       |        |
|  |       |        |
|  |       |        |
|  |       |        |
|  |       |        |
|  |       |        |
|  |       |        |
|  |       |        |
|  |       |        |
|  |       |        |
|  |       |        |
|  |       |        |
|  |       |        |
|  |       |        |
|  |       |        |
|  |       |        |
|  |       |        |
|  |       |        |

## ELDRIDGE INDUSTRIES
## Schedule of Accounts Receivable
## July 31, 2011

| | | |
|---|---|---|
| | | |
| | | |
| | | |
| | | |
| | | |
| | | |
| | | |
| | | |

## ELDRIDGE INDUSTRIES
## Schedule of Accounts Payable
## July 31, 2011

| | | |
|---|---|---|
| | | |
| | | |
| | | |
| | | |
| | | |
| | | |
| | | |

## *Problem 8-9B

### Part 1

## GENERAL LEDGER

Cash                                                    ACCOUNT NO. 101

| DATE | EXPLANATION | PR | DEBIT | CREDIT | BALANCE |
|---|---|---|---|---|---|
| | | | | | |
| | | | | | |
| | | | | | |
| | | | | | |

### Accounts Receivable    ACCOUNT NO. 106

| DATE | EXPLANATION | PR | DEBIT | CREDIT | BALANCE |
|------|-------------|----|-------|--------|---------|
|      |             |    |       |        |         |
|      |             |    |       |        |         |
|      |             |    |       |        |         |

### GST Receivable    ACCOUNT NO. 108

| DATE | EXPLANATION | PR | DEBIT | CREDIT | BALANCE |
|------|-------------|----|-------|--------|---------|
|      |             |    |       |        |         |
|      |             |    |       |        |         |
|      |             |    |       |        |         |

### Merchandise Inventory    ACCOUNT NO. 119

| DATE | EXPLANATION | PR | DEBIT | CREDIT | BALANCE |
|------|-------------|----|-------|--------|---------|
| 2011 |             |    |       |        |         |
| Oct.  31 | Balance brought forward |    |       |        | 210,000 |
|      |             |    |       |        |         |
|      |             |    |       |        |         |
|      |             |    |       |        |         |
|      |             |    |       |        |         |
|      |             |    |       |        |         |

### Office Supplies    ACCOUNT NO. 124

| DATE | EXPLANATION | PR | DEBIT | CREDIT | BALANCE |
|------|-------------|----|-------|--------|---------|
|      |             |    |       |        |         |
|      |             |    |       |        |         |
|      |             |    |       |        |         |

### Store Supplies    ACCOUNT NO. 125

| DATE | EXPLANATION | PR | DEBIT | CREDIT | BALANCE |
|------|-------------|----|-------|--------|---------|
|      |             |    |       |        |         |
|      |             |    |       |        |         |
|      |             |    |       |        |         |

### Office Equipment    ACCOUNT NO. 163

| DATE | EXPLANATION | PR | DEBIT | CREDIT | BALANCE |
|------|-------------|----|-------|--------|---------|
|      |             |    |       |        |         |
|      |             |    |       |        |         |
|      |             |    |       |        |         |

   *Name* _____

### Accounts Payable      ACCOUNT NO. 201

| DATE | EXPLANATION | PR | DEBIT | CREDIT | BALANCE |
|------|-------------|----|-------|--------|---------|
|      |             |    |       |        |         |
|      |             |    |       |        |         |
|      |             |    |       |        |         |
|      |             |    |       |        |         |
|      |             |    |       |        |         |

### PST Payable      ACCOUNT NO. 224

| DATE | EXPLANATION | PR | DEBIT | CREDIT | BALANCE |
|------|-------------|----|-------|--------|---------|
|      |             |    |       |        |         |
|      |             |    |       |        |         |
|      |             |    |       |        |         |

### GST Payable      ACCOUNT NO. 225

| DATE | EXPLANATION | PR | DEBIT | CREDIT | BALANCE |
|------|-------------|----|-------|--------|---------|
|      |             |    |       |        |         |
|      |             |    |       |        |         |
|      |             |    |       |        |         |
|      |             |    |       |        |         |
|      |             |    |       |        |         |

### Long-Term Notes Payable      ACCOUNT NO. 251

| DATE | EXPLANATION | PR | DEBIT | CREDIT | BALANCE |
|------|-------------|----|-------|--------|---------|
|      |             |    |       |        |         |
|      |             |    |       |        |         |
|      |             |    |       |        |         |

### Asha Crystal, Capital      ACCOUNT NO. 2301

| DATE | EXPLANATION | PR | DEBIT | CREDIT | BALANCE |
|------|-------------|----|-------|--------|---------|
| 2011 |             |    |       |        |         |
| Oct. 31 | Balance brought forward |  |  |  | 210,000 |
|      |             |    |       |        |         |

### Sales      ACCOUNT NO. 413

| DATE | EXPLANATION | PR | DEBIT | CREDIT | BALANCE |
|------|-------------|----|-------|--------|---------|
|      |             |    |       |        |         |
|      |             |    |       |        |         |
|      |             |    |       |        |         |

### Sales Discounts                                          ACCOUNT NO. 415

| DATE | EXPLANATION | PR | DEBIT | CREDIT | BALANCE |
|------|-------------|----|-------|--------|---------|
|      |             |    |       |        |         |
|      |             |    |       |        |         |
|      |             |    |       |        |         |

### Cost of Goods Sold                                       ACCOUNT NO. 502

| DATE | EXPLANATION | PR | DEBIT | CREDIT | BALANCE |
|------|-------------|----|-------|--------|---------|
|      |             |    |       |        |         |
|      |             |    |       |        |         |
|      |             |    |       |        |         |

### Sales Salaries Expense                                   ACCOUNT NO. 621

| DATE | EXPLANATION | PR | DEBIT | CREDIT | BALANCE |
|------|-------------|----|-------|--------|---------|
|      |             |    |       |        |         |
|      |             |    |       |        |         |

**Part 2**              ACCOUNTS RECEIVABLE SUBLEDGER

### Marjorie Cook                                            ACCOUNT NO. 106-1

| DATE | EXPLANATION | PR | DEBIT | CREDIT | BALANCE |
|------|-------------|----|-------|--------|---------|
|      |             |    |       |        |         |
|      |             |    |       |        |         |
|      |             |    |       |        |         |
|      |             |    |       |        |         |

### Leroy Holmes                                             ACCOUNT NO. 106-2

| DATE | EXPLANATION | PR | DEBIT | CREDIT | BALANCE |
|------|-------------|----|-------|--------|---------|
|      |             |    |       |        |         |
|      |             |    |       |        |         |
|      |             |    |       |        |         |

### Sam Spear                                                ACCOUNT NO. 106-3

| DATE | EXPLANATION | PR | DEBIT | CREDIT | BALANCE |
|------|-------------|----|-------|--------|---------|
|      |             |    |       |        |         |
|      |             |    |       |        |         |
|      |             |    |       |        |         |
|      |             |    |       |        |         |

Part 3         ACCOUNTS PAYABLE SUBLEDGER

### Atlas Company         ACCOUNT NO. 201-1

| DATE | EXPLANATION | PR | DEBIT | CREDIT | BALANCE |
|---|---|---|---|---|---|
|  |  |  |  |  |  |
|  |  |  |  |  |  |
|  |  |  |  |  |  |

### Defore Industries         ACCOUNT NO. 201-2

| DATE | EXPLANATION | PR | DEBIT | CREDIT | BALANCE |
|---|---|---|---|---|---|
|  |  |  |  |  |  |
|  |  |  |  |  |  |
|  |  |  |  |  |  |

### Jett Supply         ACCOUNT NO. 201-3

| DATE | EXPLANATION | PR | DEBIT | CREDIT | BALANCE |
|---|---|---|---|---|---|
|  |  |  |  |  |  |
|  |  |  |  |  |  |
|  |  |  |  |  |  |

### Welch Company         ACCOUNT NO. 201-4

| DATE | EXPLANATION | PR | DEBIT | CREDIT | BALANCE |
|---|---|---|---|---|---|
|  |  |  |  |  |  |
|  |  |  |  |  |  |
|  |  |  |  |  |  |
|  |  |  |  |  |  |

## Part 4

| | | | | Sales Journal | | | | Page |
|---|---|---|---|---|---|---|---|---|
| Date | Account Debited | Invoice No. | PR | Acct. Rec. Dr. | PST Payable Cr. | GST Payable Cr. | Sales Cr. | COGS Dr. Merch. Inv. Cr. |
|  |  |  |  |  |  |  |  |  |
|  |  |  |  |  |  |  |  |  |
|  |  |  |  |  |  |  |  |  |
|  |  |  |  |  |  |  |  |  |
|  |  |  |  |  |  |  |  |  |
|  |  |  |  |  |  |  |  |  |
|  |  |  |  |  |  |  |  |  |
|  |  |  |  |  |  |  |  |  |
|  |  |  |  |  |  |  |  |  |

## Cash Receipts Journal                                                      Page ____

| Date | Account Credited | Explanation | PR | Cash Dr. | Sales Disc. Dr. | Accts. Rec. Cr. | Sales Cr. | Other Accts. Cr. | PST Payable Cr. | GST Payable Cr. | COGS Dr. Merch. Inv. Cr. |
|------|------------------|-------------|----|----------|-----------------|-----------------|-----------|------------------|-----------------|-----------------|--------------------------|
|      |                  |             |    |          |                 |                 |           |                  |                 |                 |                          |
|      |                  |             |    |          |                 |                 |           |                  |                 |                 |                          |
|      |                  |             |    |          |                 |                 |           |                  |                 |                 |                          |
|      |                  |             |    |          |                 |                 |           |                  |                 |                 |                          |
|      |                  |             |    |          |                 |                 |           |                  |                 |                 |                          |
|      |                  |             |    |          |                 |                 |           |                  |                 |                 |                          |
|      |                  |             |    |          |                 |                 |           |                  |                 |                 |                          |
|      |                  |             |    |          |                 |                 |           |                  |                 |                 |                          |
|      |                  |             |    |          |                 |                 |           |                  |                 |                 |                          |

## Purchases Journal                                                      Page ____

| Date | Account Credited | Terms | PR | Accounts Payable Cr. | Merch. Inventory Dr. | Other Accounts Dr. | GST Receivable Dr. |
|------|------------------|-------|----|----------------------|----------------------|--------------------|--------------------|
|      |                  |       |    |                      |                      |                    |                    |
|      |                  |       |    |                      |                      |                    |                    |
|      |                  |       |    |                      |                      |                    |                    |
|      |                  |       |    |                      |                      |                    |                    |
|      |                  |       |    |                      |                      |                    |                    |
|      |                  |       |    |                      |                      |                    |                    |
|      |                  |       |    |                      |                      |                    |                    |
|      |                  |       |    |                      |                      |                    |                    |

## Cash Disbursements Journal                                             Page ____

| Date | Ch. No. | Account Debited | PR | Cash Cr. | Merch. Inventory Cr. | Other Accounts Dr. | GST Receivable Dr. | Accts. Payable Dr. |
|------|---------|-----------------|----|----------|----------------------|--------------------|--------------------|--------------------|
|      |         |                 |    |          |                      |                    |                    |                    |
|      |         |                 |    |          |                      |                    |                    |                    |
|      |         |                 |    |          |                      |                    |                    |                    |
|      |         |                 |    |          |                      |                    |                    |                    |
|      |         |                 |    |          |                      |                    |                    |                    |
|      |         |                 |    |          |                      |                    |                    |                    |
|      |         |                 |    |          |                      |                    |                    |                    |

## GENERAL JOURNAL                                Page____

| Date | Account Titles and Explanation | PR | Debit | Credit |
|------|-------------------------------|----|-------|--------|
|      |                               |    |       |        |
|      |                               |    |       |        |
|      |                               |    |       |        |
|      |                               |    |       |        |
|      |                               |    |       |        |
|      |                               |    |       |        |
|      |                               |    |       |        |
|      |                               |    |       |        |
|      |                               |    |       |        |
|      |                               |    |       |        |
|      |                               |    |       |        |
|      |                               |    |       |        |
|      |                               |    |       |        |
|      |                               |    |       |        |

**Part 5**

## CRYSTAL COMPANY
### Trial Balance
### November 30, 2011

|  | Debit | Credit |
|--|-------|--------|
|  |       |        |
|  |       |        |
|  |       |        |
|  |       |        |
|  |       |        |
|  |       |        |
|  |       |        |
|  |       |        |
|  |       |        |
|  |       |        |
|  |       |        |
|  |       |        |
|  |       |        |
|  |       |        |
|  |       |        |
|  |       |        |
|  |       |        |
|  |       |        |
|  |       |        |
|  |       |        |

*Problem 8-9B (Perpetual – concl'd.)

## CRYSTAL COMPANY
## Schedule of Accounts Receivable
## November 30,2011

|  |  |  |
|---|---|---|
|  |  |  |
|  |  |  |
|  |  |  |
|  |  |  |

## CRYSTAL COMPANY
## Schedule of Accounts Payable
## November 30,2011

|  |  |  |
|---|---|---|
|  |  |  |
|  |  |  |
|  |  |  |
|  |  |  |

*Problem 8-9B (Periodic)

Part 1

GENERAL LEDGER

Cash     ACCOUNT NO. 101

| DATE | EXPLANATION | PR | DEBIT | CREDIT | BALANCE |
|---|---|---|---|---|---|
|  |  |  |  |  |  |
|  |  |  |  |  |  |
|  |  |  |  |  |  |

Accounts Receivable     ACCOUNT NO. 106

| DATE | EXPLANATION | PR | DEBIT | CREDIT | BALANCE |
|---|---|---|---|---|---|
|  |  |  |  |  |  |
|  |  |  |  |  |  |
|  |  |  |  |  |  |

GST Receivable     ACCOUNT NO. 108

| DATE | EXPLANATION | PR | DEBIT | CREDIT | BALANCE |
|---|---|---|---|---|---|
|  |  |  |  |  |  |
|  |  |  |  |  |  |
|  |  |  |  |  |  |

Merchandise Inventory     ACCOUNT NO. 119

| DATE | EXPLANATION | PR | DEBIT | CREDIT | BALANCE |
|---|---|---|---|---|---|
| 2011 |  |  |  |  |  |
| Oct. 31 | Balance brought forward |  |  |  | 210,000 |
|  |  |  |  |  |  |

**Name** _____

### Office Supplies                                ACCOUNT NO. 124

| DATE | EXPLANATION | PR | DEBIT | CREDIT | BALANCE |
|------|-------------|----|-------|--------|---------|
|      |             |    |       |        |         |
|      |             |    |       |        |         |
|      |             |    |       |        |         |

### Store Supplies                                 ACCOUNT NO. 125

| DATE | EXPLANATION | PR | DEBIT | CREDIT | BALANCE |
|------|-------------|----|-------|--------|---------|
|      |             |    |       |        |         |
|      |             |    |       |        |         |
|      |             |    |       |        |         |

### Office Equipment                               ACCOUNT NO. 163

| DATE | EXPLANATION | PR | DEBIT | CREDIT | BALANCE |
|------|-------------|----|-------|--------|---------|
|      |             |    |       |        |         |
|      |             |    |       |        |         |
|      |             |    |       |        |         |

### Accounts Payable                               ACCOUNT NO. 201

| DATE | EXPLANATION | PR | DEBIT | CREDIT | BALANCE |
|------|-------------|----|-------|--------|---------|
|      |             |    |       |        |         |
|      |             |    |       |        |         |
|      |             |    |       |        |         |
|      |             |    |       |        |         |
|      |             |    |       |        |         |

### PST Payable                                    ACCOUNT NO. 224

| DATE | EXPLANATION | PR | DEBIT | CREDIT | BALANCE |
|------|-------------|----|-------|--------|---------|
|      |             |    |       |        |         |
|      |             |    |       |        |         |
|      |             |    |       |        |         |

### GST Payable                                    ACCOUNT NO. 225

| DATE | EXPLANATION | PR | DEBIT | CREDIT | BALANCE |
|------|-------------|----|-------|--------|---------|
|      |             |    |       |        |         |
|      |             |    |       |        |         |
|      |             |    |       |        |         |
|      |             |    |       |        |         |

### Long-Term Notes Payable                              ACCOUNT NO. 251

| DATE | EXPLANATION | PR | DEBIT | CREDIT | BALANCE |
|------|-------------|----|-------|--------|---------|
|      |             |    |       |        |         |
|      |             |    |       |        |         |
|      |             |    |       |        |         |

### Asha Crystal, Capital                                ACCOUNT NO. 2301

| DATE | EXPLANATION | PR | DEBIT | CREDIT | BALANCE |
|------|-------------|----|-------|--------|---------|
| 2011 |             |    |       |        |         |
| Oct.  31 | Balance brought forward |  |   |     | 210,000 |
|      |             |    |       |        |         |

### Sales                                                ACCOUNT NO. 413

| DATE | EXPLANATION | PR | DEBIT | CREDIT | BALANCE |
|------|-------------|----|-------|--------|---------|
|      |             |    |       |        |         |
|      |             |    |       |        |         |
|      |             |    |       |        |         |

### Sales Discounts                                      ACCOUNT NO. 415

| DATE | EXPLANATION | PR | DEBIT | CREDIT | BALANCE |
|------|-------------|----|-------|--------|---------|
|      |             |    |       |        |         |
|      |             |    |       |        |         |
|      |             |    |       |        |         |

### Purchases                                            ACCOUNT NO. 505

| DATE | EXPLANATION | PR | DEBIT | CREDIT | BALANCE |
|------|-------------|----|-------|--------|---------|
|      |             |    |       |        |         |
|      |             |    |       |        |         |
|      |             |    |       |        |         |

### Purchases Returns and Allowances                     ACCOUNT NO. 506

| DATE | EXPLANATION | PR | DEBIT | CREDIT | BALANCE |
|------|-------------|----|-------|--------|---------|
|      |             |    |       |        |         |
|      |             |    |       |        |         |
|      |             |    |       |        |         |

### Purchases Discounts                                  ACCOUNT NO. 507

| DATE | EXPLANATION | PR | DEBIT | CREDIT | BALANCE |
|------|-------------|----|-------|--------|---------|
|      |             |    |       |        |         |
|      |             |    |       |        |         |
|      |             |    |       |        |         |

| | Sales Salaries Expense | | | ACCOUNT NO. 621 | |
|---|---|---|---|---|---|
| DATE | EXPLANATION | PR | DEBIT | CREDIT | BALANCE |
| | | | | | |
| | | | | | |
| | | | | | |

NOTE:  For Parts 2, 3, and 5, use the respective forms provided in *Problem 8-9B (Perpetual).

## Part 4

| | Sales Journal | | | | | | Page |
|---|---|---|---|---|---|---|---|
| Date | Account Debited | Invoice No. | PR | Accounts Receivable Dr. | PST Payable Cr. | GST Payable Cr. | Sales Cr. |
| | | | | | | | |
| | | | | | | | |
| | | | | | | | |
| | | | | | | | |
| | | | | | | | |
| | | | | | | | |
| | | | | | | | |

| | Cash Receipts Journal | | | | | | | Page |
|---|---|---|---|---|---|---|---|---|
| Date | Account Credited | PR | Explanation | Cash Dr. | Sales Disc. Dr. | Accts. Rec. Cr. | Sales Cr. | Other Accts. Cr. |
| | | | | | | | | |
| | | | | | | | | |
| | | | | | | | | |
| | | | | | | | | |
| | | | | | | | | |
| | | | | | | | | |
| | | | | | | | | |
| | | | | | | | | |
| | | | | | | | | |

| | Purchases Journal | | | | | | Page |
|---|---|---|---|---|---|---|---|
| Date | Account Credited | Date of Invoice | Terms | PR | Accts. Payable Cr. | Purchases Dr. | Other Accounts Dr. | GST Rec'ble Dr. |
| | | | | | | | | |
| | | | | | | | | |
| | | | | | | | | |
| | | | | | | | | |
| | | | | | | | | |
| | | | | | | | | |
| | | | | | | | | |

| Cash Disbursements Journal | | | | | | | | | | Page |
|---|---|---|---|---|---|---|---|---|---|---|
| Date | Ch No | Payee | Account Debited | PR | Other Accts. Dr. | GST Rec'ble Dr. | Accts. Payable Dr. | Pur. Disc. Cr. | Cash Cr. | |
| | | | | | | | | | | |
| | | | | | | | | | | |
| | | | | | | | | | | |
| | | | | | | | | | | |
| | | | | | | | | | | |
| | | | | | | | | | | |
| | | | | | | | | | | |
| | | | | | | | | | | |

## *Problem 8-10B

| Sales Journal | | | | | | | | Page |
|---|---|---|---|---|---|---|---|---|
| Date | Account Debited | Invoice No. | PR | Acct. Rec. Dr. | PST Payable Cr. | GST Payable Cr. | Sales Cr. | COGS Dr. Merch. Inv. Cr. |
| | | | | | | | | |
| | | | | | | | | |
| | | | | | | | | |
| | | | | | | | | |
| | | | | | | | | |

| Cash Receipts Journal | | | | | | | | | | | Page |
|---|---|---|---|---|---|---|---|---|---|---|---|
| Date | Account Credited | Explanation | PR | Cash Dr. | Sales Disc. Dr. | Accts. Rec. Cr. | Sales Cr. | Other Accts. Cr. | PST Payable Cr. | GST Payable Cr. | COGS Dr. Merch. Inv. Cr. |
| | | | | | | | | | | | |
| | | | | | | | | | | | |
| | | | | | | | | | | | |
| | | | | | | | | | | | |
| | | | | | | | | | | | |

| Purchases Journal | | | | | | | Page |
|---|---|---|---|---|---|---|---|
| Date | Account Credited | Terms | PR | Accounts Payable Cr. | Merch. Inventory Dr. | Other Accounts Dr. | GST Receivable Dr. |
| | | | | | | | |
| | | | | | | | |
| | | | | | | | |
| | | | | | | | |
| | | | | | | | |

| | | | | Cash Disbursements Journal | | | | Page |
|---|---|---|---|---|---|---|---|---|
| Date | Ch No | Account Debited | PR | Cash Cr. | Merch. Inventory Cr. | Other Accounts Dr. | GST Receivable Dr. | Accts. Payable Dr. |
| | | | | | | | | |
| | | | | | | | | |
| | | | | | | | | |
| | | | | | | | | |
| | | | | | | | | |

## *Problem 8-11B

| | | | | Sales Journal | | | Page |
|---|---|---|---|---|---|---|---|
| Date | Account Debited | Invoice No. | PR | Accounts Receivable Dr. | PST Payable Cr. | GST Payable Cr. | Sales Cr. |
| | | | | | | | |
| | | | | | | | | |
| | | | | | | | | |
| | | | | | | | | |
| | | | | | | | | |

| | | | | Cash Receipts Journal | | | | Page |
|---|---|---|---|---|---|---|---|---|
| Date | Account Credited | PR | Explanation | Cash Dr. | Sales Disc. Dr. | Accts. Rec. Cr. | Sales Cr. | Other Accts. Cr. |
| | | | | | | | | |
| | | | | | | | | |
| | | | | | | | | |
| | | | | | | | | |
| | | | | | | | | |

| | | | | | Purchases Journal | | | Page |
|---|---|---|---|---|---|---|---|---|
| Date | Account Credited | Date of Invoice | Terms | PR | Accts. Payable Cr. | Purchases Dr. | Other Accounts Dr. | GST Rec'ble Dr. |
| | | | | | | | | |
| | | | | | | | | |
| | | | | | | | | |
| | | | | | | | | |
| | | | | | | | | |

| | | | | | Cash Disbursements Journal | | | Page |
|---|---|---|---|---|---|---|---|---|
| Date | Ch No | Payee | Account Debited | PR | Other Accts. Dr. | GST Rec'ble Dr. | Accts. Payable Dr. | Pur. Disc. Cr. | Cash Cr. |
| | | | | | | | | | |
| | | | | | | | | | |
| | | | | | | | | | |
| | | | | | | | | | |
| | | | | | | | | | |

## Sales Journal — Page 2

| Date | Account Debited | Invoice Number | PR | Accounts Receivable Dr. Sales Cr. | Cost of Goods Sold Dr. Merchandise Inventory Cr. |
|------|-----------------|----------------|----|-----------------------------------|--------------------------------------------------|
|      |                 |                |    |                                   |                                                  |
|      |                 |                |    |                                   |                                                  |
|      |                 |                |    |                                   |                                                  |
|      |                 |                |    |                                   |                                                  |
|      |                 |                |    |                                   |                                                  |
|      |                 |                |    |                                   |                                                  |
|      |                 |                |    |                                   |                                                  |
|      |                 |                |    |                                   |                                                  |

## Purchases Journal — Page 2

| Date | Account | Date of Invoice | Terms | PR | Accounts Payable Cr. | Merch. Inventory Dr. | Office Supplies Dr. | Other Accounts Dr. |
|------|---------|-----------------|-------|----|----------------------|----------------------|---------------------|--------------------|
|      |         |                 |       |    |                      |                      |                     |                    |
|      |         |                 |       |    |                      |                      |                     |                    |
|      |         |                 |       |    |                      |                      |                     |                    |
|      |         |                 |       |    |                      |                      |                     |                    |
|      |         |                 |       |    |                      |                      |                     |                    |
|      |         |                 |       |    |                      |                      |                     |                    |
|      |         |                 |       |    |                      |                      |                     |                    |
|      |         |                 |       |    |                      |                      |                     |                    |
|      |         |                 |       |    |                      |                      |                     |                    |
|      |         |                 |       |    |                      |                      |                     |                    |
|      |         |                 |       |    |                      |                      |                     |                    |

## Cash Receipts Journal — Page 2

| Date | Account Credited | PR | Explanation | Cash Dr. | Sales Disc. Dr. | Accts. Rec. Cr. | Sales Cr. | Other Accts. Cr. | COGS Dr. Merch. Inv. Cr. |
|------|------------------|----|-------------|----------|-----------------|-----------------|-----------|------------------|--------------------------|
|      |                  |    |             |          |                 |                 |           |                  |                          |
|      |                  |    |             |          |                 |                 |           |                  |                          |
|      |                  |    |             |          |                 |                 |           |                  |                          |
|      |                  |    |             |          |                 |                 |           |                  |                          |
|      |                  |    |             |          |                 |                 |           |                  |                          |
|      |                  |    |             |          |                 |                 |           |                  |                          |
|      |                  |    |             |          |                 |                 |           |                  |                          |
|      |                  |    |             |          |                 |                 |           |                  |                          |
|      |                  |    |             |          |                 |                 |           |                  |                          |
|      |                  |    |             |          |                 |                 |           |                  |                          |
|      |                  |    |             |          |                 |                 |           |                  |                          |

| | | | | | | Merch. | Other | Accounts |
|---|---|---|---|---|---|---|---|---|
| | Ch. | | Account | | | Inventory | Accounts | Payable |
| Date | No. | Payee | Debited | PR | Cash Cr. | Cr. | Dr. | Dr. |
| | | | | | | | | |
| | | | | | | | | |
| | | | | | | | | |
| | | | | | | | | |
| | | | | | | | | |
| | | | | | | | | |
| | | | | | | | | |
| | | | | | | | | |
| | | | | | | | | |
| | | | | | | | | |
| | | | | | | | | |
| | | | | | | | | |
| | | | | | | | | |
| | | | | | | | | |
| | | | | | | | | |
| | | | | | | | | |
| | | | | | | | | |
| | | | | | | | | |
| | | | | | | | | |

**Cash Disbursements Journal** — Page 2

### GENERAL JOURNAL     Page 3

| Date | Account Titles and Explanation | PR | Debit | Credit |
|---|---|---|---|---|
| | | | | |
| | | | | |
| | | | | |
| | | | | |
| | | | | |
| | | | | |
| | | | | |
| | | | | |
| | | | | |
| | | | | |
| | | | | |
| | | | | |
| | | | | |
| | | | | |
| | | | | |
| | | | | |
| | | | | |
| | | | | |
| | | | | |

| | GENERAL JOURNAL | | | Page 3 |
|---|---|---|---|---|

| Date | Account Titles and Explanation | PR | Debit | Credit |
|---|---|---|---|---|
| | | | | |
| | | | | |
| | | | | |
| | | | | |
| | | | | |
| | | | | |
| | | | | |
| | | | | |
| | | | | |
| | | | | |
| | | | | |
| | | | | |
| | | | | |
| | | | | |
| | | | | |
| | | | | |
| | | | | |
| | | | | |
| | | | | |
| | | | | |
| | | | | |
| | | | | |
| | | | | |
| | | | | |
| | | | | |
| | | | | |
| | | | | |
| | | | | |
| | | | | |
| | | | | |
| | | | | |
| | | | | |
| | | | | |
| | | | | |
| | | | | |
| | | | | |
| | | | | |
| | | | | |
| | | | | |

| Date | Account Titles and Explanation | PR | Debit | Credit |
|------|-------------------------------|----|-------|--------|
|      |                               |    |       |        |
|      |                               |    |       |        |
|      |                               |    |       |        |
|      |                               |    |       |        |
|      |                               |    |       |        |
|      |                               |    |       |        |
|      |                               |    |       |        |
|      |                               |    |       |        |
|      |                               |    |       |        |
|      |                               |    |       |        |
|      |                               |    |       |        |
|      |                               |    |       |        |
|      |                               |    |       |        |
|      |                               |    |       |        |
|      |                               |    |       |        |
|      |                               |    |       |        |
|      |                               |    |       |        |
|      |                               |    |       |        |
|      |                               |    |       |        |
|      |                               |    |       |        |
|      |                               |    |       |        |
|      |                               |    |       |        |
|      |                               |    |       |        |
|      |                               |    |       |        |
|      |                               |    |       |        |
|      |                               |    |       |        |
|      |                               |    |       |        |
|      |                               |    |       |        |
|      |                               |    |       |        |
|      |                               |    |       |        |
|      |                               |    |       |        |
|      |                               |    |       |        |
|      |                               |    |       |        |
|      |                               |    |       |        |
|      |                               |    |       |        |
|      |                               |    |       |        |
|      |                               |    |       |        |
|      |                               |    |       |        |
|      |                               |    |       |        |
|      |                               |    |       |        |
|      |                               |    |       |        |
|      |                               |    |       |        |

## GENERAL LEDGER

### Cash                                                                          ACCOUNT NO. 101

| DATE | EXPLANATION | PR | DEBIT | CREDIT | BALANCE |
|---|---|---|---|---|---|
| 2011 | | | | | |
| Apr.  30 | Balance | | | | 50,247 |
| | | | | | |
| | | | | | |
| | | | | | |

### Accounts Receivable                                                 ACCOUNT NO. 106

| DATE | EXPLANATION | PR | DEBIT | CREDIT | BALANCE |
|---|---|---|---|---|---|
| 2011 | | | | | |
| Apr.  30 | Balance | | | | 4,725 |
| | | | | | |
| | | | | | |
| | | | | | |
| | | | | | |

### Merchandise Inventory                                          ACCOUNT NO. 119

| DATE | EXPLANATION | PR | DEBIT | CREDIT | BALANCE |
|---|---|---|---|---|---|
| 2011 | | | | | |
| Apr.  30 | Balance | | | | 220,080 |
| | | | | | |
| | | | | | |
| | | | | | |

### Office Supplies                                                         ACCOUNT NO. 124

| DATE | EXPLANATION | PR | DEBIT | CREDIT | BALANCE |
|---|---|---|---|---|---|
| 2011 | | | | | |
| Apr. 30 | Balance | | | | 430 |
| | | | | | |
| | | | | | |
| | | | | | |

### Store Supplies                                                         ACCOUNT NO. 125

| DATE | EXPLANATION | PR | DEBIT | CREDIT | BALANCE |
|---|---|---|---|---|---|
| 2011 | | | | | |
| Apr. 30 | Balance | | | | 2,447 |
| | | | | | |
| | | | | | |
| | | | | | |

### Prepaid Insurance                          ACCOUNT NO. 128

| DATE | EXPLANATION | PR | DEBIT | CREDIT | BALANCE |
|------|-------------|----|-------|--------|---------|
| 2011 | | | | | |
| Apr. 30 | Balance | | | | 3,318 |
| | | | | | |
| | | | | | |
| | | | | | |

### Office Equipment                          ACCOUNT NO. 163

| DATE | EXPLANATION | PR | DEBIT | CREDIT | BALANCE |
|------|-------------|----|-------|--------|---------|
| 2011 | | | | | |
| Apr. 30 | Balance | | | | 22,470 |
| | | | | | |
| | | | | | |
| | | | | | |
| | | | | | |

### Accumulated Amortization, Office Equipment          ACCOUNT NO. 164

| DATE | EXPLANATION | PR | DEBIT | CREDIT | BALANCE |
|------|-------------|----|-------|--------|---------|
| 2011 | | | | | |
| Apr. 30 | Balance | | | | 9,898 |
| | | | | | |
| | | | | | |
| | | | | | |

### Store Equipment                          ACCOUNT NO. 165

| DATE | EXPLANATION | PR | DEBIT | CREDIT | BALANCE |
|------|-------------|----|-------|--------|---------|
| 2011 | | | | | |
| Apr. 30 | Balance | | | | 38,920 |
| | | | | | |
| | | | | | |

### Accumulated Amortization, Store Equipment          ACCOUNT NO. 166

| DATE | EXPLANATION | PR | DEBIT | CREDIT | BALANCE |
|------|-------------|----|-------|--------|---------|
| 2011 | | | | | |
| Apr. 30 | Balance | | | | 17,556 |
| | | | | | |
| | | | | | |
| | | | | | |

## Accounts Payable                                                     ACCOUNT NO. 201

| DATE | EXPLANATION | PR | DEBIT | CREDIT | BALANCE |
|------|-------------|----|-------|--------|---------|
| 2011 | | | | | |
| Apr.   30 | Balance | | | | 7,098 |
| | | | | | |
| | | | | | |
| | | | | | |
| | | | | | |
| | | | | | |
| | | | | | |

## Clint Barry, Capital                                                ACCOUNT NO. 301

| DATE | EXPLANATION | PR | DEBIT | CREDIT | BALANCE |
|------|-------------|----|-------|--------|---------|
| 2011 | | | | | |
| Apr.   30 | Balance | | | | 308,085 |
| | | | | | |
| | | | | | |
| | | | | | |

## Clint Barry, Withdrawals                                            ACCOUNT NO. 302

| DATE | EXPLANATION | PR | DEBIT | CREDIT | BALANCE |
|------|-------------|----|-------|--------|---------|
| 2011 | | | | | |
| | | | | | |
| | | | | | |
| | | | | | |

## Sales                                                               ACCOUNT NO. 413

| DATE | EXPLANATION | PR | DEBIT | CREDIT | BALANCE |
|------|-------------|----|-------|--------|---------|
| | | | | | |
| | | | | | |
| | | | | | |
| | | | | | |
| | | | | | |

## Sales Discounts                                                     ACCOUNT NO. 414

| DATE | EXPLANATION | PR | DEBIT | CREDIT | BALANCE |
|------|-------------|----|-------|--------|---------|
| | | | | | |
| | | | | | |
| | | | | | |
| | | | | | |

### Sales Returns and Allowances          ACCOUNT NO. 415

| DATE | EXPLANATION | PR | DEBIT | CREDIT | BALANCE |
|------|-------------|----|-------|--------|---------|
|      |             |    |       |        |         |
|      |             |    |       |        |         |
|      |             |    |       |        |         |
|      |             |    |       |        |         |

### Cost of Goods Sold          ACCOUNT NO. 502

| DATE | EXPLANATION | PR | DEBIT | CREDIT | BALANCE |
|------|-------------|----|-------|--------|---------|
|      |             |    |       |        |         |
|      |             |    |       |        |         |
|      |             |    |       |        |         |
|      |             |    |       |        |         |
|      |             |    |       |        |         |
|      |             |    |       |        |         |

### Amortization Expense, Office Equipment          ACCOUNT NO. 612

| DATE | EXPLANATION | PR | DEBIT | CREDIT | BALANCE |
|------|-------------|----|-------|--------|---------|
|      |             |    |       |        |         |
|      |             |    |       |        |         |
|      |             |    |       |        |         |
|      |             |    |       |        |         |

### Amortization Expense, Store Equipment          ACCOUNT NO. 613

| DATE | EXPLANATION | PR | DEBIT | CREDIT | BALANCE |
|------|-------------|----|-------|--------|---------|
|      |             |    |       |        |         |
|      |             |    |       |        |         |
|      |             |    |       |        |         |
|      |             |    |       |        |         |

### Office Salaries Expense          ACCOUNT NO. 620

| DATE | EXPLANATION | PR | DEBIT | CREDIT | BALANCE |
|------|-------------|----|-------|--------|---------|
|      |             |    |       |        |         |
|      |             |    |       |        |         |
|      |             |    |       |        |         |
|      |             |    |       |        |         |
|      |             |    |       |        |         |

### Sales Salaries Expense          ACCOUNT NO. 621

| DATE | EXPLANATION | PR | DEBIT | CREDIT | BALANCE |
|------|-------------|----|-------|--------|---------|
|      |             |    |       |        |         |
|      |             |    |       |        |         |
|      |             |    |       |        |         |
|      |             |    |       |        |         |
|      |             |    |       |        |         |

### Insurance Expense          ACCOUNT NO. 637

| DATE | EXPLANATION | PR | DEBIT | CREDIT | BALANCE |
|------|-------------|----|-------|--------|---------|
|      |             |    |       |        |         |
|      |             |    |       |        |         |
|      |             |    |       |        |         |
|      |             |    |       |        |         |

### Rent Expense, Office Space          ACCOUNT NO. 641

| DATE | EXPLANATION | PR | DEBIT | CREDIT | BALANCE |
|------|-------------|----|-------|--------|---------|
|      |             |    |       |        |         |
|      |             |    |       |        |         |
|      |             |    |       |        |         |
|      |             |    |       |        |         |

### Rent Expense, Selling Space          ACCOUNT NO. 642

| DATE | EXPLANATION | PR | DEBIT | CREDIT | BALANCE |
|------|-------------|----|-------|--------|---------|
|      |             |    |       |        |         |
|      |             |    |       |        |         |
|      |             |    |       |        |         |
|      |             |    |       |        |         |

### Office Supplies Expense          ACCOUNT NO. 650

| DATE | EXPLANATION | PR | DEBIT | CREDIT | BALANCE |
|------|-------------|----|-------|--------|---------|
|      |             |    |       |        |         |
|      |             |    |       |        |         |
|      |             |    |       |        |         |
|      |             |    |       |        |         |

## Store Supplies Expense                          ACCOUNT NO. 651

| DATE | EXPLANATION | PR | DEBIT | CREDIT | BALANCE |
|------|-------------|----|-------|--------|---------|
| 2011 |             |    |       |        |         |
|      |             |    |       |        |         |
|      |             |    |       |        |         |

## Utilities Expense                              ACCOUNT NO. 690

| DATE | EXPLANATION | PR | DEBIT | CREDIT | BALANCE |
|------|-------------|----|-------|--------|---------|
| 2011 |             |    |       |        |         |
|      |             |    |       |        |         |
|      |             |    |       |        |         |

## Income Summary                                 ACCOUNT NO. 901

| DATE | EXPLANATION | PR | DEBIT | CREDIT | BALANCE |
|------|-------------|----|-------|--------|---------|
|      |             |    |       |        |         |
|      |             |    |       |        |         |
|      |             |    |       |        |         |
|      |             |    |       |        |         |

## ACCOUNTS RECEIVABLE LEDGER

**NAME**    Deaver Corp.

| DATE | EXPLANATION | PR | DEBIT | CREDIT | BALANCE |
|------|-------------|----|-------|--------|---------|
|      |             |    |       |        |         |
|      |             |    |       |        |         |
|      |             |    |       |        |         |

**NAME**    Essex Company

| DATE | EXPLANATION | PR | DEBIT | CREDIT | BALANCE |
|------|-------------|----|-------|--------|---------|
|      |             |    |       |        |         |
|      |             |    |       |        |         |
|      |             |    |       |        |         |
|      |             |    |       |        |         |

**NAME**    Nabors, Inc.

| DATE    | EXPLANATION | PR | DEBIT | CREDIT | BALANCE |
|---------|-------------|----|-------|--------|---------|
| 2011    |             |    |       |        |         |
| Apr. 28 |             | S2 | 4,725 |        | 4,725   |
|         |             |    |       |        |         |
|         |             |    |       |        |         |

NAME          Oscar Services.          _____

| DATE | EXPLANATION | PR | DEBIT | CREDIT | BALANCE |
|------|-------------|-----|-------|--------|---------|
| 2011 | | | | | |
| | | | | | |
| | | | | | |

## ACCOUNTS PAYABLE LEDGER

NAME          Chandler Corp.          _____

| DATE | EXPLANATION | PR | DEBIT | CREDIT | BALANCE |
|------|-------------|-----|-------|--------|---------|
| 2011 | | | | | |
| | | | | | |
| | | | | | |

NAME          Gale, Inc.          _____

| DATE | EXPLANATION | PR | DEBIT | CREDIT | BALANCE |
|------|-------------|-----|-------|--------|---------|
| 2011 | | | | | |
| | | | | | |
| | | | | | |

NAME          Parkay Products          _____

| DATE | EXPLANATION | PR | DEBIT | CREDIT | BALANCE |
|------|-------------|-----|-------|--------|---------|
| 2011 | | | | | |
| Apr.  29 | | P2 | | 7,098 | 7,098 |
| | | | | | |
| | | | | | |
| | | | | | |

NAME          Thompson Supply Co.          _____

| DATE | EXPLANATION | PR | DEBIT | CREDIT | BALANCE |
|------|-------------|-----|-------|--------|---------|
| | | | | | |
| | | | | | |
| | | | | | |
| | | | | | |

Alpine Company
Work Sheet
For Month Ended May 31, 2011

| Account Titles | Trial Balance | | Adjustments | | Income Statement | | Balance Sheet and Statement of Owner's Equity | |
|---|---|---|---|---|---|---|---|---|
| | Debit | Credit | Debit | Credit | Debit | Credit | Debit | Credit |
| | | | | | | | | |

### Alpine Company
### Income Statement
### For Month Ended May 31, 2011

| | | | |
|---|---|---|---|
| | | | |
| | | | |
| | | | |
| | | | |
| | | | |
| | | | |
| | | | |
| | | | |
| | | | |
| | | | |
| | | | |
| | | | |
| | | | |
| | | | |
| | | | |
| | | | |
| | | | |
| | | | |
| | | | |
| | | | |
| | | | |
| | | | |
| | | | |
| | | | |
| | | | |
| | | | |
| | | | |
| | | | |
| | | | |
| | | | |
| | | | |
| | | | |

**Alpine Company**

**Statement of Owner's Equity**

**For Month Ended May 31, 2011**

| | | | |
|---|---|---|---|
| | | | |
| | | | |
| | | | |
| | | | |
| | | | |
| | | | |
| | | | |
| | | | |

**Alpine Company**

**Balance Sheet**

**May 31, 2011**

| | | | |
|---|---|---|---|
| | | | |
| | | | |
| | | | |
| | | | |
| | | | |
| | | | |
| | | | |
| | | | |
| | | | |
| | | | |
| | | | |
| | | | |
| | | | |
| | | | |
| | | | |
| | | | |
| | | | |
| | | | |
| | | | |
| | | | |
| | | | |
| | | | |
| | | | |
| | | | |
| | | | |

## Alpine Company
## Post-Closing Trial Balance
## May 31, 2011

|  | Debit | Credit |
|---|---|---|
|  |  |  |
|  |  |  |
|  |  |  |
|  |  |  |
|  |  |  |
|  |  |  |
|  |  |  |
|  |  |  |
|  |  |  |
|  |  |  |
|  |  |  |
|  |  |  |
|  |  |  |
|  |  |  |
|  |  |  |
|  |  |  |
|  |  |  |
|  |  |  |
|  |  |  |
|  |  |  |
|  |  |  |
|  |  |  |

## Alpine Company
## Schedule of Accounts Receivable
## May 31, 2011

|  |  |  |
|---|---|---|
|  |  |  |
|  |  |  |
|  |  |  |
|  |  |  |
|  |  |  |

## Alpine Company
## Schedule of Accounts Payable
## May 31, 2011

|  |  |  |
|---|---|---|
|  |  |  |
|  |  |  |
|  |  |  |
|  |  |  |
|  |  |  |

## Sales Journal                                                                   Page 2

| Date | Account Debited | Invoice Number | PR | Accts. Receivable Dr. Sales Cr. |
|------|-----------------|----------------|----|---------------------------------|
|      |                 |                |    |                                 |
|      |                 |                |    |                                 |
|      |                 |                |    |                                 |
|      |                 |                |    |                                 |
|      |                 |                |    |                                 |
|      |                 |                |    |                                 |
|      |                 |                |    |                                 |
|      |                 |                |    |                                 |

## Purchases Journal                                                               Page 2

| Date | Account | Date of Inv. | Terms | PR | Accts. Pay. Cr. | Purchases Dr. | Office Supplies Dr. | Other Accts. Dr. |
|------|---------|--------------|-------|----|-----------------|---------------|---------------------|------------------|
|      |         |              |       |    |                 |               |                     |                  |
|      |         |              |       |    |                 |               |                     |                  |
|      |         |              |       |    |                 |               |                     |                  |
|      |         |              |       |    |                 |               |                     |                  |
|      |         |              |       |    |                 |               |                     |                  |
|      |         |              |       |    |                 |               |                     |                  |
|      |         |              |       |    |                 |               |                     |                  |
|      |         |              |       |    |                 |               |                     |                  |
|      |         |              |       |    |                 |               |                     |                  |
|      |         |              |       |    |                 |               |                     |                  |

## Cash Receipts Journal                                                           Page 2

| Date | Accounts Credited | Explanation | PR | Cash Dr. | Sales Disc. Dr. | Accts. Rec. Cr. | Sales Cr. | Other Accts. Cr. |
|------|-------------------|-------------|----|----------|-----------------|-----------------|-----------|------------------|
|      |                   |             |    |          |                 |                 |           |                  |
|      |                   |             |    |          |                 |                 |           |                  |
|      |                   |             |    |          |                 |                 |           |                  |
|      |                   |             |    |          |                 |                 |           |                  |
|      |                   |             |    |          |                 |                 |           |                  |
|      |                   |             |    |          |                 |                 |           |                  |
|      |                   |             |    |          |                 |                 |           |                  |
|      |                   |             |    |          |                 |                 |           |                  |
|      |                   |             |    |          |                 |                 |           |                  |

| | | | Cash Disbursements Journal | | | | | Page 2 |
| | | | | | | | | |

| Date | Ch. No. | Payee | Account Debited | PR | Cash Cr. | Purch. Disc. Cr. | Other Accts. Dr. | Accts. Payable Dr. |
|------|---------|-------|-----------------|-----|----------|------------------|------------------|--------------------|
| | | | | | | | | |
| | | | | | | | | |
| | | | | | | | | |
| | | | | | | | | |
| | | | | | | | | |
| | | | | | | | | |
| | | | | | | | | |
| | | | | | | | | |
| | | | | | | | | |
| | | | | | | | | |
| | | | | | | | | |
| | | | | | | | | |
| | | | | | | | | |
| | | | | | | | | |
| | | | | | | | | |

### GENERAL JOURNAL                                   Page 3

| Date | Account Titles and Explanation | PR | Debit | Credit |
|------|-------------------------------|-----|-------|--------|
| | | | | |
| | | | | |
| | | | | |
| | | | | |
| | | | | |
| | | | | |
| | | | | |
| | | | | |
| | | | | |
| | | | | |
| | | | | |
| | | | | |
| | | | | |
| | | | | |
| | | | | |
| | | | | |
| | | | | |
| | | | | |
| | | | | |
| | | | | |
| | | | | |

## GENERAL JOURNAL  Page 3

| Date | Account Titles and Explanation | PR | Debit | Credit |
|------|-------------------------------|----|-------|--------|
|  |  |  |  |  |
|  |  |  |  |  |
|  |  |  |  |  |
|  |  |  |  |  |
|  |  |  |  |  |
|  |  |  |  |  |
|  |  |  |  |  |
|  |  |  |  |  |
|  |  |  |  |  |
|  |  |  |  |  |
|  |  |  |  |  |
|  |  |  |  |  |
|  |  |  |  |  |
|  |  |  |  |  |
|  |  |  |  |  |
|  |  |  |  |  |
|  |  |  |  |  |
|  |  |  |  |  |
|  |  |  |  |  |
|  |  |  |  |  |
|  |  |  |  |  |
|  |  |  |  |  |
|  |  |  |  |  |
|  |  |  |  |  |
|  |  |  |  |  |
|  |  |  |  |  |
|  |  |  |  |  |
|  |  |  |  |  |
|  |  |  |  |  |
|  |  |  |  |  |
|  |  |  |  |  |
|  |  |  |  |  |
|  |  |  |  |  |
|  |  |  |  |  |
|  |  |  |  |  |
|  |  |  |  |  |
|  |  |  |  |  |
|  |  |  |  |  |
|  |  |  |  |  |

## GENERAL LEDGER

### Cash                                          ACCOUNT NO. 101

| DATE | EXPLANATION | PR | DEBIT | CREDIT | BALANCE |
|------|-------------|----|-------|--------|---------|
| 2011 | | | | | |
| Apr.   30 | Balance | | | | 50,247 |
| | | | | | |
| | | | | | |

### Accounts Receivable                          ACCOUNT NO. 106

| DATE | EXPLANATION | PR | DEBIT | CREDIT | BALANCE |
|------|-------------|----|-------|--------|---------|
| 2011 | | | | | |
| Apr.   30 | Balance | | | | 4,725 |
| | | | | | |
| | | | | | |
| | | | | | |

### Merchandise Inventory                        ACCOUNT NO. 119

| DATE | EXPLANATION | PR | DEBIT | CREDIT | BALANCE |
|------|-------------|----|-------|--------|---------|
| 2011 | | | | | |
| Apr.   30 | Balance | | | | 220,080 |
| | | | | | |
| | | | | | |
| | | | | | |

### Office Supplies                              ACCOUNT NO. 124

| DATE | EXPLANATION | PR | DEBIT | CREDIT | BALANCE |
|------|-------------|----|-------|--------|---------|
| 2011 | | | | | |
| Apr. 30 | Balance | | | | 430 |
| | | | | | |
| | | | | | |
| | | | | | |

### Store Supplies                              ACCOUNT NO. 125

| DATE | EXPLANATION | PR | DEBIT | CREDIT | BALANCE |
|------|-------------|----|-------|--------|---------|
| 2011 | | | | | |
| Apr. 30 | Balance | | | | 2,447 |
| | | | | | |
| | | | | | |
| | | | | | |
| | | | | | |

### Prepaid Insurance                                      ACCOUNT NO. 128

| DATE | EXPLANATION | PR | DEBIT | CREDIT | BALANCE |
|------|-------------|----|-------|--------|---------|
| 2011 | | | | | |
| Apr. 30 | Balance | | | | 3,318 |
| | | | | | |
| | | | | | |
| | | | | | |

### Office Equipment                                      ACCOUNT NO. 163

| DATE | EXPLANATION | PR | DEBIT | CREDIT | BALANCE |
|------|-------------|----|-------|--------|---------|
| 2011 | | | | | |
| Apr. 30 | Balance | | | | 22,470 |
| | | | | | |
| | | | | | |
| | | | | | |

### Accumulated Amortization, Office Equipment            ACCOUNT NO. 164

| DATE | EXPLANATION | PR | DEBIT | CREDIT | BALANCE |
|------|-------------|----|-------|--------|---------|
| 2011 | | | | | |
| Apr. 30 | Balance | | | | 9,898 |
| | | | | | |
| | | | | | |
| | | | | | |

### Store Equipment                                       ACCOUNT NO. 165

| DATE | EXPLANATION | PR | DEBIT | CREDIT | BALANCE |
|------|-------------|----|-------|--------|---------|
| 2011 | | | | | |
| Apr. 30 | Balance | | | | 38,920 |
| | | | | | |
| | | | | | |

### Accumulated Amortization, Store Equipment             ACCOUNT NO. 166

| DATE | EXPLANATION | PR | DEBIT | CREDIT | BALANCE |
|------|-------------|----|-------|--------|---------|
| 2011 | | | | | |
| Apr. 30 | Balance | | | | 17,556 |
| | | | | | |
| | | | | | |
| | | | | | |

### Accounts Payable                          ACCOUNT NO. 201

| DATE | EXPLANATION | PR | DEBIT | CREDIT | BALANCE |
|------|-------------|----|-------|--------|---------|
| 2011 | | | | | |
| Apr. 30 | Balance | | | | 7,098 |
| | | | | | |
| | | | | | |
| | | | | | |
| | | | | | |

### Clint Barry, Capital                       ACCOUNT NO. 301

| DATE | EXPLANATION | PR | DEBIT | CREDIT | BALANCE |
|------|-------------|----|-------|--------|---------|
| 2011 | | | | | |
| Apr. 30 | Balance | | | | 308,085 |
| | | | | | |
| | | | | | |

### Clint Barry, Withdrawals                   ACCOUNT NO. 302

| DATE | EXPLANATION | PR | DEBIT | CREDIT | BALANCE |
|------|-------------|----|-------|--------|---------|
| 2011 | | | | | |
| | | | | | |
| | | | | | |

### Sales                                      ACCOUNT NO. 413

| DATE | EXPLANATION | PR | DEBIT | CREDIT | BALANCE |
|------|-------------|----|-------|--------|---------|
| | | | | | |
| | | | | | |
| | | | | | |
| | | | | | |

### Sales Discounts                            ACCOUNT NO. 414

| DATE | EXPLANATION | PR | DEBIT | CREDIT | BALANCE |
|------|-------------|----|-------|--------|---------|
| | | | | | |
| | | | | | |
| | | | | | |

### Sales Returns and Allowances               ACCOUNT NO. 415

| DATE | EXPLANATION | PR | DEBIT | CREDIT | BALANCE |
|------|-------------|----|-------|--------|---------|
| | | | | | |
| | | | | | |
| | | | | | |

## Purchases      ACCOUNT NO. 505

| DATE | EXPLANATION | PR | DEBIT | CREDIT | BALANCE |
|------|-------------|-----|-------|--------|---------|
|      |             |     |       |        |         |
|      |             |     |       |        |         |
|      |             |     |       |        |         |

## Purchases Discounts      ACCOUNT NO. 506

| DATE | EXPLANATION | PR | DEBIT | CREDIT | BALANCE |
|------|-------------|-----|-------|--------|---------|
|      |             |     |       |        |         |
|      |             |     |       |        |         |
|      |             |     |       |        |         |

## Purchases Returns and Allowances      ACCOUNT NO. 507

| DATE | EXPLANATION | PR | DEBIT | CREDIT | BALANCE |
|------|-------------|-----|-------|--------|---------|
|      |             |     |       |        |         |
|      |             |     |       |        |         |
|      |             |     |       |        |         |

## Amortization Expense, Office Equipment      ACCOUNT NO. 612

| DATE | EXPLANATION | PR | DEBIT | CREDIT | BALANCE |
|------|-------------|-----|-------|--------|---------|
|      |             |     |       |        |         |
|      |             |     |       |        |         |
|      |             |     |       |        |         |
|      |             |     |       |        |         |

## Amortization Expense, Store Equipment      ACCOUNT NO. 613

| DATE | EXPLANATION | PR | DEBIT | CREDIT | BALANCE |
|------|-------------|-----|-------|--------|---------|
|      |             |     |       |        |         |
|      |             |     |       |        |         |
|      |             |     |       |        |         |
|      |             |     |       |        |         |

## Office Salaries Expense      ACCOUNT NO. 620

| DATE | EXPLANATION | PR | DEBIT | CREDIT | BALANCE |
|------|-------------|-----|-------|--------|---------|
|      |             |     |       |        |         |
|      |             |     |       |        |         |
|      |             |     |       |        |         |
|      |             |     |       |        |         |
|      |             |     |       |        |         |

## Sales Salaries Expense                    ACCOUNT NO. 621

| DATE | EXPLANATION | PR | DEBIT | CREDIT | BALANCE |
|------|-------------|-----|-------|--------|---------|
|      |             |     |       |        |         |
|      |             |     |       |        |         |
|      |             |     |       |        |         |
|      |             |     |       |        |         |
|      |             |     |       |        |         |

## Insurance Expense                         ACCOUNT NO. 637

| DATE | EXPLANATION | PR | DEBIT | CREDIT | BALANCE |
|------|-------------|-----|-------|--------|---------|
|      |             |     |       |        |         |
|      |             |     |       |        |         |
|      |             |     |       |        |         |
|      |             |     |       |        |         |

## Rent Expense, Office Space                ACCOUNT NO. 641

| DATE | EXPLANATION | PR | DEBIT | CREDIT | BALANCE |
|------|-------------|-----|-------|--------|---------|
|      |             |     |       |        |         |
|      |             |     |       |        |         |
|      |             |     |       |        |         |
|      |             |     |       |        |         |

## Rent Expense, Selling Space               ACCOUNT NO. 642

| DATE | EXPLANATION | PR | DEBIT | CREDIT | BALANCE |
|------|-------------|-----|-------|--------|---------|
|      |             |     |       |        |         |
|      |             |     |       |        |         |
|      |             |     |       |        |         |
|      |             |     |       |        |         |

## Office Supplies Expense                   ACCOUNT NO. 650

| DATE | EXPLANATION | PR | DEBIT | CREDIT | BALANCE |
|------|-------------|-----|-------|--------|---------|
|      |             |     |       |        |         |
|      |             |     |       |        |         |
|      |             |     |       |        |         |
|      |             |     |       |        |         |

### Store Supplies Expense                ACCOUNT NO. 651

| DATE | EXPLANATION | PR | DEBIT | CREDIT | BALANCE |
|------|-------------|-----|-------|--------|---------|
| 2011 | | | | | |
| | | | | | |
| | | | | | |

### Utilities Expense                    ACCOUNT NO. 690

| DATE | EXPLANATION | PR | DEBIT | CREDIT | BALANCE |
|------|-------------|-----|-------|--------|---------|
| 2011 | | | | | |
| | | | | | |
| | | | | | |

### Income Summary                       ACCOUNT NO. 901

| DATE | EXPLANATION | PR | DEBIT | CREDIT | BALANCE |
|------|-------------|-----|-------|--------|---------|
| | | | | | |
| | | | | | |
| | | | | | |
| | | | | | |

## ACCOUNTS RECEIVABLE LEDGER

**NAME**        Deaver Corp. _____

| DATE | EXPLANATION | PR | DEBIT | CREDIT | BALANCE |
|------|-------------|-----|-------|--------|---------|
| | | | | | |
| | | | | | |
| | | | | | |

**NAME**        Essex Company _____

| DATE | EXPLANATION | PR | DEBIT | CREDIT | BALANCE |
|------|-------------|-----|-------|--------|---------|
| | | | | | |
| | | | | | |
| | | | | | |
| | | | | | |

**NAME**        Nabors, Inc. _____

| DATE | EXPLANATION | PR | DEBIT | CREDIT | BALANCE |
|------|-------------|-----|-------|--------|---------|
| 2011 | | | | | |
| Apr.   28 | | S2 | 4,725 | | 4,725 |
| | | | | | |
| | | | | | |

NAME          Oscar Services.

| DATE | EXPLANATION | PR | DEBIT | CREDIT | BALANCE |
|------|-------------|----|----|----|----|
| 2011 |  |  |  |  |  |
|  |  |  |  |  |  |
|  |  |  |  |  |  |

## ACCOUNTS PAYABLE LEDGER

NAME          Chandler Corp.

| DATE | EXPLANATION | PR | DEBIT | CREDIT | BALANCE |
|------|-------------|----|----|----|----|
| 2011 |  |  |  |  |  |
|  |  |  |  |  |  |
|  |  |  |  |  |  |

NAME          Gale, Inc.

| DATE | EXPLANATION | PR | DEBIT | CREDIT | BALANCE |
|------|-------------|----|----|----|----|
| 2011 |  |  |  |  |  |
|  |  |  |  |  |  |
|  |  |  |  |  |  |

NAME          Parkay Products

| DATE | EXPLANATION | PR | DEBIT | CREDIT | BALANCE |
|------|-------------|----|----|----|----|
| 2011 |  |  |  |  |  |
| Apr.  29 |  | P2 |  | 7,098 | 7,098 |
|  |  |  |  |  |  |
|  |  |  |  |  |  |
|  |  |  |  |  |  |

NAME          Thompson Supply Co.

| DATE | EXPLANATION | PR | DEBIT | CREDIT | BALANCE |
|------|-------------|----|----|----|----|
|  |  |  |  |  |  |
|  |  |  |  |  |  |
|  |  |  |  |  |  |
|  |  |  |  |  |  |

Alpine Company
Work Sheet
For Month Ended May 31, 2011

| Account Titles | Trial Balance | | Adjustments | | Income Statement | | Balance Sheet and Statement of Owner's Equity | |
|---|---|---|---|---|---|---|---|---|
| | Debit | Credit | Debit | Credit | Debit | Credit | Debit | Credit |
| | | | | | | | | |

Alpine Company
Income Statement
For Month Ended May 31, 2011

| | | | |
|---|---|---|---|
| | | | |
| | | | |
| | | | |
| | | | |
| | | | |
| | | | |
| | | | |
| | | | |
| | | | |
| | | | |
| | | | |
| | | | |
| | | | |
| | | | |
| | | | |
| | | | |
| | | | |
| | | | |
| | | | |
| | | | |
| | | | |
| | | | |
| | | | |
| | | | |
| | | | |
| | | | |
| | | | |
| | | | |
| | | | |
| | | | |
| | | | |
| | | | |
| | | | |
| | | | |
| | | | |
| | | | |
| | | | |

**Alpine Company**

**Statement of Owner's Equity**

**For Month Ended May 31, 2011**

| | | | |
|---|---|---|---|
| | | | |
| | | | |
| | | | |
| | | | |
| | | | |
| | | | |

**Alpine Company**

**Balance Sheet**

**May 31, 2011**

| | | | |
|---|---|---|---|
| | | | |
| | | | |
| | | | |
| | | | |
| | | | |
| | | | |
| | | | |
| | | | |
| | | | |
| | | | |
| | | | |
| | | | |
| | | | |
| | | | |
| | | | |
| | | | |
| | | | |
| | | | |
| | | | |
| | | | |
| | | | |
| | | | |
| | | | |
| | | | |
| | | | |
| | | | |
| | | | |

### Alpine Company
### Post-Closing Trial Balance
### May 31, 2011

| | Debit | Credit |
|---|---|---|
| | | |
| | | |
| | | |
| | | |
| | | |
| | | |
| | | |
| | | |
| | | |
| | | |
| | | |
| | | |
| | | |
| | | |
| | | |
| | | |
| | | |
| | | |
| | | |
| | | |
| | | |
| | | |

### Alpine Company
### Schedule of Accounts Receivable
### May 31, 2011

| | | |
|---|---|---|
| | | |
| | | |
| | | |
| | | |

### Alpine Company
### Schedule of Accounts Payable
### May 31, 2011

| | | |
|---|---|---|
| | | |
| | | |
| | | |
| | | |

**(a)** _____

_____

_____

_____

_____

_____

_____

**(b)** _____

_____

_____

_____

_____

_____

_____

**(c)** _____

_____

_____

_____

## Quick Study 9-2

**a.** _____

_____

_____

_____

**b.** _____

_____

_____

_____

## Quick Study 9-3

**(1) Establishment of the fund:**

### GENERAL JOURNAL                                  Page____

| Date | Account Titles and Explanation | PR | Debit | Credit |
|------|-------------------------------|----|-------|--------|
|      |                               |    |       |        |
|      |                               |    |       |        |
|      |                               |    |       |        |
|      |                               |    |       |        |
|      |                               |    |       |        |

## (2) Summary of petty cash receipts and entry to reimburse the fund at month-end:

**Wee Ones Agency**
**Petty Cash Payments Report**
**May 1 – 31, 2011**

Receipts:

_____

_____

_____

_____

_____

_____

Fund total

Less:  Cash remaining

Equals:  Cash required to replenish petty cash

Cash over/(short)

### GENERAL JOURNAL                                    Page____

| Date | Account Titles and Explanation | PR | Debit | Credit |
|---|---|---|---|---|
| | | | | |
| | | | | |
| | | | | |
| | | | | |
| | | | | |

(3) _____

_____

_____

_____

## Quick Study 9-4

### GENERAL JOURNAL                                    Page____

| Date | Account Titles and Explanation | PR | Debit | Credit |
|---|---|---|---|---|
| | | | | |
| | | | | |
| | | | | |
| | | | | |
| | | | | |
| | | | | |
| | | | | |
| | | | | |
| | | | | |

## GENERAL JOURNAL                                      Page____

| Date | Account Titles and Explanation | PR | Debit | Credit |
|------|-------------------------------|----|-------|--------|
|      |                               |    |       |        |
|      |                               |    |       |        |
|      |                               |    |       |        |
|      |                               |    |       |        |
|      |                               |    |       |        |
|      |                               |    |       |        |
|      |                               |    |       |        |
|      |                               |    |       |        |
|      |                               |    |       |        |
|      |                               |    |       |        |
|      |                               |    |       |        |

## Quick Study 9-6

## GENERAL JOURNAL                                      Page____

| Date | Account Titles and Explanation | PR | Debit | Credit |
|------|-------------------------------|----|-------|--------|
|      |                               |    |       |        |
|      |                               |    |       |        |
|      |                               |    |       |        |
|      |                               |    |       |        |
|      |                               |    |       |        |
|      |                               |    |       |        |
|      |                               |    |       |        |
|      |                               |    |       |        |
|      |                               |    |       |        |
|      |                               |    |       |        |
|      |                               |    |       |        |
|      |                               |    |       |        |
|      |                               |    |       |        |
|      |                               |    |       |        |
|      |                               |    |       |        |
|      |                               |    |       |        |
|      |                               |    |       |        |
|      |                               |    |       |        |
|      |                               |    |       |        |
|      |                               |    |       |        |
|      |                               |    |       |        |
|      |                               |    |       |        |
|      |                               |    |       |        |
|      |                               |    |       |        |
|      |                               |    |       |        |

## GENERAL JOURNAL                                    Page____

| Date | Account Titles and Explanation | PR | Debit | Credit |
|------|-------------------------------|-----|-------|--------|
|      |                               |     |       |        |
|      |                               |     |       |        |
|      |                               |     |       |        |
|      |                               |     |       |        |
|      |                               |     |       |        |
|      |                               |     |       |        |
|      |                               |     |       |        |
|      |                               |     |       |        |
|      |                               |     |       |        |
|      |                               |     |       |        |
|      |                               |     |       |        |
|      |                               |     |       |        |
|      |                               |     |       |        |
|      |                               |     |       |        |
|      |                               |     |       |        |
|      |                               |     |       |        |
|      |                               |     |       |        |
|      |                               |     |       |        |
|      |                               |     |       |        |
|      |                               |     |       |        |
|      |                               |     |       |        |
|      |                               |     |       |        |
|      |                               |     |       |        |
|      |                               |     |       |        |

## Quick Study 9-8     Parts 1 and 2:

| | **Bank or Book Effect** | **Add or Subtract** | **Journal Entry Required or Not** |
|---|---|---|---|
| (a) | | | |
| (b) | | | |
| (c) | | | |
| (d) | | | |
| (e) | | | |
| (f) | | | |
| (g) | | | |

## Bank Reconciliation

| | | | |
|---|---|---|---|
| | | | |
| | | | |
| | | | |
| | | | |
| | | | |
| | | | |
| | | | |
| | | | |
| | | | |
| | | | |
| | | | |
| | | | |

### GENERAL JOURNAL                          Page____

| Date | Account Titles and Explanation | PR | Debit | Credit |
|---|---|---|---|---|
| | | | | |
| | | | | |
| | | | | |
| | | | | |

## Quick Study 9-10

_____
_____
_____
_____
_____
_____
_____
_____
_____
_____

**Exercise 9-2**

_____
_____
_____
_____
_____
_____
_____
_____
_____
_____
_____
_____
_____
_____
_____

**Exercise 9-3**

(a)
_____
_____
_____
_____
_____
_____

(b)
_____
_____
_____
_____
_____
_____

Internal Control Problem: _____

_____

_____

_____

_____

_____

_____

_____

_____

Internal Control Recommendation: _____

_____

_____

_____

_____

_____

**Exercise 9-5**

Part 1(a) Establish the Fund

GENERAL JOURNAL                                                    Page____

| Date | Account Titles and Explanation | PR | Debit | Credit |
|------|-------------------------------|----|-------|--------|
|      |                               |    |       |        |
|      |                               |    |       |        |
|      |                               |    |       |        |
|      |                               |    |       |        |
|      |                               |    |       |        |
|      |                               |    |       |        |

Part 1(b) Prepare a summary of petty cash receipts

Eanes Co.
Petty Cash Payments Report
January 1 – 8, 2011

Receipts: _____

_____

_____

_____

_____

_____

_____

Fund total

Less:  Cash remaining

Equals:  Cash required to replenish petty cash

Cash over/(short)

**Record the reimbursement:**

### GENERAL JOURNAL                                    Page____

| Date | Account Titles and Explanation | PR | Debit | Credit |
|------|-------------------------------|----|-------|--------|
|      |                               |    |       |        |
|      |                               |    |       |        |
|      |                               |    |       |        |
|      |                               |    |       |        |
|      |                               |    |       |        |
|      |                               |    |       |        |

**Part 2:  Reimburse and Increase the Fund**

### GENERAL JOURNAL                                    Page____

| Date | Account Titles and Explanation | PR | Debit | Credit |
|------|-------------------------------|----|-------|--------|
|      |                               |    |       |        |
|      |                               |    |       |        |
|      |                               |    |       |        |
|      |                               |    |       |        |
|      |                               |    |       |        |
|      |                               |    |       |        |
|      |                               |    |       |        |
|      |                               |    |       |        |

*Analysis component:* _____

_____

_____

_____

_____

**Exercise 9-6**

**(a) Establish the Fund**

### GENERAL JOURNAL                                    Page____

| Date | Account Titles and Explanation | PR | Debit | Credit |
|------|-------------------------------|----|-------|--------|
|      |                               |    |       |        |
|      |                               |    |       |        |
|      |                               |    |       |        |
|      |                               |    |       |        |
|      |                               |    |       |        |
|      |                               |    |       |        |
|      |                               |    |       |        |
|      |                               |    |       |        |

**(b) Prepare a summary of petty cash receipts**

**Brady Company**
**Petty Cash Payments Report**
**September 9 – 30, 2011**

| | |
|---|---|
| Receipts: | |
| | |
| | |
| | |
| | |
| | |
| | |
| Fund total | |
| Less:  Cash remaining | |
| Equals:  Cash required to replenish petty cash | |
| Cash over/(short) | |

**Reimburse and reduce the fund**

**GENERAL JOURNAL**                    Page____

| Date | Account Titles and Explanation | PR | Debit | Credit |
|---|---|---|---|---|
| | | | | |
| | | | | |
| | | | | |
| | | | | |
| | | | | |
| | | | | |
| | | | | |
| | | | | |

*Analysis component:* _____

_____
_____
_____
_____
_____
_____
_____

## GENERAL JOURNAL                                    Page____

| Date | Account Titles and Explanation | PR | Debit | Credit |
|------|-------------------------------|----|-------|--------|
| a. | | | | |
| | | | | |
| | | | | |
| | | | | |
| | | | | |
| | | | | |
| | | | | |
| b. | | | | |
| | | | | |
| | | | | |
| | | | | |
| | | | | |
| | | | | |
| | | | | |
| c. | | | | |
| | | | | |
| | | | | |
| | | | | |
| | | | | |
| | | | | |
| | | | | |

## Exercise 9-8

## GENERAL JOURNAL                                    Page____

| Date | Account Titles and Explanation | PR | Debit | Credit |
|------|-------------------------------|----|-------|--------|
| | | | | |
| | | | | |
| | | | | |
| | | | | |
| | | | | |
| | | | | |
| | | | | |
| | | | | |
| | | | | |
| | | | | |
| | | | | |
| | | | | |

## GENERAL JOURNAL                                          Page____

| Date | | Account Titles and Explanation | PR | Debit | Credit |
|------|---|-------------------------------|----|----|----|
| | | | | | |
| | | | | | |
| | | | | | |
| | | | | | |
| | | | | | |
| | | | | | |
| | | | | | |
| | | | | | |
| | | | | | |
| | | | | | |
| | | | | | |
| | | | | | |
| | | | | | |
| | | | | | |
| | | | | | |
| | | | | | |

## Exercise 9-9

## GENERAL JOURNAL                                          Page____

| Date | | Account Titles and Explanation | PR | Debit | Credit |
|------|---|-------------------------------|----|----|----|
| | | | | | |
| | | | | | |
| | | | | | |
| | | | | | |
| | | | | | |
| | | | | | |
| | | | | | |
| | | | | | |
| | | | | | |
| | | | | | |
| | | | | | |
| | | | | | |
| | | | | | |
| | | | | | |
| | | | | | |
| | | | | | |
| | | | | | |
| | | | | | |
| | | | | | |
| | | | | | |

## GENERAL JOURNAL                                          Page____

| Date | Account Titles and Explanation | PR | Debit | Credit |
|------|-------------------------------|----|-------|--------|
|      |                               |    |       |        |
|      |                               |    |       |        |
|      |                               |    |       |        |
|      |                               |    |       |        |
|      |                               |    |       |        |
|      |                               |    |       |        |
|      |                               |    |       |        |
|      |                               |    |       |        |
|      |                               |    |       |        |
|      |                               |    |       |        |
|      |                               |    |       |        |
|      |                               |    |       |        |
|      |                               |    |       |        |
|      |                               |    |       |        |
|      |                               |    |       |        |
|      |                               |    |       |        |
|      |                               |    |       |        |
|      |                               |    |       |        |
|      |                               |    |       |        |
|      |                               |    |       |        |
|      |                               |    |       |        |
|      |                               |    |       |        |
|      |                               |    |       |        |
|      |                               |    |       |        |
|      |                               |    |       |        |
|      |                               |    |       |        |

*Analysis component:* _____
_____
_____
_____
_____
_____
_____
_____
_____
_____

_____
_____

| | | | | | | | |
|---|---|---|---|---|---|---|---|
| | | | | | | | |
| | | | | | | | |
| | | | | | | | |
| | | | | | | | |
| | | | | | | | |
| | | | | | | | |
| | | | | | | | |
| | | | | | | | |
| | | | | | | | |
| | | | | | | | |
| | | | | | | | |

**2.**

### GENERAL JOURNAL                                   Page____

| Date | Account Titles and Explanation | PR | Debit | Credit |
|---|---|---|---|---|
| | | | | |
| | | | | |
| | | | | |
| | | | | |
| | | | | |

*Analysis component:* _____

_____
_____
_____
_____

### Exercise 9-11

**a.** _____

_____

| | | | |
|---|---|---|---|
| | | | |
| | | | |
| | | | |
| | | | |
| | | | |
| | | | |
| | | | |
| | | | |
| | | | |

b.                          GENERAL JOURNAL                          Page____

| Date | Account Titles and Explanation | PR | Debit | Credit |
|------|-------------------------------|----|-------|--------|
|      |                               |    |       |        |
|      |                               |    |       |        |
|      |                               |    |       |        |
|      |                               |    |       |        |
|      |                               |    |       |        |
|      |                               |    |       |        |
|      |                               |    |       |        |
|      |                               |    |       |        |
|      |                               |    |       |        |
|      |                               |    |       |        |
|      |                               |    |       |        |

*Analysis component:* _____
_____
_____
_____
_____
_____
_____

|  | | Bank Balance | | Book Balance | | | Not Shown on the Reconciliation |
|---|---|---|---|---|---|---|---|
|  | | Add | Deduct | Add | Deduct | Adjust | |
| 1. | Interest earned on the account. | | | | | | |
| 2. | Deposit made on September 30 after the bank was closed. | | | | | | |
| 3. | Cheques outstanding on August 31 that cleared the bank in September. | | | | | | |
| 4. | NSF cheque from customer returned on September 15 but not recorded by the company | | | | | | |
| 5. | Cheques written and mailed to payees on September 30. | | | | | | |
| 6. | Deposit made on September 5 that was processed on September 8. | | | | | | |
| 7. | Bank service charge. | | | | | | |
| 8. | Cheques written and mailed to payees on October 5. | | | | | | |
| 9. | Cheque written by another depositor but charged against the company's account. | | | | | | |
| 10. | Principal and interest collected by the bank but not recorded by the company. | | | | | | |
| 11. | Special charge for collection of note in No. 10 on company's behalf. | | | | | | |
| 12. | Cheque written against the account and cleared by the bank; erroneously omitted by the company recordkeeper. | | | | | | |

| | Case X | Case Y | Case Z |
|---|---|---|---|
| | | | |

_____
_____
_____
_____
_____
_____
_____
_____
_____
_____
_____
_____
_____
_____
_____
_____
_____

## Problem 9-1A

| (1) Principle Violated: |
|---|
| Recommendation: |
| |
| |
| |

| (2) Principle Violated: |
|---|
| Recommendation: |
| |
| |
| |

| (3) Principle Violated: |
|---|
| Recommendation: |
| |
| |
| |

| (4) Principle Violated: |
|---|
| Recommendation: |
| |
| |
| |

| (5) Principle Violated: |
|---|
| Recommendation: |
| |
| |
| |

Part 1                     **GENERAL JOURNAL**                     Page____

| Date | Account Titles and Explanation | PR | Debit | Credit |
|------|-------------------------------|----|-------|--------|
|      |                               |    |       |        |
|      |                               |    |       |        |
|      |                               |    |       |        |
|      |                               |    |       |        |
|      |                               |    |       |        |

Part 2

**Palladium Art Gallery**
**Petty Cash Payments Report**
**February 2 – 28, 2011**

Receipts:

Fund total
Less:  Cash remaining
Equals:  Cash required to replenish petty cash
Cash over/(short)

Part 3                     **GENERAL JOURNAL**                     Page____

| Date | Account Titles and Explanation | PR | Debit | Credit |
|------|-------------------------------|----|-------|--------|
|      |                               |    |       |        |
|      |                               |    |       |        |
|      |                               |    |       |        |
|      |                               |    |       |        |
|      |                               |    |       |        |
|      |                               |    |       |        |
|      |                               |    |       |        |
|      |                               |    |       |        |
|      |                               |    |       |        |
|      |                               |    |       |        |

*Analysis component:*  _____

_____

_____

_____

_____

_____

_____

_____

_____


## Problem 9-3A

**Part 1**                    **GENERAL JOURNAL**                    Page____

| Date | Account Titles and Explanation | PR | Debit | Credit |
|------|-------------------------------|----|-------|--------|
|      |                               |    |       |        |
|      |                               |    |       |        |
|      |                               |    |       |        |
|      |                               |    |       |        |
|      |                               |    |       |        |
|      |                               |    |       |        |
|      |                               |    |       |        |
|      |                               |    |       |        |
|      |                               |    |       |        |
|      |                               |    |       |        |
|      |                               |    |       |        |
|      |                               |    |       |        |
|      |                               |    |       |        |
|      |                               |    |       |        |
|      |                               |    |       |        |
|      |                               |    |       |        |
|      |                               |    |       |        |
|      |                               |    |       |        |
|      |                               |    |       |        |
|      |                               |    |       |        |
|      |                               |    |       |        |
|      |                               |    |       |        |
|      |                               |    |       |        |

*Analysis component:*  _____

_____

_____

_____

_____

_____

_____

**a.**

_____
_____

| | | | |
|---|---|---|---|
| | | | |
| | | | |
| | | | |
| | | | |
| | | | |
| | | | |
| | | | |
| | | | |
| | | | |
| | | | |
| | | | |
| | | | |
| | | | |
| | | | |
| | | | |
| | | | |

**b.**                    **GENERAL JOURNAL**                    Page____

| Date | Account Titles and Explanation | PR | Debit | Credit |
|---|---|---|---|---|
| | | | | |
| | | | | |
| | | | | |
| | | | | |
| | | | | |
| | | | | |
| | | | | |
| | | | | |
| | | | | |
| | | | | |
| | | | | |
| | | | | |
| | | | | |
| | | | | |
| | | | | |
| | | | | |

*Analysis component:* _____
_____
_____
_____
_____
_____
_____

a.

_____

|  |  |  |  |
|---|---|---|---|
|  |  |  |  |
|  |  |  |  |
|  |  |  |  |
|  |  |  |  |
|  |  |  |  |
|  |  |  |  |
|  |  |  |  |
|  |  |  |  |
|  |  |  |  |
|  |  |  |  |
|  |  |  |  |
|  |  |  |  |

b.

## GENERAL JOURNAL                                                    Page____

| Date | Account Titles and Explanation | PR | Debit | Credit |
|---|---|---|---|---|
|  |  |  |  |  |
|  |  |  |  |  |
|  |  |  |  |  |
|  |  |  |  |  |
|  |  |  |  |  |
|  |  |  |  |  |
|  |  |  |  |  |
|  |  |  |  |  |
|  |  |  |  |  |
|  |  |  |  |  |
|  |  |  |  |  |
|  |  |  |  |  |
|  |  |  |  |  |
|  |  |  |  |  |
|  |  |  |  |  |
|  |  |  |  |  |
|  |  |  |  |  |
|  |  |  |  |  |
|  |  |  |  |  |
|  |  |  |  |  |

## GENERAL JOURNAL                                    Page____

| Date | Account Titles and Explanation | PR | Debit | Credit |
|------|-------------------------------|----|-------|--------|
|      |                               |    |       |        |
|      |                               |    |       |        |
|      |                               |    |       |        |
|      |                               |    |       |        |
|      |                               |    |       |        |
|      |                               |    |       |        |
|      |                               |    |       |        |
|      |                               |    |       |        |
|      |                               |    |       |        |
|      |                               |    |       |        |
|      |                               |    |       |        |
|      |                               |    |       |        |
|      |                               |    |       |        |
|      |                               |    |       |        |
|      |                               |    |       |        |
|      |                               |    |       |        |
|      |                               |    |       |        |
|      |                               |    |       |        |

**Problem 9-6A**

**Part 1**

_____
_____

|   |   |   |   |
|---|---|---|---|
|   |   |   |   |
|   |   |   |   |
|   |   |   |   |
|   |   |   |   |
|   |   |   |   |
|   |   |   |   |
|   |   |   |   |
|   |   |   |   |
|   |   |   |   |
|   |   |   |   |
|   |   |   |   |
|   |   |   |   |
|   |   |   |   |
|   |   |   |   |
|   |   |   |   |
|   |   |   |   |
|   |   |   |   |
|   |   |   |   |
|   |   |   |   |

## GENERAL JOURNAL                                    Page____

| Date | Account Titles and Explanation | PR | Debit | Credit |
|------|-------------------------------|----|-------|--------|
|      |                               |    |       |        |
|      |                               |    |       |        |
|      |                               |    |       |        |
|      |                               |    |       |        |
|      |                               |    |       |        |
|      |                               |    |       |        |
|      |                               |    |       |        |
|      |                               |    |       |        |
|      |                               |    |       |        |
|      |                               |    |       |        |
|      |                               |    |       |        |
|      |                               |    |       |        |
|      |                               |    |       |        |
|      |                               |    |       |        |
|      |                               |    |       |        |
|      |                               |    |       |        |
|      |                               |    |       |        |
|      |                               |    |       |        |
|      |                               |    |       |        |
|      |                               |    |       |        |
|      |                               |    |       |        |
|      |                               |    |       |        |
|      |                               |    |       |        |
|      |                               |    |       |        |
|      |                               |    |       |        |

*Analysis component:* _____

_____
_____
_____
_____
_____
_____
_____
_____
_____
_____
_____
_____
_____

Chapter 9    Problem 9-7A          *Name* _____

Part 1

_____
_____
_____

|  |  |  |  |
|---|---|---|---|
|  |  |  |  |
|  |  |  |  |
|  |  |  |  |
|  |  |  |  |
|  |  |  |  |
|  |  |  |  |
|  |  |  |  |
|  |  |  |  |
|  |  |  |  |
|  |  |  |  |
|  |  |  |  |
|  |  |  |  |
|  |  |  |  |
|  |  |  |  |

Part 2

### GENERAL JOURNAL                                    Page____

| Date | Account Titles and Explanation | PR | Debit | Credit |
|---|---|---|---|---|
|  |  |  |  |  |
|  |  |  |  |  |
|  |  |  |  |  |
|  |  |  |  |  |
|  |  |  |  |  |
|  |  |  |  |  |
|  |  |  |  |  |
|  |  |  |  |  |
|  |  |  |  |  |
|  |  |  |  |  |
|  |  |  |  |  |
|  |  |  |  |  |
|  |  |  |  |  |
|  |  |  |  |  |
|  |  |  |  |  |
|  |  |  |  |  |
|  |  |  |  |  |
|  |  |  |  |  |
|  |  |  |  |  |
|  |  |  |  |  |
|  |  |  |  |  |
|  |  |  |  |  |
|  |  |  |  |  |

*Analysis component:* _____

_____
_____
_____
_____
_____
_____
_____
_____
_____
_____

## Problem 9-8A

a.

_____
_____

|  |  |  |  |
|---|---|---|---|
|  |  |  |  |
|  |  |  |  |
|  |  |  |  |
|  |  |  |  |
|  |  |  |  |
|  |  |  |  |
|  |  |  |  |
|  |  |  |  |
|  |  |  |  |
|  |  |  |  |
|  |  |  |  |
|  |  |  |  |
|  |  |  |  |
|  |  |  |  |
|  |  |  |  |
|  |  |  |  |
|  |  |  |  |

## GENERAL JOURNAL                               Page____

| Date | Account Titles and Explanation | PR | Debit | Credit |
|------|-------------------------------|----|-------|--------|
|      |                               |    |       |        |
|      |                               |    |       |        |
|      |                               |    |       |        |
|      |                               |    |       |        |
|      |                               |    |       |        |
|      |                               |    |       |        |
|      |                               |    |       |        |
|      |                               |    |       |        |
|      |                               |    |       |        |
|      |                               |    |       |        |
|      |                               |    |       |        |
|      |                               |    |       |        |
|      |                               |    |       |        |
|      |                               |    |       |        |
|      |                               |    |       |        |
|      |                               |    |       |        |
|      |                               |    |       |        |
|      |                               |    |       |        |
|      |                               |    |       |        |
|      |                               |    |       |        |
|      |                               |    |       |        |
|      |                               |    |       |        |
|      |                               |    |       |        |
|      |                               |    |       |        |
|      |                               |    |       |        |

## Problem 9-9A

a. _____

_____

| | | | |
|---|---|---|---|
| | | | |
| | | | |
| | | | |
| | | | |
| | | | |
| | | | |
| | | | |
| | | | |
| | | | |
| | | | |
| | | | |
| | | | |
| | | | |
| | | | |

**b.**             **GENERAL JOURNAL**               Page____

| Date | Account Titles and Explanation | PR | Debit | Credit |
|------|-------------------------------|----|----|----|
|  |  |  |  |  |
|  |  |  |  |  |
|  |  |  |  |  |
|  |  |  |  |  |
|  |  |  |  |  |
|  |  |  |  |  |
|  |  |  |  |  |
|  |  |  |  |  |
|  |  |  |  |  |
|  |  |  |  |  |
|  |  |  |  |  |
|  |  |  |  |  |
|  |  |  |  |  |
|  |  |  |  |  |
|  |  |  |  |  |
|  |  |  |  |  |

**Problem 9-10A**

**a.**

_____

_____

_____

| | | | |
|---|---|---|---|
|  |  |  |  |
|  |  |  |  |
|  |  |  |  |
|  |  |  |  |
|  |  |  |  |
|  |  |  |  |
|  |  |  |  |
|  |  |  |  |
|  |  |  |  |
|  |  |  |  |
|  |  |  |  |
|  |  |  |  |
|  |  |  |  |
|  |  |  |  |
|  |  |  |  |
|  |  |  |  |
|  |  |  |  |
|  |  |  |  |
|  |  |  |  |
|  |  |  |  |

b.

## GENERAL JOURNAL                              Page____

| Date | Account Titles and Explanation | PR | Debit | Credit |
|------|-------------------------------|----|-------|--------|
|      |                               |    |       |        |
|      |                               |    |       |        |
|      |                               |    |       |        |
|      |                               |    |       |        |
|      |                               |    |       |        |
|      |                               |    |       |        |
|      |                               |    |       |        |
|      |                               |    |       |        |
|      |                               |    |       |        |
|      |                               |    |       |        |
|      |                               |    |       |        |
|      |                               |    |       |        |
|      |                               |    |       |        |
|      |                               |    |       |        |
|      |                               |    |       |        |
|      |                               |    |       |        |
|      |                               |    |       |        |
|      |                               |    |       |        |
|      |                               |    |       |        |
|      |                               |    |       |        |
|      |                               |    |       |        |
|      |                               |    |       |        |
|      |                               |    |       |        |
|      |                               |    |       |        |

*Analysis component:* _____

_____
_____
_____
_____
_____
_____

**Problem 9-1B**

| (1) **Principle Violated:** |
|---|
| **Recommendation:** |
| |
| |
| |

| (2) **Principle Violated:** |
|---|
| **Recommendation:** |
| |
| |
| |

| (3) **Principle Violated:** |
|---|
| **Recommendation:** |
| |
| |
| |

| (4) **Principle Violated:** |
|---|
| **Recommendation:** |
| |
| |
| |

| (5) **Principle Violated:** |
|---|
| **Recommendation:** |
| |
| |
| |

**Part 1**                              GENERAL JOURNAL                              Page____

| Date | | Account Titles and Explanation | PR | Debit | Credit |
|---|---|---|---|---|---|
| | | | | | |
| | | | | | |
| | | | | | |
| | | | | | |

**Part 2**

Dodge & Sons
Petty Cash Payments Report
July 5 – 31, 2011

Receipts:

Fund total
Less:  Cash remaining
Equals:  Cash required to replenish petty cash
Cash over/(short)

**Part 3**                              GENERAL JOURNAL                              Page____

| Date | | Account Titles and Explanation | PR | Debit | Credit |
|---|---|---|---|---|---|
| | | | | | |
| | | | | | |
| | | | | | |
| | | | | | |
| | | | | | |
| | | | | | |
| | | | | | |
| | | | | | |
| | | | | | |
| | | | | | |

*Analysis component:* _____

_____
_____
_____
_____
_____
_____
_____
_____

## Problem 9-3B

Part 1                     GENERAL JOURNAL                     Page____

| Date | Account Titles and Explanation | PR | Debit | Credit |
|------|-------------------------------|----|-------|--------|
|      |                               |    |       |        |
|      |                               |    |       |        |
|      |                               |    |       |        |
|      |                               |    |       |        |
|      |                               |    |       |        |
|      |                               |    |       |        |
|      |                               |    |       |        |
|      |                               |    |       |        |
|      |                               |    |       |        |
|      |                               |    |       |        |
|      |                               |    |       |        |
|      |                               |    |       |        |
|      |                               |    |       |        |
|      |                               |    |       |        |
|      |                               |    |       |        |
|      |                               |    |       |        |
|      |                               |    |       |        |
|      |                               |    |       |        |
|      |                               |    |       |        |
|      |                               |    |       |        |
|      |                               |    |       |        |
|      |                               |    |       |        |
|      |                               |    |       |        |
|      |                               |    |       |        |

*Analysis component:* _____

_____
_____
_____
_____
_____
_____

*Name* _____

a.

_____
_____
_____

|  |  |  |  |
|---|---|---|---|
|  |  |  |  |
|  |  |  |  |
|  |  |  |  |
|  |  |  |  |
|  |  |  |  |
|  |  |  |  |
|  |  |  |  |
|  |  |  |  |
|  |  |  |  |
|  |  |  |  |
|  |  |  |  |
|  |  |  |  |
|  |  |  |  |
|  |  |  |  |
|  |  |  |  |
|  |  |  |  |
|  |  |  |  |
|  |  |  |  |

b.                           **GENERAL JOURNAL**                          Page____

| Date | Account Titles and Explanation | PR | Debit | Credit |
|---|---|---|---|---|
|  |  |  |  |  |
|  |  |  |  |  |
|  |  |  |  |  |
|  |  |  |  |  |

*Analysis component:* _____

_____
_____
_____
_____
_____
_____
_____
_____
_____
_____

a.

_____

_____

_____

|  |  |  |  |
|---|---|---|---|
|  |  |  |  |
|  |  |  |  |
|  |  |  |  |
|  |  |  |  |
|  |  |  |  |
|  |  |  |  |
|  |  |  |  |
|  |  |  |  |
|  |  |  |  |
|  |  |  |  |
|  |  |  |  |
|  |  |  |  |
|  |  |  |  |
|  |  |  |  |

b.

## GENERAL JOURNAL                                    Page____

| Date | Account Titles and Explanation | PR | Debit | Credit |
|---|---|---|---|---|
|  |  |  |  |  |
|  |  |  |  |  |
|  |  |  |  |  |
|  |  |  |  |  |
|  |  |  |  |  |
|  |  |  |  |  |
|  |  |  |  |  |
|  |  |  |  |  |
|  |  |  |  |  |
|  |  |  |  |  |
|  |  |  |  |  |
|  |  |  |  |  |

Chapter 9     Problem 9-6B          *Name* _____

**Part 1**

_____
_____
_____

| | | | |
|---|---|---|---|
| | | | |
| | | | |
| | | | |
| | | | |
| | | | |
| | | | |
| | | | |
| | | | |
| | | | |
| | | | |
| | | | |
| | | | |
| | | | |
| | | | |
| | | | |

**Part 2**

### GENERAL JOURNAL                                   Page____

| Date | Account Titles and Explanation | PR | Debit | Credit |
|---|---|---|---|---|
| | | | | |
| | | | | |
| | | | | |
| | | | | |
| | | | | |
| | | | | |
| | | | | |
| | | | | |
| | | | | |
| | | | | |
| | | | | |
| | | | | |
| | | | | |
| | | | | |
| | | | | |
| | | | | |
| | | | | |
| | | | | |
| | | | | |
| | | | | |

*Analysis component:*   _____

_____
_____
_____
_____
_____
_____
_____
_____
_____
_____
_____

## Problem 9-7B    Part 1

_____
_____

|  |  |  |  |
|---|---|---|---|
|  |  |  |  |
|  |  |  |  |
|  |  |  |  |
|  |  |  |  |
|  |  |  |  |
|  |  |  |  |
|  |  |  |  |
|  |  |  |  |
|  |  |  |  |
|  |  |  |  |
|  |  |  |  |
|  |  |  |  |

## Part 2

### GENERAL JOURNAL                                    Page____

| Date | Account Titles and Explanation | PR | Debit | Credit |
|------|-------------------------------|----|-------|--------|
|  |  |  |  |  |
|  |  |  |  |  |
|  |  |  |  |  |
|  |  |  |  |  |
|  |  |  |  |  |
|  |  |  |  |  |
|  |  |  |  |  |
|  |  |  |  |  |
|  |  |  |  |  |
|  |  |  |  |  |
|  |  |  |  |  |

## GENERAL JOURNAL                                                     Page____

| Date | Account Titles and Explanation | PR | Debit | Credit |
|------|-------------------------------|-----|-------|--------|
|      |                               |     |       |        |
|      |                               |     |       |        |
|      |                               |     |       |        |
|      |                               |     |       |        |
|      |                               |     |       |        |
|      |                               |     |       |        |
|      |                               |     |       |        |
|      |                               |     |       |        |
|      |                               |     |       |        |
|      |                               |     |       |        |
|      |                               |     |       |        |

*Analysis component:* _____

_____
_____
_____
_____
_____
_____
_____
_____
_____
_____

## Problem 9-8B     Part 1

_____
_____

|  |  |  |  |
|--|--|--|--|
|  |  |  |  |
|  |  |  |  |
|  |  |  |  |
|  |  |  |  |
|  |  |  |  |
|  |  |  |  |
|  |  |  |  |
|  |  |  |  |
|  |  |  |  |
|  |  |  |  |
|  |  |  |  |
|  |  |  |  |
|  |  |  |  |
|  |  |  |  |
|  |  |  |  |

## GENERAL JOURNAL                                     Page____

| Date | Account Titles and Explanation | PR | Debit | Credit |
|------|-------------------------------|----|-------|--------|
|      |                               |    |       |        |
|      |                               |    |       |        |
|      |                               |    |       |        |
|      |                               |    |       |        |
|      |                               |    |       |        |
|      |                               |    |       |        |
|      |                               |    |       |        |
|      |                               |    |       |        |
|      |                               |    |       |        |
|      |                               |    |       |        |
|      |                               |    |       |        |
|      |                               |    |       |        |
|      |                               |    |       |        |
|      |                               |    |       |        |
|      |                               |    |       |        |
|      |                               |    |       |        |
|      |                               |    |       |        |
|      |                               |    |       |        |
|      |                               |    |       |        |
|      |                               |    |       |        |
|      |                               |    |       |        |
|      |                               |    |       |        |

## Problem 9-9B     Part 1

_____

_____

|  |  |  |  |
|---|---|---|---|
|  |  |  |  |
|  |  |  |  |
|  |  |  |  |
|  |  |  |  |
|  |  |  |  |
|  |  |  |  |
|  |  |  |  |
|  |  |  |  |
|  |  |  |  |
|  |  |  |  |
|  |  |  |  |
|  |  |  |  |
|  |  |  |  |
|  |  |  |  |
|  |  |  |  |

Part 2                         GENERAL JOURNAL                         Page____

| Date | Account Titles and Explanation | PR | Debit | Credit |
|------|-------------------------------|----|-------|--------|
|      |                               |    |       |        |
|      |                               |    |       |        |
|      |                               |    |       |        |
|      |                               |    |       |        |
|      |                               |    |       |        |
|      |                               |    |       |        |
|      |                               |    |       |        |
|      |                               |    |       |        |
|      |                               |    |       |        |
|      |                               |    |       |        |
|      |                               |    |       |        |
|      |                               |    |       |        |
|      |                               |    |       |        |
|      |                               |    |       |        |
|      |                               |    |       |        |
|      |                               |    |       |        |
|      |                               |    |       |        |
|      |                               |    |       |        |
|      |                               |    |       |        |
|      |                               |    |       |        |
|      |                               |    |       |        |
|      |                               |    |       |        |
|      |                               |    |       |        |
|      |                               |    |       |        |
|      |                               |    |       |        |
|      |                               |    |       |        |

## Problem 9-10B     Part 1

_____

_____

|  |  |  |  |
|--|--|--|--|
|  |  |  |  |
|  |  |  |  |
|  |  |  |  |
|  |  |  |  |
|  |  |  |  |
|  |  |  |  |
|  |  |  |  |
|  |  |  |  |
|  |  |  |  |
|  |  |  |  |
|  |  |  |  |
|  |  |  |  |
|  |  |  |  |
|  |  |  |  |

**2.**

GENERAL JOURNAL                                    Page____

| Date | Account Titles and Explanation | PR | Debit | Credit |
|------|-------------------------------|----|-------|--------|
|      |                               |    |       |        |
|      |                               |    |       |        |
|      |                               |    |       |        |
|      |                               |    |       |        |
|      |                               |    |       |        |
|      |                               |    |       |        |
|      |                               |    |       |        |
|      |                               |    |       |        |
|      |                               |    |       |        |
|      |                               |    |       |        |
|      |                               |    |       |        |
|      |                               |    |       |        |
|      |                               |    |       |        |
|      |                               |    |       |        |
|      |                               |    |       |        |
|      |                               |    |       |        |
|      |                               |    |       |        |
|      |                               |    |       |        |
|      |                               |    |       |        |
|      |                               |    |       |        |
|      |                               |    |       |        |
|      |                               |    |       |        |
|      |                               |    |       |        |
|      |                               |    |       |        |
|      |                               |    |       |        |
|      |                               |    |       |        |
|      |                               |    |       |        |
|      |                               |    |       |        |
|      |                               |    |       |        |
|      |                               |    |       |        |

*Analysis component:* _____

_____
_____
_____
_____
_____
_____

## GENERAL JOURNAL

| Date | Account Titles and Explanation | PR | Debit | Credit |
|------|-------------------------------|-----|-------|--------|
|  |  |  |  |  |
|  |  |  |  |  |
|  |  |  |  |  |
|  |  |  |  |  |
|  |  |  |  |  |
|  |  |  |  |  |
|  |  |  |  |  |
|  |  |  |  |  |
|  |  |  |  |  |
|  |  |  |  |  |
|  |  |  |  |  |
|  |  |  |  |  |
|  |  |  |  |  |
|  |  |  |  |  |
|  |  |  |  |  |
|  |  |  |  |  |
|  |  |  |  |  |
|  |  |  |  |  |

## Quick Study 10-2

a.

## GENERAL JOURNAL

| Date | Account Titles and Explanation | PR | Debit | Credit |
|------|-------------------------------|-----|-------|--------|
|  |  |  |  |  |
|  |  |  |  |  |
|  |  |  |  |  |
|  |  |  |  |  |
|  |  |  |  |  |
|  |  |  |  |  |
|  |  |  |  |  |
|  |  |  |  |  |
|  |  |  |  |  |
|  |  |  |  |  |
|  |  |  |  |  |
|  |  |  |  |  |
|  |  |  |  |  |
|  |  |  |  |  |
|  |  |  |  |  |
|  |  |  |  |  |
|  |  |  |  |  |
|  |  |  |  |  |
|  |  |  |  |  |
|  |  |  |  |  |

## GENERAL JOURNAL

| Date | Account Titles and Explanation | PR | Debit | Credit |
|------|-------------------------------|----|-------|--------|
|      |                               |    |       |        |
|      |                               |    |       |        |
|      |                               |    |       |        |
|      |                               |    |       |        |
|      |                               |    |       |        |
|      |                               |    |       |        |
|      |                               |    |       |        |
|      |                               |    |       |        |
|      |                               |    |       |        |
|      |                               |    |       |        |
|      |                               |    |       |        |
|      |                               |    |       |        |
|      |                               |    |       |        |
|      |                               |    |       |        |
|      |                               |    |       |        |
|      |                               |    |       |        |
|      |                               |    |       |        |
|      |                               |    |       |        |
|      |                               |    |       |        |
|      |                               |    |       |        |

## Quick Study 10-4

## GENERAL JOURNAL

| Date | Account Titles and Explanation | PR | Debit | Credit |
|------|-------------------------------|----|-------|--------|
|      |                               |    |       |        |
|      |                               |    |       |        |
|      |                               |    |       |        |
|      |                               |    |       |        |
|      |                               |    |       |        |
|      |                               |    |       |        |
|      |                               |    |       |        |
|      |                               |    |       |        |
|      |                               |    |       |        |
|      |                               |    |       |        |
|      |                               |    |       |        |
|      |                               |    |       |        |
|      |                               |    |       |        |
|      |                               |    |       |        |
|      |                               |    |       |        |
|      |                               |    |       |        |
|      |                               |    |       |        |
|      |                               |    |       |        |
|      |                               |    |       |        |
|      |                               |    |       |        |

### GENERAL JOURNAL

| Date | | Account Titles and Explanation | PR | Debit | Credit |
|---|---|---|---|---|---|
| | | | | | |
| | | | | | |
| | | | | | |
| | | | | | |
| | | | | | |
| | | | | | |
| | | | | | |
| | | | | | |
| | | | | | |
| | | | | | |
| | | | | | |
| | | | | | |
| | | | | | |
| | | | | | |
| | | | | | |
| | | | | | |
| | | | | | |
| | | | | | |
| | | | | | |
| | | | | | |
| | | | | | |
| | | | | | |
| | | | | | |
| | | | | | |

## Quick Study 10-5

### Partial Balance Sheet

| | | |
|---|---|---|
| | | |
| | | |
| | | |
| | | |
| | | |
| | | |
| | | |
| | | |
| | | |
| | | |
| | | |
| | | |
| | | |
| | | |
| | | |
| | | |

## GENERAL JOURNAL

| Date | | Account Titles and Explanation | PR | Debit | Credit |
|---|---|---|---|---|---|
| | | | | | |
| | | | | | |
| | | | | | |
| | | | | | |
| | | | | | |
| | | | | | |
| | | | | | |

## Quick Study 10-7

### Allowance for Doubtful Accounts

## GENERAL JOURNAL                                    Page____

| Date | | Account Titles and Explanation | PR | Debit | Credit |
|---|---|---|---|---|---|
| | | | | | |
| | | | | | |
| | | | | | |
| | | | | | |
| | | | | | |

## Quick Study 10-8

a.                                  ## GENERAL JOURNAL                                    Page____

| Date | | Account Titles and Explanation | PR | Debit | Credit |
|---|---|---|---|---|---|
| | | | | | |
| | | | | | |
| | | | | | |
| | | | | | |

b. _____

c. _____

## GENERAL JOURNAL                                          Page____

| Date | Account Titles and Explanation | PR | Debit | Credit |
|------|-------------------------------|----|----|----|
|      |                               |    |    |    |
|      |                               |    |    |    |
|      |                               |    |    |    |
|      |                               |    |    |    |
|      |                               |    |    |    |

**Allowance for Doubtful Accounts**

## Quick Study 10-10

### GENERAL JOURNAL                                          Page____

| Date | Account Titles and Explanation | PR | Debit | Credit |
|------|-------------------------------|----|----|----|
|      |                               |    |    |    |
|      |                               |    |    |    |
|      |                               |    |    |    |
|      |                               |    |    |    |
|      |                               |    |    |    |

## Quick Study 10-11

### GENERAL JOURNAL                                          Page____

| Date | Account Titles and Explanation | PR | Debit | Credit |
|------|-------------------------------|----|----|----|
|      |                               |    |    |    |
|      |                               |    |    |    |
|      |                               |    |    |    |
|      |                               |    |    |    |
|      |                               |    |    |    |
|      |                               |    |    |    |
|      |                               |    |    |    |
|      |                               |    |    |    |
|      |                               |    |    |    |
|      |                               |    |    |    |
|      |                               |    |    |    |

## GENERAL JOURNAL

| Date | | Account Titles and Explanation | PR | Debit | Credit |
|---|---|---|---|---|---|
| | | | | | |
| | | | | | |
| | | | | | |
| | | | | | |
| | | | | | |
| | | | | | |
| | | | | | |
| | | | | | |
| | | | | | |
| | | | | | |
| | | | | | |

## Quick Study 10-13

### GENERAL JOURNAL

| Date | | Account Titles and Explanation | PR | Debit | Credit |
|---|---|---|---|---|---|
| | | | | | |
| | | | | | |
| | | | | | |
| | | | | | |
| | | | | | |
| | | | | | |
| | | | | | |

## *Quick Study 10-14

### GENERAL JOURNAL

| Date | | Account Titles and Explanation | PR | Debit | Credit |
|---|---|---|---|---|---|
| | | | | | |
| | | | | | |
| | | | | | |
| | | | | | |
| | | | | | |
| | | | | | |
| | | | | | |

## GENERAL JOURNAL

| Date | Account Titles and Explanation | PR | Debit | Credit |
|---|---|---|---|---|
|  |  |  |  |  |
|  |  |  |  |  |
|  |  |  |  |  |
|  |  |  |  |  |

*Calculations:*

---

## *Quick Study 10-16

a.

b.

c.

## Exercise 10-1

## GENERAL JOURNAL

| Date | Account Titles and Explanation | PR | Debit | Credit |
|---|---|---|---|---|
|  |  |  |  |  |
|  |  |  |  |  |
|  |  |  |  |  |
|  |  |  |  |  |
|  |  |  |  |  |
|  |  |  |  |  |
|  |  |  |  |  |
|  |  |  |  |  |
|  |  |  |  |  |
|  |  |  |  |  |
|  |  |  |  |  |
|  |  |  |  |  |
|  |  |  |  |  |
|  |  |  |  |  |
|  |  |  |  |  |
|  |  |  |  |  |
|  |  |  |  |  |
|  |  |  |  |  |
|  |  |  |  |  |
|  |  |  |  |  |
|  |  |  |  |  |
|  |  |  |  |  |
|  |  |  |  |  |

## GENERAL LEDGER

| Accounts Receivable | Sales | Sales Returns and Allowances |
|---|---|---|
| | | |

## ACCOUNTS RECEIVABLE SUBLEDGER

| ABC Shop | Colt Enterprises | Red McKenzie |
|---|---|---|
| | | |

**Part 2**

| | | |
|---|---|---|
| | | |
| | | |
| | | |
| | | |
| | | |
| | | |

<u>Comparison:</u>

## GENERAL JOURNAL

| Date | Account Titles and Explanation | PR | Debit | Credit |
|------|-------------------------------|-----|-------|--------|
|      |                               |     |       |        |
|      |                               |     |       |        |
|      |                               |     |       |        |
|      |                               |     |       |        |
|      |                               |     |       |        |
|      |                               |     |       |        |
|      |                               |     |       |        |
|      |                               |     |       |        |
|      |                               |     |       |        |
|      |                               |     |       |        |
|      |                               |     |       |        |
|      |                               |     |       |        |
|      |                               |     |       |        |
|      |                               |     |       |        |
|      |                               |     |       |        |
|      |                               |     |       |        |

## Exercise 10-4

## GENERAL JOURNAL

| Date | Account Titles and Explanation | PR | Debit | Credit |
|------|-------------------------------|-----|-------|--------|
|      |                               |     |       |        |
|      |                               |     |       |        |
|      |                               |     |       |        |
|      |                               |     |       |        |
|      |                               |     |       |        |
|      |                               |     |       |        |
|      |                               |     |       |        |
|      |                               |     |       |        |
|      |                               |     |       |        |
|      |                               |     |       |        |
|      |                               |     |       |        |
|      |                               |     |       |        |
|      |                               |     |       |        |
|      |                               |     |       |        |
|      |                               |     |       |        |
|      |                               |     |       |        |
|      |                               |     |       |        |
|      |                               |     |       |        |
|      |                               |     |       |        |
|      |                               |     |       |        |
|      |                               |     |       |        |
|      |                               |     |       |        |

a.

| Accounts Receivable | Allowance for Doubtful Accounts |
|---|---|

### GENERAL JOURNAL

| Date | Account Titles and Explanation | PR | Debit | Credit |
|---|---|---|---|---|
|  |  |  |  |  |
|  |  |  |  |  |
|  |  |  |  |  |
|  |  |  |  |  |

b.

| Accounts Receivable | Allowance for Doubtful Accounts |
|---|---|

### GENERAL JOURNAL

| Date | Account Titles and Explanation | PR | Debit | Credit |
|---|---|---|---|---|
|  |  |  |  |  |
|  |  |  |  |  |
|  |  |  |  |  |
|  |  |  |  |  |

## Exercise 10-6

a. _____

b. _____

c. _____

d. _____

e. _____

*Name* _____

## Partial Balance Sheet

| | | |
|---|---|---|
| | | |
| | | |
| | | |
| | | |
| | | |
| | | |
| | | |
| | | |
| | | |
| | | |
| | | |

### Exercise 10-8

**a, b, and c**                    **GENERAL JOURNAL**                    Page____

| Date | Account Titles and Explanation | PR | Debit | Credit |
|---|---|---|---|---|
| | | | | |
| | | | | |
| | | | | |
| | | | | |
| | | | | |
| | | | | |
| | | | | |
| | | | | |
| | | | | |
| | | | | |
| | | | | |
| | | | | |
| | | | | |
| | | | | |
| | | | | |
| | | | | |
| | | | | |
| | | | | |
| | | | | |
| | | | | |
| | | | | |
| | | | | |
| | | | | |
| | | | | |
| | | | | |

a, b, and c (cont'd.)           **GENERAL JOURNAL**                    Page____

| Date | Account Titles and Explanation | PR | Debit | Credit |
|------|-------------------------------|----|-------|--------|
|      |                               |    |       |        |
|      |                               |    |       |        |
|      |                               |    |       |        |
|      |                               |    |       |        |
|      |                               |    |       |        |
|      |                               |    |       |        |
|      |                               |    |       |        |
|      |                               |    |       |        |
|      |                               |    |       |        |
|      |                               |    |       |        |
|      |                               |    |       |        |
|      |                               |    |       |        |

*Calculations:*

| Accounts Receivable | Allowance for Doubtful Accounts |
|---------------------|---------------------------------|
|                     |                                 |

**d.**

**Partial Balance Sheet**

|  |  |  |
|--|--|--|
|  |  |  |
|  |  |  |
|  |  |  |
|  |  |  |

*Analysis component:*

_____

_____

_____

_____

_____

*Name* _____

a, b, and c.                    **GENERAL JOURNAL**                    Page____

| Date | Account Titles and Explanation | PR | Debit | Credit |
|------|-------------------------------|----|-------|--------|
|      |                               |    |       |        |
|      |                               |    |       |        |
|      |                               |    |       |        |
|      |                               |    |       |        |
|      |                               |    |       |        |
|      |                               |    |       |        |
|      |                               |    |       |        |
|      |                               |    |       |        |
|      |                               |    |       |        |
|      |                               |    |       |        |
|      |                               |    |       |        |
|      |                               |    |       |        |
|      |                               |    |       |        |
|      |                               |    |       |        |
|      |                               |    |       |        |
|      |                               |    |       |        |
|      |                               |    |       |        |
|      |                               |    |       |        |
|      |                               |    |       |        |
|      |                               |    |       |        |
|      |                               |    |       |        |
|      |                               |    |       |        |
|      |                               |    |       |        |
|      |                               |    |       |        |
|      |                               |    |       |        |
|      |                               |    |       |        |
|      |                               |    |       |        |
|      |                               |    |       |        |
|      |                               |    |       |        |
|      |                               |    |       |        |
|      |                               |    |       |        |
|      |                               |    |       |        |
|      |                               |    |       |        |
|      |                               |    |       |        |

*Calculations:*

| Accounts Receivable | Allowance for Doubtful Accounts |
|---------------------|---------------------------------|
|                     |                                 |

**d.**

| Partial Balance Sheet | | |
|---|---|---|
| | | |
| | | |
| | | |
| | | |
| | | |

*Analysis component:* _____

_____

_____

_____

_____

## Exercise 10-10

**a and b.**                        GENERAL JOURNAL                        Page____

| Date | Account Titles and Explanation | PR | Debit | Credit |
|---|---|---|---|---|
| | | | | |
| | | | | |
| | | | | |
| | | | | |
| | | | | |
| | | | | |
| | | | | |
| | | | | |
| | | | | |
| | | | | |
| | | | | |
| | | | | |

*Calculations:*

| Accounts Receivable | Allowance for Doubtful Accounts |
|---|---|
| | |

d.

| Partial Balance Sheet | | |
|---|---|---|
| | | |
| | | |
| | | |
| | | |
| | | |

*Analysis component:*

_____
_____
_____
_____
_____

**Exercise 10-11**

GENERAL JOURNAL                                         Page____

| Date | Account Titles and Explanation | PR | Debit | Credit |
|---|---|---|---|---|
| | | | | |
| | | | | |
| | | | | |
| | | | | |
| | | | | |
| | | | | |
| | | | | |
| | | | | |

*Analysis component:*

_____
_____
_____
_____
_____
_____
_____

## GENERAL JOURNAL

| Date | Account Titles and Explanation | PR | Debit | Credit |
|------|-------------------------------|----|-------|--------|
|      |                               |    |       |        |
|      |                               |    |       |        |
|      |                               |    |       |        |
|      |                               |    |       |        |
|      |                               |    |       |        |
|      |                               |    |       |        |
|      |                               |    |       |        |
|      |                               |    |       |        |
|      |                               |    |       |        |
|      |                               |    |       |        |
|      |                               |    |       |        |
|      |                               |    |       |        |
|      |                               |    |       |        |
|      |                               |    |       |        |
|      |                               |    |       |        |
|      |                               |    |       |        |
|      |                               |    |       |        |

### Exercise 10-13

## GENERAL JOURNAL

| Date | Account Titles and Explanation | PR | Debit | Credit |
|------|-------------------------------|----|-------|--------|
|      |                               |    |       |        |
|      |                               |    |       |        |
|      |                               |    |       |        |
|      |                               |    |       |        |
|      |                               |    |       |        |
|      |                               |    |       |        |
|      |                               |    |       |        |
|      |                               |    |       |        |
|      |                               |    |       |        |
|      |                               |    |       |        |
|      |                               |    |       |        |
|      |                               |    |       |        |
|      |                               |    |       |        |
|      |                               |    |       |        |
|      |                               |    |       |        |
|      |                               |    |       |        |
|      |                               |    |       |        |
|      |                               |    |       |        |
|      |                               |    |       |        |

*Name* _____

## GENERAL JOURNAL

| Date | Account Titles and Explanation | PR | Debit | Credit |
|------|-------------------------------|-----|-------|--------|
|      |                               |     |       |        |
|      |                               |     |       |        |
|      |                               |     |       |        |
|      |                               |     |       |        |
|      |                               |     |       |        |
|      |                               |     |       |        |
|      |                               |     |       |        |
|      |                               |     |       |        |
|      |                               |     |       |        |
|      |                               |     |       |        |
|      |                               |     |       |        |
|      |                               |     |       |        |
|      |                               |     |       |        |
|      |                               |     |       |        |
|      |                               |     |       |        |
|      |                               |     |       |        |
|      |                               |     |       |        |
|      |                               |     |       |        |
|      |                               |     |       |        |
|      |                               |     |       |        |
|      |                               |     |       |        |
|      |                               |     |       |        |
|      |                               |     |       |        |
|      |                               |     |       |        |
|      |                               |     |       |        |
|      |                               |     |       |        |
|      |                               |     |       |        |
|      |                               |     |       |        |
|      |                               |     |       |        |
|      |                               |     |       |        |
|      |                               |     |       |        |
|      |                               |     |       |        |
|      |                               |     |       |        |
|      |                               |     |       |        |
|      |                               |     |       |        |
|      |                               |     |       |        |
|      |                               |     |       |        |
|      |                               |     |       |        |
|      |                               |     |       |        |
|      |                               |     |       |        |

## GENERAL JOURNAL

| Date | Account Titles and Explanation | PR | Debit | Credit |
|------|-------------------------------|----|-------|--------|
|      |                               |    |       |        |
|      |                               |    |       |        |
|      |                               |    |       |        |
|      |                               |    |       |        |
|      |                               |    |       |        |
|      |                               |    |       |        |
|      |                               |    |       |        |
|      |                               |    |       |        |
|      |                               |    |       |        |
|      |                               |    |       |        |
|      |                               |    |       |        |
|      |                               |    |       |        |
|      |                               |    |       |        |
|      |                               |    |       |        |
|      |                               |    |       |        |
|      |                               |    |       |        |
|      |                               |    |       |        |
|      |                               |    |       |        |
|      |                               |    |       |        |
|      |                               |    |       |        |
|      |                               |    |       |        |
|      |                               |    |       |        |
|      |                               |    |       |        |
|      |                               |    |       |        |
|      |                               |    |       |        |

**Financial Statement Note(s):**

_____
_____
_____
_____

*Name*

## GENERAL JOURNAL

| Date | | Account Titles and Explanation | PR | Debit | Credit |
|---|---|---|---|---|---|
| | | | | | |
| | | | | | |
| | | | | | |
| | | | | | |
| | | | | | |
| | | | | | |
| | | | | | |
| | | | | | |
| | | | | | |
| | | | | | |
| | | | | | |
| | | | | | |

*Calculations:*

_____

_____

_____

_____

_____

_____

## *Exercise 10-17

### Part 1

Accounts Receivable Turnover          Days' Sales Uncollected

_____

_____

_____

_____

_____

_____

_____

### Part 2

_____

_____

_____

_____

_____

_____

_____

_____

_____

## GENERAL JOURNAL

| Date | Account Titles and Explanation | PR | Debit | Credit |
|------|-------------------------------|----|-------|--------|
|  |  |  |  |  |
|  |  |  |  |  |
|  |  |  |  |  |
|  |  |  |  |  |
|  |  |  |  |  |
|  |  |  |  |  |
|  |  |  |  |  |
|  |  |  |  |  |
|  |  |  |  |  |
|  |  |  |  |  |
|  |  |  |  |  |
|  |  |  |  |  |
|  |  |  |  |  |
|  |  |  |  |  |
|  |  |  |  |  |
|  |  |  |  |  |
|  |  |  |  |  |
|  |  |  |  |  |
|  |  |  |  |  |
|  |  |  |  |  |
|  |  |  |  |  |
|  |  |  |  |  |
|  |  |  |  |  |
|  |  |  |  |  |
|  |  |  |  |  |
|  |  |  |  |  |
|  |  |  |  |  |
|  |  |  |  |  |
|  |  |  |  |  |
|  |  |  |  |  |
|  |  |  |  |  |
|  |  |  |  |  |
|  |  |  |  |  |
|  |  |  |  |  |
|  |  |  |  |  |
|  |  |  |  |  |
|  |  |  |  |  |
|  |  |  |  |  |

## GENERAL JOURNAL

| Date | | Account Titles and Explanation | PR | Debit | Credit |
|---|---|---|---|---|---|
| | | | | | |
| | | | | | |
| | | | | | |
| | | | | | |
| | | | | | |
| | | | | | |
| | | | | | |
| | | | | | |

*Analysis component:*

| | Advantages | Disadvantages |
|---|---|---|
| a. bank credit cards | | |
| b. non-bank credit cards | | |
| c. debit cards | | |
| d. cash | | |

Chapter 10    Problem 10-2A          *Name*  _____

a. **Expense is 2% of credit sales:**

### GENERAL JOURNAL

| Date | Account Titles and Explanation | PR | Debit | Credit |
|------|-------------------------------|----|-------|--------|
|      |                               |    |       |        |
|      |                               |    |       |        |
|      |                               |    |       |        |
|      |                               |    |       |        |

b. **Allowance is 5% of accounts receivable:**

### GENERAL JOURNAL

| Date | Account Titles and Explanation | PR | Debit | Credit |
|------|-------------------------------|----|-------|--------|
|      |                               |    |       |        |
|      |                               |    |       |        |
|      |                               |    |       |        |

*Calculations for Part b:*

**Accounts Receivable**

## Part 2

|  |  |  |
|--|--|--|
|  |  |  |
|  |  |  |
|  |  |  |

## Part 3

|  |  |  |
|--|--|--|
|  |  |  |
|  |  |  |
|  |  |  |

*Analysis component:*

_____
_____
_____
_____
_____

Calculation of the required balance of the allowance (using an aging analysis):

_____
_____
_____
_____
_____
_____
_____

| Accounts Receivable | |
|---|---|
| | |
| | |
| | |

**Part 2**

## GENERAL JOURNAL

| Date | Account Titles and Explanation | PR | Debit | Credit |
|---|---|---|---|---|
| | | | | |
| | | | | |
| | | | | |
| | | | | |

*Analysis component:*

_____
_____
_____
_____
_____
_____

## GENERAL JOURNAL

| Date | Account Titles and Explanation | PR | Debit | Credit |
|------|-------------------------------|----|-------|--------|
|  |  |  |  |  |
|  |  |  |  |  |
|  |  |  |  |  |
|  |  |  |  |  |
|  |  |  |  |  |
|  |  |  |  |  |
|  |  |  |  |  |
|  |  |  |  |  |
|  |  |  |  |  |
|  |  |  |  |  |
|  |  |  |  |  |
|  |  |  |  |  |
|  |  |  |  |  |
|  |  |  |  |  |
|  |  |  |  |  |
|  |  |  |  |  |
|  |  |  |  |  |
|  |  |  |  |  |
|  |  |  |  |  |
|  |  |  |  |  |
|  |  |  |  |  |
|  |  |  |  |  |
|  |  |  |  |  |
|  |  |  |  |  |
|  |  |  |  |  |
|  |  |  |  |  |
|  |  |  |  |  |
|  |  |  |  |  |
|  |  |  |  |  |
|  |  |  |  |  |
|  |  |  |  |  |
|  |  |  |  |  |
|  |  |  |  |  |
|  |  |  |  |  |
|  |  |  |  |  |
|  |  |  |  |  |
|  |  |  |  |  |
|  |  |  |  |  |
|  |  |  |  |  |
|  |  |  |  |  |
|  |  |  |  |  |
|  |  |  |  |  |

Part 2

### GENERAL JOURNAL                                          Page____

| Date | Account Titles and Explanation | PR | Debit | Credit |
|------|-------------------------------|----|-------|--------|
|      |                               |    |       |        |
|      |                               |    |       |        |
|      |                               |    |       |        |
|      |                               |    |       |        |

Part 3

| | | | | |
|--|--|--|--|--|
|  |  |  |  |  |
|  |  |  |  |  |
|  |  |  |  |  |

Part 4

_____

Part 5

### GENERAL JOURNAL                                          Page____

| Date | Account Titles and Explanation | PR | Debit | Credit |
|------|-------------------------------|----|-------|--------|
|      |                               |    |       |        |
|      |                               |    |       |        |
|      |                               |    |       |        |
|      |                               |    |       |        |

*Calculations:*

| Accounts Receivable | Allowance for Doubtful Accounts |
|---------------------|---------------------------------|
|                     |                                 |

Part 6

| | | | | |
|--|--|--|--|--|
|  |  |  |  |  |
|  |  |  |  |  |
|  |  |  |  |  |

Part 7

_____

*Name* _____

## GENERAL JOURNAL

| Date | Account Titles and Explanation | PR | Debit | Credit |
|------|-------------------------------|----|-------|--------|
| 2011 | | | | |
| a. | | | | |
| | | | | |
| | | | | |
| | | | | |
| | | | | |
| | | | | |
| | | | | |
| | | | | |
| b. | | | | |
| | | | | |
| | | | | |
| | | | | |
| c. | | | | |
| | | | | |
| | | | | |
| | | | | |
| d. | | | | |
| | | | | |
| | | | | |
| | | | | |
| | | | | |

*Calculations:*

Accounts Receivable                    Allowance for Doubtful Accounts

## GENERAL JOURNAL

| Date | Account Titles and Explanation | PR | Debit | Credit |
|---|---|---|---|---|
| 2012 | | | | |
| e. | | | | |
| | | | | |
| | | | | |
| | | | | |
| | | | | |
| | | | | |
| | | | | |
| | | | | |
| | | | | |
| f. | | | | |
| | | | | |
| | | | | |
| | | | | |
| | | | | |
| g. | | | | |
| | | | | |
| | | | | |
| | | | | |
| h. | | | | |
| | | | | |
| | | | | |
| | | | | |
| | | | | |

*Calculations:*

|   Accounts Receivable   |   Allowance for Doubtful Accounts   |
|---|---|

Part a

## GENERAL JOURNAL

| Date | Account Titles and Explanation | PR | Debit | Credit |
|------|-------------------------------|----|-------|--------|
| 2011 | | | | |
| | | | | |
| | | | | |
| | | | | |
| | | | | |

### Allowance for Doubtful Accounts

Part b

| | | |
|---|---|---|
| | | |
| | | |
| | | |
| | | |

Part c

## GENERAL JOURNAL

| Date | Account Titles and Explanation | PR | Debit | Credit |
|------|-------------------------------|----|-------|--------|
| 2011 | | | | |
| | | | | |
| | | | | |
| | | | | |

*Calculations:*

### Allowance for Doubtful Accounts

Part d

| | | |
|---|---|---|
| | | |
| | | |
| | | |
| | | |

*Name* _____

## Part 1

### GENERAL JOURNAL

| Date | | Account Titles and Explanation | PR | Debit | Credit |
|---|---|---|---|---|---|
| | | | | | |
| | | | | | |
| | | | | | |
| | | | | | |

## Part 2

### GENERAL JOURNAL

| Date | | Account Titles and Explanation | PR | Debit | Credit |
|---|---|---|---|---|---|
| | | | | | |
| | | | | | |
| | | | | | |
| | | | | | |

*Calculations:*

| Accounts Receivable | Allowance for Doubtful Accounts |
|---|---|
| | |

## Problem 10-8A

a.

**Month**

| Customer | Not yet due<br>0.5% | 1 to 29 days past due<br>1% | 30 to 59 days past due<br>4% | 60 to 89 days past due<br>10% | 90 to 119 days past due<br>20% | Over 119 days past due<br>50% |
|---|---|---|---|---|---|---|
| B. Axley | | | | | | |
| T. Holton | | | | | | |
| W. Nix | | | | | | |
| C. Percy | | | | | | |
| K. Willis | | | | | | |
| | | | | | | |
| | | | | | | |
| | | | | | | |
| | | | | | | |

**b.** <center>**GENERAL JOURNAL**</center> Page____

| Date | Account Titles and Explanation | PR | Debit | Credit |
|------|-------------------------------|----|-------|--------|
|      |                               |    |       |        |
|      |                               |    |       |        |
|      |                               |    |       |        |
|      |                               |    |       |        |

*Calculations:*

| Accounts Receivable | Allowance for Doubtful Accounts |
|---------------------|--------------------------------|
|                     |                                |

**Problem 10-9A**

**a.** <center>**GENERAL JOURNAL**</center> Page____

| Date | Account Titles and Explanation | PR | Debit | Credit |
|------|-------------------------------|----|-------|--------|
| 2011 |                               |    |       |        |
|      |                               |    |       |        |
|      |                               |    |       |        |
|      |                               |    |       |        |
|      |                               |    |       |        |
| 2012 |                               |    |       |        |
|      |                               |    |       |        |
|      |                               |    |       |        |
|      |                               |    |       |        |
|      |                               |    |       |        |
| 2013 |                               |    |       |        |
|      |                               |    |       |        |
|      |                               |    |       |        |
|      |                               |    |       |        |
|      |                               |    |       |        |
|      |                               |    |       |        |

*Calculations:*

| Accounts Receivable | Allowance for Doubtful Accounts |
|---|---|
| | |

*Analysis component:* _____

_____

_____

_____

_____

_____

_____

## Problem 10-10A

### Parts a, b, and c.

| Date of Note | Principal | Interest Rate | Term | Maturity Date | Days of Accrued Interest at Dec. 31, 2011 | Accrued Interest at Dec. 31, 2011 |
|---|---|---|---|---|---|---|
| Nov. 1/10 | $120,000 | 7% | 180 days | | | |
| Jan. 5/11 | 50,000 | 8% | 90 days | | | |
| Nov. 20/11 | 45,000 | 10% | 45 days | | | |
| Dec. 10/11 | 60,000 | 12% | 30 days | | | |

*Calculations:*

_____

_____

_____

_____

_____

_____

_____

_____

_____

_____

_____

_____

_____

_____

_____

**d.**                          GENERAL JOURNAL                          Page____

| Date | Account Titles and Explanation | PR | Debit | Credit |
|------|-------------------------------|----|-------|--------|
|      |                               |    |       |        |
|      |                               |    |       |        |
|      |                               |    |       |        |
|      |                               |    |       |        |

**e.**                          GENERAL JOURNAL                          Page____

| Date | Account Titles and Explanation | PR | Debit | Credit |
|------|-------------------------------|----|-------|--------|
|      |                               |    |       |        |
|      |                               |    |       |        |
|      |                               |    |       |        |
|      |                               |    |       |        |
|      |                               |    |       |        |

**Problem 10-11A**

**a.**                          GENERAL JOURNAL                          Page____

| Date | Account Titles and Explanation | PR | Debit | Credit |
|------|-------------------------------|----|-------|--------|
|      |                               |    |       |        |
|      |                               |    |       |        |
|      |                               |    |       |        |
|      |                               |    |       |        |
|      |                               |    |       |        |
|      |                               |    |       |        |
|      |                               |    |       |        |
|      |                               |    |       |        |
|      |                               |    |       |        |
|      |                               |    |       |        |
|      |                               |    |       |        |
|      |                               |    |       |        |
|      |                               |    |       |        |
|      |                               |    |       |        |
|      |                               |    |       |        |
|      |                               |    |       |        |
|      |                               |    |       |        |
|      |                               |    |       |        |
|      |                               |    |       |        |
|      |                               |    |       |        |

### GENERAL JOURNAL                                    Page____

| Date | Account Titles and Explanation | PR | Debit | Credit |
|------|-------------------------------|----|-------|--------|
|      |                               |    |       |        |
|      |                               |    |       |        |
|      |                               |    |       |        |
|      |                               |    |       |        |
|      |                               |    |       |        |
|      |                               |    |       |        |
|      |                               |    |       |        |
|      |                               |    |       |        |
|      |                               |    |       |        |
|      |                               |    |       |        |
|      |                               |    |       |        |
|      |                               |    |       |        |
|      |                               |    |       |        |
|      |                               |    |       |        |
|      |                               |    |       |        |
|      |                               |    |       |        |
|      |                               |    |       |        |
|      |                               |    |       |        |

b.  Determine the maturity date of the note dated March 2:

_____
_____
_____
_____
_____
_____

Prepare the entry on the maturity date:

### GENERAL JOURNAL                                    Page____

| Date | Account Titles and Explanation | PR | Debit | Credit |
|------|-------------------------------|----|-------|--------|
|      |                               |    |       |        |
|      |                               |    |       |        |
|      |                               |    |       |        |
|      |                               |    |       |        |
|      |                               |    |       |        |

## GENERAL JOURNAL                                    Page____

| Date | Account Titles and Explanation | PR | Debit | Credit |
|------|-------------------------------|----|----|----|
|  |  |  |  |  |
|  |  |  |  |  |
|  |  |  |  |  |
|  |  |  |  |  |
|  |  |  |  |  |
|  |  |  |  |  |
|  |  |  |  |  |
|  |  |  |  |  |
|  |  |  |  |  |
|  |  |  |  |  |
|  |  |  |  |  |
|  |  |  |  |  |
|  |  |  |  |  |
|  |  |  |  |  |
|  |  |  |  |  |
|  |  |  |  |  |
|  |  |  |  |  |
|  |  |  |  |  |
|  |  |  |  |  |
|  |  |  |  |  |
|  |  |  |  |  |
|  |  |  |  |  |
|  |  |  |  |  |
|  |  |  |  |  |
|  |  |  |  |  |
|  |  |  |  |  |
|  |  |  |  |  |
|  |  |  |  |  |
|  |  |  |  |  |
|  |  |  |  |  |
|  |  |  |  |  |
|  |  |  |  |  |
|  |  |  |  |  |
|  |  |  |  |  |
|  |  |  |  |  |
|  |  |  |  |  |

Analysis component: _____
_____
_____
_____
_____
_____

**Preparation component:**

## GENERAL JOURNAL                                    Page____

| Date | Account Titles and Explanation | PR | Debit | Credit |
|------|-------------------------------|----|----|----|
|  |  |  |  |  |
|  |  |  |  |  |
|  |  |  |  |  |
|  |  |  |  |  |
|  |  |  |  |  |
|  |  |  |  |  |
|  |  |  |  |  |
|  |  |  |  |  |
|  |  |  |  |  |
|  |  |  |  |  |
|  |  |  |  |  |
|  |  |  |  |  |
|  |  |  |  |  |
|  |  |  |  |  |
|  |  |  |  |  |
|  |  |  |  |  |
|  |  |  |  |  |
|  |  |  |  |  |
|  |  |  |  |  |
|  |  |  |  |  |
|  |  |  |  |  |
|  |  |  |  |  |
|  |  |  |  |  |
|  |  |  |  |  |
|  |  |  |  |  |
|  |  |  |  |  |
|  |  |  |  |  |
|  |  |  |  |  |
|  |  |  |  |  |
|  |  |  |  |  |
|  |  |  |  |  |
|  |  |  |  |  |
|  |  |  |  |  |

**Analysis component:** _____
_____
_____
_____
_____
_____

## GENERAL JOURNAL                                                    Page____

| Date | Account Titles and Explanation | PR | Debit | Credit |
|------|-------------------------------|----|-------|--------|
|      |                               |    |       |        |
|      |                               |    |       |        |
|      |                               |    |       |        |
|      |                               |    |       |        |
|      |                               |    |       |        |
|      |                               |    |       |        |
|      |                               |    |       |        |
|      |                               |    |       |        |
|      |                               |    |       |        |
|      |                               |    |       |        |
|      |                               |    |       |        |
|      |                               |    |       |        |
|      |                               |    |       |        |
|      |                               |    |       |        |
|      |                               |    |       |        |
|      |                               |    |       |        |
|      |                               |    |       |        |
|      |                               |    |       |        |
|      |                               |    |       |        |
|      |                               |    |       |        |
|      |                               |    |       |        |
|      |                               |    |       |        |
|      |                               |    |       |        |
|      |                               |    |       |        |
|      |                               |    |       |        |
|      |                               |    |       |        |
|      |                               |    |       |        |
|      |                               |    |       |        |
|      |                               |    |       |        |
|      |                               |    |       |        |
|      |                               |    |       |        |
|      |                               |    |       |        |
|      |                               |    |       |        |
|      |                               |    |       |        |
|      |                               |    |       |        |
|      |                               |    |       |        |
|      |                               |    |       |        |
|      |                               |    |       |        |
|      |                               |    |       |        |
|      |                               |    |       |        |
|      |                               |    |       |        |

## GENERAL JOURNAL

| Date | Account Titles and Explanation | PR | Debit | Credit |
|---|---|---|---|---|
|  |  |  |  |  |
|  |  |  |  |  |
|  |  |  |  |  |
|  |  |  |  |  |
|  |  |  |  |  |
|  |  |  |  |  |
|  |  |  |  |  |
|  |  |  |  |  |
|  |  |  |  |  |
|  |  |  |  |  |
|  |  |  |  |  |
|  |  |  |  |  |
|  |  |  |  |  |
|  |  |  |  |  |
|  |  |  |  |  |
|  |  |  |  |  |
|  |  |  |  |  |
|  |  |  |  |  |
|  |  |  |  |  |
|  |  |  |  |  |
|  |  |  |  |  |
|  |  |  |  |  |
|  |  |  |  |  |
|  |  |  |  |  |
|  |  |  |  |  |
|  |  |  |  |  |
|  |  |  |  |  |
|  |  |  |  |  |
|  |  |  |  |  |
|  |  |  |  |  |
|  |  |  |  |  |
|  |  |  |  |  |
|  |  |  |  |  |
|  |  |  |  |  |
|  |  |  |  |  |
|  |  |  |  |  |
|  |  |  |  |  |
|  |  |  |  |  |
|  |  |  |  |  |

## GENERAL JOURNAL

| Date | Account Titles and Explanation | PR | Debit | Credit |
|------|-------------------------------|----|----|----|
|  |  |  |  |  |
|  |  |  |  |  |
|  |  |  |  |  |
|  |  |  |  |  |
|  |  |  |  |  |
|  |  |  |  |  |
|  |  |  |  |  |
|  |  |  |  |  |
|  |  |  |  |  |
|  |  |  |  |  |
|  |  |  |  |  |
|  |  |  |  |  |
|  |  |  |  |  |
|  |  |  |  |  |
|  |  |  |  |  |
|  |  |  |  |  |
|  |  |  |  |  |
|  |  |  |  |  |
|  |  |  |  |  |
|  |  |  |  |  |
|  |  |  |  |  |
|  |  |  |  |  |
|  |  |  |  |  |
|  |  |  |  |  |
|  |  |  |  |  |
|  |  |  |  |  |
|  |  |  |  |  |
|  |  |  |  |  |
|  |  |  |  |  |
|  |  |  |  |  |
|  |  |  |  |  |
|  |  |  |  |  |
|  |  |  |  |  |
|  |  |  |  |  |
|  |  |  |  |  |
|  |  |  |  |  |
|  |  |  |  |  |
|  |  |  |  |  |
|  |  |  |  |  |
|  |  |  |  |  |

## GENERAL JOURNAL

| Date | | Account Titles and Explanation | PR | Debit | Credit |
|---|---|---|---|---|---|
|  |  |  |  |  |  |
|  |  |  |  |  |  |
|  |  |  |  |  |  |
|  |  |  |  |  |  |
|  |  |  |  |  |  |
|  |  |  |  |  |  |
|  |  |  |  |  |  |
|  |  |  |  |  |  |

*Analysis component:*

|  | Advantages | Disadvantages |
|---|---|---|
| a.  cash |  |  |
| b.  debit cards |  |  |
| c.  credit cards |  |  |
| d.  cheques |  |  |

*Name*  _____

## a. Expense is 2.5% of credit sales:

### GENERAL JOURNAL

| Date | Account Titles and Explanation | PR | Debit | Credit |
|---|---|---|---|---|
|  |  |  |  |  |
|  |  |  |  |  |
|  |  |  |  |  |

## b. Allowance is 6% of accounts receivable:

### GENERAL JOURNAL

| Date | Account Titles and Explanation | PR | Debit | Credit |
|---|---|---|---|---|
|  |  |  |  |  |
|  |  |  |  |  |
|  |  |  |  |  |

*Calculations for Part b:*

### Accounts Receivable

## Part 2

|  |  |  |
|---|---|---|
|  |  |  |
|  |  |  |
|  |  |  |

## Part 3

|  |  |  |
|---|---|---|
|  |  |  |
|  |  |  |
|  |  |  |

*Analysis component:* _____

_____

_____

_____

_____

_____

**Calculation of the required balance of the allowance (using an aging analysis):**

_____
_____
_____
_____
_____
_____
_____

**Accounts Receivable**

**Part 2**

## GENERAL JOURNAL

| Date | Account Titles and Explanation | PR | Debit | Credit |
|------|-------------------------------|-----|-------|--------|
|      |                               |     |       |        |
|      |                               |     |       |        |
|      |                               |     |       |        |
|      |                               |     |       |        |

*Analysis component:*

_____
_____
_____
_____
_____
_____

## GENERAL JOURNAL

| Date | Account Titles and Explanation | PR | Debit | Credit |
|------|-------------------------------|----|-------|--------|
|      |                               |    |       |        |
|      |                               |    |       |        |
|      |                               |    |       |        |
|      |                               |    |       |        |
|      |                               |    |       |        |
|      |                               |    |       |        |
|      |                               |    |       |        |
|      |                               |    |       |        |
|      |                               |    |       |        |
|      |                               |    |       |        |
|      |                               |    |       |        |
|      |                               |    |       |        |
|      |                               |    |       |        |
|      |                               |    |       |        |
|      |                               |    |       |        |
|      |                               |    |       |        |
|      |                               |    |       |        |
|      |                               |    |       |        |
|      |                               |    |       |        |
|      |                               |    |       |        |
|      |                               |    |       |        |
|      |                               |    |       |        |
|      |                               |    |       |        |
|      |                               |    |       |        |
|      |                               |    |       |        |
|      |                               |    |       |        |
|      |                               |    |       |        |
|      |                               |    |       |        |
|      |                               |    |       |        |
|      |                               |    |       |        |
|      |                               |    |       |        |
|      |                               |    |       |        |
|      |                               |    |       |        |
|      |                               |    |       |        |
|      |                               |    |       |        |
|      |                               |    |       |        |
|      |                               |    |       |        |
|      |                               |    |       |        |
|      |                               |    |       |        |

Part 2

### GENERAL JOURNAL                                      Page____

| Date | Account Titles and Explanation | PR | Debit | Credit |
|------|-------------------------------|----|-------|--------|
|      |                               |    |       |        |
|      |                               |    |       |        |
|      |                               |    |       |        |
|      |                               |    |       |        |

Part 3

| | | | | |
|---|---|---|---|---|
|   |   |   |   |   |
|   |   |   |   |   |
|   |   |   |   |   |
|   |   |   |   |   |

Part 4

_____

_____

Part 5

### GENERAL JOURNAL                                      Page____

| Date | Account Titles and Explanation | PR | Debit | Credit |
|------|-------------------------------|----|-------|--------|
|      |                               |    |       |        |
|      |                               |    |       |        |
|      |                               |    |       |        |
|      |                               |    |       |        |

*Calculations:*

| Accounts Receivable | Allowance for Doubtful Accounts |
|---------------------|---------------------------------|
|                     |                                 |

Part 6

| | | | |
|---|---|---|---|
|   |   |   |   |
|   |   |   |   |
|   |   |   |   |
|   |   |   |   |

Part 7

_____

_____

Name _____

## GENERAL JOURNAL

| Date | Account Titles and Explanation | PR | Debit | Credit |
|------|-------------------------------|-----|-------|--------|
| 2011 | | | | |
| a. | | | | |
| | | | | |
| | | | | |
| | | | | |
| | | | | |
| | | | | |
| | | | | |
| | | | | |
| b. | | | | |
| | | | | |
| | | | | |
| | | | | |
| c. | | | | |
| | | | | |
| | | | | |
| | | | | |
| d. | | | | |
| | | | | |
| | | | | |
| | | | | |
| | | | | |

*Calculations:*

| Accounts Receivable | Allowance for Doubtful Accounts |
|---------------------|----------------------------------|
| | |

*Name* _____

## GENERAL JOURNAL

| Date | Account Titles and Explanation | PR | Debit | Credit |
|------|-------------------------------|----|-------|--------|
| 2012 | | | | |
| e. | | | | |
| | | | | |
| | | | | |
| | | | | |
| | | | | |
| | | | | |
| | | | | |
| | | | | |
| f. | | | | |
| | | | | |
| | | | | |
| | | | | |
| g. | | | | |
| | | | | |
| | | | | |
| | | | | |
| h. | | | | |
| | | | | |
| | | | | |
| | | | | |
| | | | | |

*Calculations:*

**Accounts Receivable** _____        **Allowance for Doubtful Accounts** _____

**Name** _____

**Part a**

### GENERAL JOURNAL

| Date | Account Titles and Explanation | PR | Debit | Credit |
|------|-------------------------------|----|-------|--------|
| 2011 | | | | |
| | | | | |
| | | | | |
| | | | | |
| | | | | |

**Allowance for Doubtful Accounts**

**Part b**

| | | |
|--|--|--|
| | | |
| | | |
| | | |
| | | |

**Part c**

### GENERAL JOURNAL

| Date | Account Titles and Explanation | PR | Debit | Credit |
|------|-------------------------------|----|-------|--------|
| 2011 | | | | |
| | | | | |
| | | | | |
| | | | | |

*Calculations:*

**Allowance for Doubtful Accounts**

**Part d**

| | | |
|--|--|--|
| | | |
| | | |
| | | |
| | | |

Part 1

## GENERAL JOURNAL

| Date | Account Titles and Explanation | PR | Debit | Credit |
|------|-------------------------------|----|-------|--------|
|      |                               |    |       |        |
|      |                               |    |       |        |
|      |                               |    |       |        |
|      |                               |    |       |        |

Part 2

## GENERAL JOURNAL

| Date | Account Titles and Explanation | PR | Debit | Credit |
|------|-------------------------------|----|-------|--------|
|      |                               |    |       |        |
|      |                               |    |       |        |
|      |                               |    |       |        |
|      |                               |    |       |        |

*Calculations:*

| Accounts Receivable | Allowance for Doubtful Accounts |
|---------------------|----------------------------------|
|                     |                                  |

### Problem 10-8B

a.

Month

| Customer | Not yet due 1% | 1 to 29 days past due 2% | 30 to 59 days past due 5% | 60 to 89 days past due 20% | 90 to 119 days past due 35% | Over 119 days past due 50% |
|----------|----------------|--------------------------|---------------------------|----------------------------|-----------------------------|----------------------------|
| A. Leslie |  |  |  |  |  |  |
| T. Meston |  |  |  |  |  |  |
| P. Obrian |  |  |  |  |  |  |
| L. Timms |  |  |  |  |  |  |
| W. Victor |  |  |  |  |  |  |
|  |  |  |  |  |  |  |
|  |  |  |  |  |  |  |
|  |  |  |  |  |  |  |
|  |  |  |  |  |  |  |

**b.**                          **GENERAL JOURNAL**                          Page____

| Date | Account Titles and Explanation | PR | Debit | Credit |
|------|-------------------------------|----|-------|--------|
|      |                               |    |       |        |
|      |                               |    |       |        |
|      |                               |    |       |        |
|      |                               |    |       |        |

*Calculations:*

| Accounts Receivable | | Allowance for Doubtful Accounts | |
|---|---|---|---|
| | | | |

**Problem 10-9B**

**a.**                          **GENERAL JOURNAL**                          Page____

| Date | Account Titles and Explanation | PR | Debit | Credit |
|------|-------------------------------|----|-------|--------|
| 2011 |                               |    |       |        |
|      |                               |    |       |        |
|      |                               |    |       |        |
|      |                               |    |       |        |
|      |                               |    |       |        |
| 2012 |                               |    |       |        |
|      |                               |    |       |        |
|      |                               |    |       |        |
|      |                               |    |       |        |
|      |                               |    |       |        |
| 2013 |                               |    |       |        |
|      |                               |    |       |        |
|      |                               |    |       |        |
|      |                               |    |       |        |
|      |                               |    |       |        |
|      |                               |    |       |        |

*Calculations:*

| Accounts Receivable | Allowance for Doubtful Accounts |
|---|---|
| | |

*Analysis component:* _____

_____

_____

_____

_____

_____

_____

## Problem 10-10B

Parts a, b, and c.

| Date of Note | Principal | Interest Rate | Term | Maturity Date | Days of Accrued Interest at Dec. 31, 2011 | Accrued Interest at Dec. 31, 2011 |
|---|---|---|---|---|---|---|
| Sept. 20/10 | $245,000 | 7% | 120 days | | | |
| June 01/11 | 120,000 | 9% | 45 days | | | |
| Nov. 23/11 | 82,000 | 9% | 90 days | | | |
| Dec. 18/11 | 60,000 | 10% | 30 days | | | |

*Calculations:*

_____

_____

_____

_____

_____

_____

_____

_____

_____

_____

_____

_____

_____

_____

_____

d.                                    GENERAL JOURNAL                          Page____

| Date | Account Titles and Explanation | PR | Debit | Credit |
|------|-------------------------------|-----|-------|--------|
|      |                               |     |       |        |
|      |                               |     |       |        |
|      |                               |     |       |        |
|      |                               |     |       |        |

e.                                    GENERAL JOURNAL                          Page____

| Date | Account Titles and Explanation | PR | Debit | Credit |
|------|-------------------------------|-----|-------|--------|
|      |                               |     |       |        |
|      |                               |     |       |        |
|      |                               |     |       |        |
|      |                               |     |       |        |
|      |                               |     |       |        |

## Problem 10-11B

a.                                    GENERAL JOURNAL                          Page____

| Date | Account Titles and Explanation | PR | Debit | Credit |
|------|-------------------------------|-----|-------|--------|
|      |                               |     |       |        |
|      |                               |     |       |        |
|      |                               |     |       |        |
|      |                               |     |       |        |
|      |                               |     |       |        |
|      |                               |     |       |        |
|      |                               |     |       |        |
|      |                               |     |       |        |
|      |                               |     |       |        |
|      |                               |     |       |        |
|      |                               |     |       |        |
|      |                               |     |       |        |
|      |                               |     |       |        |
|      |                               |     |       |        |
|      |                               |     |       |        |
|      |                               |     |       |        |
|      |                               |     |       |        |
|      |                               |     |       |        |
|      |                               |     |       |        |
|      |                               |     |       |        |

## GENERAL JOURNAL                                    Page____

| Date | Account Titles and Explanation | PR | Debit | Credit |
|------|-------------------------------|----|----|--------|
|  |  |  |  |  |
|  |  |  |  |  |
|  |  |  |  |  |
|  |  |  |  |  |
|  |  |  |  |  |
|  |  |  |  |  |
|  |  |  |  |  |
|  |  |  |  |  |
|  |  |  |  |  |
|  |  |  |  |  |
|  |  |  |  |  |
|  |  |  |  |  |
|  |  |  |  |  |
|  |  |  |  |  |
|  |  |  |  |  |
|  |  |  |  |  |
|  |  |  |  |  |
|  |  |  |  |  |
|  |  |  |  |  |
|  |  |  |  |  |
|  |  |  |  |  |

**b. Determine the maturity date of the note dated March 1:**

_____

_____

_____

_____

_____

_____

**Prepare the entry on the maturity date:**

## GENERAL JOURNAL                                    Page____

| Date | Account Titles and Explanation | PR | Debit | Credit |
|------|-------------------------------|----|----|--------|
|  |  |  |  |  |
|  |  |  |  |  |
|  |  |  |  |  |
|  |  |  |  |  |
|  |  |  |  |  |
|  |  |  |  |  |

## GENERAL JOURNAL                                    Page____

| Date | Account Titles and Explanation | PR | Debit | Credit |
|------|-------------------------------|----|-------|--------|
|      |                               |    |       |        |
|      |                               |    |       |        |
|      |                               |    |       |        |
|      |                               |    |       |        |
|      |                               |    |       |        |
|      |                               |    |       |        |
|      |                               |    |       |        |
|      |                               |    |       |        |
|      |                               |    |       |        |
|      |                               |    |       |        |
|      |                               |    |       |        |
|      |                               |    |       |        |
|      |                               |    |       |        |
|      |                               |    |       |        |
|      |                               |    |       |        |
|      |                               |    |       |        |
|      |                               |    |       |        |
|      |                               |    |       |        |
|      |                               |    |       |        |
|      |                               |    |       |        |
|      |                               |    |       |        |
|      |                               |    |       |        |
|      |                               |    |       |        |
|      |                               |    |       |        |
|      |                               |    |       |        |
|      |                               |    |       |        |
|      |                               |    |       |        |
|      |                               |    |       |        |
|      |                               |    |       |        |
|      |                               |    |       |        |
|      |                               |    |       |        |
|      |                               |    |       |        |
|      |                               |    |       |        |
|      |                               |    |       |        |
|      |                               |    |       |        |
|      |                               |    |       |        |
|      |                               |    |       |        |
|      |                               |    |       |        |

**Analysis component:** _____
_____
_____
_____
_____
_____

**Preparation component:**

## GENERAL JOURNAL                                    Page____

| Date | Account Titles and Explanation | PR | Debit | Credit |
|------|-------------------------------|----|----|----|
|  |  |  |  |  |
|  |  |  |  |  |
|  |  |  |  |  |
|  |  |  |  |  |
|  |  |  |  |  |
|  |  |  |  |  |
|  |  |  |  |  |
|  |  |  |  |  |
|  |  |  |  |  |
|  |  |  |  |  |
|  |  |  |  |  |
|  |  |  |  |  |
|  |  |  |  |  |
|  |  |  |  |  |
|  |  |  |  |  |
|  |  |  |  |  |
|  |  |  |  |  |
|  |  |  |  |  |
|  |  |  |  |  |
|  |  |  |  |  |
|  |  |  |  |  |
|  |  |  |  |  |
|  |  |  |  |  |
|  |  |  |  |  |
|  |  |  |  |  |
|  |  |  |  |  |
|  |  |  |  |  |
|  |  |  |  |  |
|  |  |  |  |  |
|  |  |  |  |  |
|  |  |  |  |  |
|  |  |  |  |  |
|  |  |  |  |  |
|  |  |  |  |  |
|  |  |  |  |  |
|  |  |  |  |  |

**Analysis component:** _____

_____

_____

_____

_____

_____

## GENERAL JOURNAL                                    Page____

| Date | Account Titles and Explanation | PR | Debit | Credit |
|------|-------------------------------|----|-------|--------|
|      |                               |    |       |        |
|      |                               |    |       |        |
|      |                               |    |       |        |
|      |                               |    |       |        |
|      |                               |    |       |        |
|      |                               |    |       |        |
|      |                               |    |       |        |
|      |                               |    |       |        |
|      |                               |    |       |        |
|      |                               |    |       |        |
|      |                               |    |       |        |
|      |                               |    |       |        |
|      |                               |    |       |        |
|      |                               |    |       |        |
|      |                               |    |       |        |
|      |                               |    |       |        |
|      |                               |    |       |        |
|      |                               |    |       |        |
|      |                               |    |       |        |
|      |                               |    |       |        |
|      |                               |    |       |        |
|      |                               |    |       |        |
|      |                               |    |       |        |
|      |                               |    |       |        |
|      |                               |    |       |        |
|      |                               |    |       |        |
|      |                               |    |       |        |
|      |                               |    |       |        |
|      |                               |    |       |        |
|      |                               |    |       |        |
|      |                               |    |       |        |
|      |                               |    |       |        |
|      |                               |    |       |        |
|      |                               |    |       |        |
|      |                               |    |       |        |
|      |                               |    |       |        |
|      |                               |    |       |        |
|      |                               |    |       |        |
|      |                               |    |       |        |
|      |                               |    |       |        |
|      |                               |    |       |        |

## GENERAL JOURNAL

| Date | Account Titles and Explanation | PR | Debit | Credit |
|------|-------------------------------|----|-------|--------|
|      |                               |    |       |        |
|      |                               |    |       |        |
|      |                               |    |       |        |
|      |                               |    |       |        |
|      |                               |    |       |        |
|      |                               |    |       |        |
|      |                               |    |       |        |
|      |                               |    |       |        |
|      |                               |    |       |        |
|      |                               |    |       |        |
|      |                               |    |       |        |
|      |                               |    |       |        |
|      |                               |    |       |        |
|      |                               |    |       |        |
|      |                               |    |       |        |
|      |                               |    |       |        |
|      |                               |    |       |        |
|      |                               |    |       |        |
|      |                               |    |       |        |
|      |                               |    |       |        |
|      |                               |    |       |        |
|      |                               |    |       |        |
|      |                               |    |       |        |
|      |                               |    |       |        |
|      |                               |    |       |        |
|      |                               |    |       |        |
|      |                               |    |       |        |
|      |                               |    |       |        |
|      |                               |    |       |        |
|      |                               |    |       |        |
|      |                               |    |       |        |
|      |                               |    |       |        |
|      |                               |    |       |        |
|      |                               |    |       |        |
|      |                               |    |       |        |
|      |                               |    |       |        |
|      |                               |    |       |        |

_____
_____
_____
_____
_____
_____
_____
_____

## Quick Study 11-2

### GENERAL JOURNAL

| Date | Account Titles and Explanation | PR | Debit | Credit |
|------|-------------------------------|-----|-------|--------|
|      |                               |     |       |        |
|      |                               |     |       |        |
|      |                               |     |       |        |
|      |                               |     |       |        |
|      |                               |     |       |        |
|      |                               |     |       |        |
|      |                               |     |       |        |
|      |                               |     |       |        |

## Quick Study 11-3

### GENERAL JOURNAL

| Date | Account Titles and Explanation | PR | Debit | Credit |
|------|-------------------------------|-----|-------|--------|
|      |                               |     |       |        |
|      |                               |     |       |        |
|      |                               |     |       |        |
|      |                               |     |       |        |
|      |                               |     |       |        |

## Quick Study 11-4

| Employee | Gross Pay | EI Premium | Taxes | CPP | Deductions Total | Net Pay | Office Salaries | Sales Salaries |
|----------|-----------|-----------|-------|------|------------------|---------|-----------------|----------------|
|          |           | **Deductions** | | | | **Pay** | **Distribution** | |
| Johnson, S. | 1,200.00 | 22.44 | 298.70 | 56.07 | | | | |
| Waverley, N. | 530.00 | 9.91 | 85.30 | 22.90 | | | | |
| Zender, B. | 675.00 | 12.62 | 120.20 | 30.08 | | | | |
| Totals | 2,405.00 | 44.97 | 504.20 | 109.05 | | | | |

| Employee | Gross Pay | Deductions | | | | Pay | Salaries Expense |
| | | EI Premium | Taxes | CPP | Deductions Total | Net Pay | |
|---|---|---|---|---|---|---|---|
| Bentley, A. | 2,010.00 | | | | | | |
| Craig, T. | 2,115.00 | | | | | | |
| Totals | 4,125.00 | | | | | | |

## Quick Study 11-6

| Employee | Gross Pay | Deductions | | | | Pay | Distribution | |
| | | EI Premium | Income Taxes | CPP | Total Deductions | Net Pay | Office Salaries | Sales Salaries |
|---|---|---|---|---|---|---|---|---|
| Withers, S. | 2,500.00 | | | | | | 2,500.00 | |
| Volt. C. | 1,800.00 | | | | | | | 1,800.00 |
| Totals | | | | | | | | |

*Calculations:*

_____
_____
_____
_____
_____
_____
_____
_____
_____

## Quick Study 11-7

**GENERAL JOURNAL**                              Page____

| Date | Account Titles and Explanation | PR | Debit | Credit |
|---|---|---|---|---|
| | | | | |
| | | | | |
| | | | | |
| | | | | |
| | | | | |
| | | | | |
| | | | | |
| | | | | |
| | | | | |

## GENERAL JOURNAL

| Date | Account Titles and Explanation | PR | Debit | Credit |
|------|-------------------------------|----|-------|--------|
|  |  |  |  |  |
|  |  |  |  |  |
|  |  |  |  |  |
|  |  |  |  |  |
|  |  |  |  |  |
|  |  |  |  |  |
|  |  |  |  |  |
|  |  |  |  |  |
|  |  |  |  |  |
|  |  |  |  |  |

## Quick Study 11-9

## GENERAL JOURNAL

| Date | Account Titles and Explanation | PR | Debit | Credit |
|------|-------------------------------|----|-------|--------|
|  |  |  |  |  |
|  |  |  |  |  |
|  |  |  |  |  |
|  |  |  |  |  |
|  |  |  |  |  |
|  |  |  |  |  |
|  |  |  |  |  |
|  |  |  |  |  |
|  |  |  |  |  |
|  |  |  |  |  |

## Quick Study 11-10

## GENERAL JOURNAL

| Date | Account Titles and Explanation | PR | Debit | Credit |
|------|-------------------------------|----|-------|--------|
|  |  |  |  |  |
|  |  |  |  |  |
|  |  |  |  |  |
|  |  |  |  |  |
|  |  |  |  |  |
|  |  |  |  |  |
|  |  |  |  |  |
|  |  |  |  |  |
|  |  |  |  |  |
|  |  |  |  |  |

## GENERAL JOURNAL

| Date | Account Titles and Explanation | PR | Debit | Credit |
|------|-------------------------------|----|-------|--------|
|      |                               |    |       |        |
|      |                               |    |       |        |
|      |                               |    |       |        |
|      |                               |    |       |        |
|      |                               |    |       |        |
|      |                               |    |       |        |
|      |                               |    |       |        |
|      |                               |    |       |        |

## Exercise 11-1

|  |  |  |
|--|--|--|
|  |  |  |
|  |  |  |
|  |  |  |
|  |  |  |
|  |  |  |
|  |  |  |
|  |  |  |
|  |  |  |
|  |  |  |
|  |  |  |
|  |  |  |
|  |  |  |

## Exercise 11-2

| Employee | Gross Pay | EI Premium | Income Taxes | CPP | Health Insurance | Total Deductions | Net Pay |
|----------|-----------|------------|--------------|-----|------------------|------------------|---------|
| H. Chea | 720.00 | | 133.55 | | 24.00 | | |
| J. Lim | | | 104.65 | | 24.00 | | |
| D. Patelli | 2,500.00 | | 169.70 | | 24.00 | | |
| S. Qulnata | 1,800.00 | | 486.90 | | 24.00 | | |
| Totals | 3,860.00 | | 894.80 | | 108.00 | | |

*Calculations:*

_____
_____
_____
_____
_____
_____
_____
_____

## GENERAL JOURNAL

| Date | Account Titles and Explanation | PR | Debit | Credit |
|---|---|---|---|---|
| | | | | |
| | | | | |
| | | | | |
| | | | | |
| | | | | |
| | | | | |
| | | | | |
| | | | | |
| | | | | |

## Exercise 11-3

| Employee | Gross Pay | EI Prem. | Income Taxes | United Way | CPP | Total Deductions | Net Pay | Admin. Salaries | Sales Salaries |
|---|---|---|---|---|---|---|---|---|---|
| | | | Deductions | | | | Pay | Distribution | |
| Akerley, D. | 1,900.00 | 35.53 | 421.65 | 80.00 | 87.39 | | | | |
| Nesbitt, M. | 1,260.00 | 23.56 | 218.60 | 50.00 | 55.71 | | | | |
| Trent, F. | 1,680.00 | 31.42 | 348.35 | 40.00 | 76.50 | | | | |
| Vacon, M. | 3,000.00 | 56.10 | 815.00 | 300.00 | 141.84 | | | | |
| Totals | 7,840.00 | 146.61 | 1803.60 | 470.00 | 361.44 | | | | |

## Exercise 11-4

| Employee | Gross Pay | EI Prem. | Income Taxes | Canada Savings Bonds | CPP | United Way | Total Deductions | Net Pay | Office Salaries | Sales Salaries |
|---|---|---|---|---|---|---|---|---|---|---|
| | | | | Deductions | | | | Payment | Distribution | |
| Crimson | 1,995.00 | | | | | | | | 1,995.00 | |
| Long | 2,040.00 | | | | | | | | | 2,040.00 |
| Morris | 2,000.00 | | | | | | | | | 2,000.00 |
| Peterson | 2,280.00 | | | | | | | | | 2,280.00 |
| Totals | | | | | | | | | | |

*Name* _____

| Employee | Gross Pay | Deductions | | | | | | Payment | Distribution | |
| | | EI Prem. | Income Taxes | Medical Ins. | CPP | United Way | Total Deductions | Net Pay | Office Salaries | Guide Salaries |
|---|---|---|---|---|---|---|---|---|---|---|
| Crimson | 1,995.00 | | | 65.00 | | 40.00 | | | | 1,995.00 |
| Long | 2,040.00 | | | 65.00 | | 100.00 | | | 2,040.00 | |
| Morris | 2,000.00 | | | 65.00 | | 0 | | | | 2,000.00 |
| Peterson | 2,350.00 | | | 65.00 | | 50.00 | | | | 2,350.00 |
| Totals | | | | | | | | | | |

*Calculations:*

_____
_____
_____
_____
_____
_____
_____
_____
_____
_____

## Exercise 11-6

| | | |
|---|---|---|
| | | |
| | | |
| | | |
| | | |
| | | |
| | | |
| | | |
| | | |
| | | |

## GENERAL JOURNAL

| Date | Account Titles and Explanation | PR | Debit | Credit |
|---|---|---|---|---|
| | | | | |
| | | | | |
| | | | | |
| | | | | |
| | | | | |
| | | | | |
| | | | | |

## GENERAL JOURNAL

| Date | Account Titles and Explanation | PR | Debit | Credit |
|------|-------------------------------|-----|-------|--------|
|      |                               |     |       |        |
|      |                               |     |       |        |
|      |                               |     |       |        |
|      |                               |     |       |        |
|      |                               |     |       |        |
|      |                               |     |       |        |
|      |                               |     |       |        |
|      |                               |     |       |        |
|      |                               |     |       |        |
|      |                               |     |       |        |
|      |                               |     |       |        |

## Exercise 11-8

## GENERAL JOURNAL

| Date | Account Titles and Explanation | PR | Debit | Credit |
|------|-------------------------------|-----|-------|--------|
|      |                               |     |       |        |
|      |                               |     |       |        |
|      |                               |     |       |        |
|      |                               |     |       |        |
|      |                               |     |       |        |
|      |                               |     |       |        |
|      |                               |     |       |        |
|      |                               |     |       |        |
|      |                               |     |       |        |

## Exercise 11-9

## GENERAL JOURNAL

| Date | Account Titles and Explanation | PR | Debit | Credit |
|------|-------------------------------|-----|-------|--------|
|      |                               |     |       |        |
|      |                               |     |       |        |
|      |                               |     |       |        |
|      |                               |     |       |        |
|      |                               |     |       |        |
|      |                               |     |       |        |
|      |                               |     |       |        |
|      |                               |     |       |        |
|      |                               |     |       |        |

## GENERAL JOURNAL

| Date | Account Titles and Explanation | PR | Debit | Credit |
|------|-------------------------------|----|-------|--------|
|      |                               |    |       |        |
|      |                               |    |       |        |
|      |                               |    |       |        |
|      |                               |    |       |        |
|      |                               |    |       |        |
|      |                               |    |       |        |
|      |                               |    |       |        |
|      |                               |    |       |        |
|      |                               |    |       |        |
|      |                               |    |       |        |
|      |                               |    |       |        |
|      |                               |    |       |        |
|      |                               |    |       |        |
|      |                               |    |       |        |
|      |                               |    |       |        |

## Exercise 11-11

| Employee | CPP Contribution | EI Contribution | Retirement Fund Contributions | Health Insurance |
|----------|------------------|-----------------|-------------------------------|------------------|
|          |                  |                 |                               |                  |
|          |                  |                 |                               |                  |
|          |                  |                 |                               |                  |
|          |                  |                 |                               |                  |
|          |                  |                 |                               |                  |
|          |                  |                 |                               |                  |
|          |                  |                 |                               |                  |

## *Calculations:*

_____

_____

_____

_____

_____

_____

_____

_____

_____

_____

## GENERAL JOURNAL

| Date | Account Titles and Explanation | PR | Debit | Credit |
|------|-------------------------------|----|-------|--------|
| | | | | |
| | | | | |
| | | | | |
| | | | | |
| | | | | |
| | | | | |
| | | | | |
| | | | | |
| | | | | |
| | | | | |
| | | | | |
| | | | | |
| | | | | |
| | | | | |
| | | | | |
| | | | | |
| | | | | |
| | | | | |
| | | | | |
| | | | | |
| | | | | |
| | | | | |
| | | | | |
| | | | | |
| | | | | |
| | | | | |
| | | | | |
| | | | | |
| | | | | |
| | | | | |
| | | | | |

**Exercise 11-13**

## GENERAL JOURNAL

| Date | Account Titles and Explanation | PR | Debit | Credit |
|------|-------------------------------|----|-------|--------|
| | | | | |
| | | | | |
| | | | | |
| | | | | |
| | | | | |
| | | | | |
| | | | | |
| | | | | |

## Part 1

| Employee | Daily Time | | | | | | | Total Hrs. | O.T. Hrs. | Reg. Pay Rate | Earnings | | |
|---|---|---|---|---|---|---|---|---|---|---|---|---|---|
| | M | T | W | T | F | S | S | | | | Regular Pay | Premium Pay | Gross Pay |
| Loran | 8 | 8 | 8 | 8 | 8 | 4 | 0 | | | 40.00 | | | |
| Sousa | 7 | 8 | 6 | 7 | 8 | 4 | 0 | | | 36.00 | | | |
| Smith | 8 | 8 | 0 | 8 | 8 | 4 | 4 | | | 32.00 | | | |
| Parton | 8 | 8 | 8 | 8 | 8 | 0 | 0 | | | 40.00 | | | |
| Wood | 0 | 6 | 6 | 6 | 6 | 8 | 8 | | | 36.00 | | | |
| | | | | | | | | | | | | | |

| Employee | Deductions | | | | | | Payment | Distribution | |
|---|---|---|---|---|---|---|---|---|---|
| | EI Prem. | CPP | Income Tax | Hosp. Ins. | Union Dues | Total Deductions | Net Pay | Office Salaries Expense | Service Wages Expense |
| Loran | | | | 40.00 | 16.00 | | | | |
| Sousa | | | | 40.00 | 15.00 | | | | |
| Smith | | | | 40.00 | 14.00 | | | | |
| Parton | | | | 40.00 | 16.00 | | | | |
| Wood | | | | 40.00 | 15.00 | | | | |
| Totals | | | | 200.00 | 76.00 | | | | |

## Part 2

### GENERAL JOURNAL

| Date | Account Titles and Explanation | PR | Debit | Credit |
|---|---|---|---|---|
| | | | | |
| | | | | |
| | | | | |
| | | | | |
| | | | | |
| | | | | |
| | | | | |
| | | | | |
| | | | | |
| | | | | |
| | | | | |
| | | | | |
| | | | | |
| | | | | |
| | | | | |
| | | | | |

Part 1

## GENERAL JOURNAL

| Date | Account Titles and Explanation | PR | Debit | Credit |
|------|-------------------------------|----|-------|--------|
|      |                               |    |       |        |
|      |                               |    |       |        |
|      |                               |    |       |        |
|      |                               |    |       |        |
|      |                               |    |       |        |
|      |                               |    |       |        |
|      |                               |    |       |        |
|      |                               |    |       |        |
|      |                               |    |       |        |
|      |                               |    |       |        |
|      |                               |    |       |        |
|      |                               |    |       |        |
|      |                               |    |       |        |
|      |                               |    |       |        |

Part 2

## GENERAL JOURNAL

| Date | Account Titles and Explanation | PR | Debit | Credit |
|------|-------------------------------|----|-------|--------|
|      |                               |    |       |        |
|      |                               |    |       |        |
|      |                               |    |       |        |
|      |                               |    |       |        |
|      |                               |    |       |        |
|      |                               |    |       |        |

## Problem 11-3A

Part 1

## GENERAL JOURNAL

| Date | Account Titles and Explanation | PR | Debit | Credit |
|------|-------------------------------|----|-------|--------|
|      |                               |    |       |        |
|      |                               |    |       |        |
|      |                               |    |       |        |
|      |                               |    |       |        |
|      |                               |    |       |        |
|      |                               |    |       |        |
|      |                               |    |       |        |
|      |                               |    |       |        |
|      |                               |    |       |        |
|      |                               |    |       |        |
|      |                               |    |       |        |
|      |                               |    |       |        |
|      |                               |    |       |        |

**Part 2**

## GENERAL JOURNAL

| Date | Account Titles and Explanation | PR | Debit | Credit |
|------|-------------------------------|----|-------|--------|
|      |                               |    |       |        |
|      |                               |    |       |        |
|      |                               |    |       |        |
|      |                               |    |       |        |
|      |                               |    |       |        |
|      |                               |    |       |        |

**Part 3**

## GENERAL JOURNAL

| Date | Account Titles and Explanation | PR | Debit | Credit |
|------|-------------------------------|----|-------|--------|
|      |                               |    |       |        |
|      |                               |    |       |        |
|      |                               |    |       |        |
|      |                               |    |       |        |
|      |                               |    |       |        |
|      |                               |    |       |        |
|      |                               |    |       |        |
|      |                               |    |       |        |

**Problem 11-4A**

## GENERAL JOURNAL

| Date | Account Titles and Explanation | PR | Debit | Credit |
|------|-------------------------------|----|-------|--------|
|      |                               |    |       |        |
|      |                               |    |       |        |
|      |                               |    |       |        |
|      |                               |    |       |        |
|      |                               |    |       |        |
|      |                               |    |       |        |
|      |                               |    |       |        |
|      |                               |    |       |        |
|      |                               |    |       |        |
|      |                               |    |       |        |
|      |                               |    |       |        |
|      |                               |    |       |        |
|      |                               |    |       |        |
|      |                               |    |       |        |
|      |                               |    |       |        |
|      |                               |    |       |        |
|      |                               |    |       |        |

## GENERAL JOURNAL

| Date | Account Titles and Explanation | PR | Debit | Credit |
|------|-------------------------------|----|-------|--------|
|      |                               |    |       |        |
|      |                               |    |       |        |
|      |                               |    |       |        |
|      |                               |    |       |        |
|      |                               |    |       |        |
|      |                               |    |       |        |
|      |                               |    |       |        |
|      |                               |    |       |        |
|      |                               |    |       |        |
|      |                               |    |       |        |
|      |                               |    |       |        |
|      |                               |    |       |        |
|      |                               |    |       |        |
|      |                               |    |       |        |
|      |                               |    |       |        |
|      |                               |    |       |        |
|      |                               |    |       |        |
|      |                               |    |       |        |
|      |                               |    |       |        |
|      |                               |    |       |        |
|      |                               |    |       |        |
|      |                               |    |       |        |
|      |                               |    |       |        |
|      |                               |    |       |        |
|      |                               |    |       |        |
|      |                               |    |       |        |
|      |                               |    |       |        |
|      |                               |    |       |        |
|      |                               |    |       |        |
|      |                               |    |       |        |
|      |                               |    |       |        |
|      |                               |    |       |        |
|      |                               |    |       |        |
|      |                               |    |       |        |
|      |                               |    |       |        |
|      |                               |    |       |        |
|      |                               |    |       |        |
|      |                               |    |       |        |
|      |                               |    |       |        |
|      |                               |    |       |        |
|      |                               |    |       |        |
|      |                               |    |       |        |
|      |                               |    |       |        |
|      |                               |    |       |        |
|      |                               |    |       |        |
|      |                               |    |       |        |

**Part 1**

| Employee | Daily Time | | | | | | | Total Hrs. | O.T. Hrs. | Reg. Pay Rate | Earnings | | |
|---|---|---|---|---|---|---|---|---|---|---|---|---|---|
| | M | T | W | T | F | S | S | | | | Regular Pay | Premium Pay | Gross Pay |
| Amoko | 8 | 8 | 8 | 8 | 8 | 0 | 0 | | | 17.00 | | | |
| Carson | 7 | 8 | 8 | 7 | 8 | 4 | 0 | | | 18.00 | | | |
| Mitale De | 8 | 8 | 0 | 8 | 8 | 4 | 4 | | | 18.00 | | | |
| Deszca | 8 | 8 | 8 | 8 | 8 | 0 | 0 | | | 15.00 | | | |
| Tan | 0 | 6 | 6 | 6 | 6 | 8 | 8 | | | 15.00 | | | |
| | | | | | | | | | | | | | |

| Employee | Deductions | | | | | | Payment | Distribution | |
|---|---|---|---|---|---|---|---|---|---|
| | EI Prem. | CPP | Income Tax | Hosp. Ins. | Union Dues | Total Deductions | Net Pay | Office Salaries Expense | Service Wages Expense |
| Amoko | | | | 30.00 | 12.00 | | | | |
| Carson | | | | 30.00 | 12.00 | | | | |
| Mitale De | | | | 30.00 | 12.00 | | | | |
| Deszca | | | | 30.00 | 12.00 | | | | |
| Tan | | | | 30.00 | 12.00 | | | | |
| Totals | | | | 150.00 | 60.00 | | | | |

**Part 2**

## GENERAL JOURNAL

| Date | Account Titles and Explanation | PR | Debit | Credit |
|---|---|---|---|---|
| | | | | |
| | | | | |
| | | | | |
| | | | | |
| | | | | |
| | | | | |
| | | | | |
| | | | | |
| | | | | |
| | | | | |
| | | | | |
| | | | | |
| | | | | |
| | | | | |
| | | | | |
| | | | | |
| | | | | |
| | | | | |

*Name* _____

**Part 1**

## GENERAL JOURNAL

| Date | Account Titles and Explanation | PR | Debit | Credit |
|------|-------------------------------|----|-------|--------|
|  |  |  |  |  |
|  |  |  |  |  |
|  |  |  |  |  |
|  |  |  |  |  |
|  |  |  |  |  |
|  |  |  |  |  |
|  |  |  |  |  |
|  |  |  |  |  |
|  |  |  |  |  |
|  |  |  |  |  |
|  |  |  |  |  |
|  |  |  |  |  |

**Part 2**

## GENERAL JOURNAL

| Date | Account Titles and Explanation | PR | Debit | Credit |
|------|-------------------------------|----|-------|--------|
|  |  |  |  |  |
|  |  |  |  |  |
|  |  |  |  |  |
|  |  |  |  |  |
|  |  |  |  |  |

## Problem 11-3B

**Part 1**

## GENERAL JOURNAL

| Date | Account Titles and Explanation | PR | Debit | Credit |
|------|-------------------------------|----|-------|--------|
|  |  |  |  |  |
|  |  |  |  |  |
|  |  |  |  |  |
|  |  |  |  |  |
|  |  |  |  |  |
|  |  |  |  |  |
|  |  |  |  |  |
|  |  |  |  |  |
|  |  |  |  |  |
|  |  |  |  |  |
|  |  |  |  |  |
|  |  |  |  |  |

**Part 2**

## GENERAL JOURNAL

| Date | Account Titles and Explanation | PR | Debit | Credit |
|------|-------------------------------|-----|-------|--------|
|      |                               |     |       |        |
|      |                               |     |       |        |
|      |                               |     |       |        |
|      |                               |     |       |        |
|      |                               |     |       |        |
|      |                               |     |       |        |

**Part 3**

## GENERAL JOURNAL

| Date | Account Titles and Explanation | PR | Debit | Credit |
|------|-------------------------------|-----|-------|--------|
|      |                               |     |       |        |
|      |                               |     |       |        |
|      |                               |     |       |        |
|      |                               |     |       |        |
|      |                               |     |       |        |
|      |                               |     |       |        |
|      |                               |     |       |        |
|      |                               |     |       |        |
|      |                               |     |       |        |

**Problem 11-4B**

## GENERAL JOURNAL

| Date | Account Titles and Explanation | PR | Debit | Credit |
|------|-------------------------------|-----|-------|--------|
|      |                               |     |       |        |
|      |                               |     |       |        |
|      |                               |     |       |        |
|      |                               |     |       |        |
|      |                               |     |       |        |
|      |                               |     |       |        |
|      |                               |     |       |        |
|      |                               |     |       |        |
|      |                               |     |       |        |
|      |                               |     |       |        |
|      |                               |     |       |        |
|      |                               |     |       |        |
|      |                               |     |       |        |
|      |                               |     |       |        |

## GENERAL JOURNAL

| Date | Account Titles and Explanation | PR | Debit | Credit |
|------|-------------------------------|----|----|----|
|  |  |  |  |  |
|  |  |  |  |  |
|  |  |  |  |  |
|  |  |  |  |  |
|  |  |  |  |  |
|  |  |  |  |  |
|  |  |  |  |  |
|  |  |  |  |  |
|  |  |  |  |  |
|  |  |  |  |  |
|  |  |  |  |  |
|  |  |  |  |  |
|  |  |  |  |  |
|  |  |  |  |  |
|  |  |  |  |  |
|  |  |  |  |  |
|  |  |  |  |  |
|  |  |  |  |  |
|  |  |  |  |  |
|  |  |  |  |  |
|  |  |  |  |  |
|  |  |  |  |  |
|  |  |  |  |  |
|  |  |  |  |  |
|  |  |  |  |  |
|  |  |  |  |  |
|  |  |  |  |  |
|  |  |  |  |  |
|  |  |  |  |  |
|  |  |  |  |  |
|  |  |  |  |  |
|  |  |  |  |  |
|  |  |  |  |  |
|  |  |  |  |  |
|  |  |  |  |  |
|  |  |  |  |  |
|  |  |  |  |  |
|  |  |  |  |  |
|  |  |  |  |  |
|  |  |  |  |  |
|  |  |  |  |  |
|  |  |  |  |  |
|  |  |  |  |  |
|  |  |  |  |  |
|  |  |  |  |  |